8131

APPLIED THERMODYNAMICS PROBLEMS FOR ENGINEERS

BY

W. J. PECK

M.Eng.(Sheffield), M.I.Mech.E.

ASSISTANT HEAD, MECHANICAL AND CIVIL ENGINEERING DEPT.,
BATTERSEA POLYTECHNIC, LONDON.

AND

A. J. RICHMOND

B.Sc.(Eng.) (Lond.), A.M.I.Mech.E.

SENIOR LECTURER, MECHANICAL AND CIVIL ENGINEERING DEPT.,
BATTERSEA POLYTECHNIC, LONDON.

LONDON

EDWARD ARNOLD & CO.

Printed in Great Britain by
Butler & Tanner Ltd., Frome and London

PREFACE

This book is intended for the use of students preparing for the final degree examinations in Engineering of the Universities, the Associate Membership examinations of the professional institutions, Higher National Certificates, and Whitworth and Senior Whitworth Scholarships. It is hoped that it may also prove of interest to some practising engineers as a synopsis of the fundamental calculations in the subject.

The purpose of this book is to provide a widely representative selection of fully worked examples together with such explanatory matter as would enable an average student to follow the solutions logically. With this object in mind, standard proofs of mathematical expressions have been omitted except where it was thought desirable to present the solution to a question as a whole, rather than to deal with numerical substitutions only. The book is therefore in no way intended to supersede existing textbooks, nor to be a substitute for that valuable aspect of the learning of a subject which derives from the personal contact between teacher and student. The authors rather feel that the diversity and continual growth of the subject as a whole and of the syllabuses of many examining bodies have created a need for a book in this particular form as a means of supplementing both the above methods of learning the subject. It is hoped that the hints, intermediate and final answers given to the unworked examples at the end of each chapter will be found especially useful, as the student may thus check his own solution from stage to stage and recognize any mistake at an early moment.

The subject as a whole is too large to be covered completely in one volume, from its fundamentals to the advanced standard aimed at. The present volume deals therefore with the prevalent need of the more advanced section of the work, assuming the knowledge of a first-year course in Applied Heat or Heat Engines. In order to facilitate cross-references, however, and to establish the basis for much of the work, chapter I has been devoted entirely to a summary (without proofs) of the fundamental principles of Thermodynamics as used by Engineers, and concise explanations are given whenever our experience has shown that difficulties are most likely to arise in the student's mind. For similar reasons, some chapters contain general introductory remarks to the topic under discussion.

The symbols used are those in common use in Great Britain ; so far as is possible, both Callendar's notation in regard to the properties of steam and the general notation in regard to scientific terms (in accordance with the B.S.S. 560—1934) have been followed. *Abridged Callendar Steam Tables*, Fahrenheit Units, 4th edition (Edward Arnold & Co.), and the same publisher's *Total Heat-Entropy Chart for Steam*, 1939, in Fahrenheit Units, have been used where appropriate. The use of the British Thermal

iii

Unit and ° F. are in keeping with the bulk of current practice. A deliberate change has been made in referring to the British Thermal Unit as the B.T.U. and not as hitherto the B.Th.U. This is justified on the grounds of simplicity and the rather remote possibility of any confusion with the Board of Trade Unit for which the abbreviation B.T.U. is usually reserved in Great Britain. It may be observed that the unit adopted in the United States is the British Thermal Unit, abbreviated to Btu.

Grateful acknowledgements are made to the various bodies who have readily co-operated in giving permission to reprint questions from past examination papers; viz. the Senate of the University of London, the Manchester University Press, the Senate of the University of Durham, the University Court of the University of Glasgow, the University of Cambridge, Birmingham University, the Senate of the University of Sheffield, the University of Melbourne, the University of Sydney, the University of the Witwatersrand (Johannesburg), the Controller of H.M. Stationery Office, the Council of the Union of Lancashire and Cheshire Institutes, the Council of the Institution of Mechanical Engineers, the Council of the Institution of Civil Engineers, and the Council of the Institution of Chemical Engineers.

All numerical results have been obtained with the aid of a slide rule, as a higher degree of accuracy is not usually required. Every care has been taken to exclude mistakes of all sorts, but in a work of this nature it cannot be hoped that all errors have in fact been eliminated. The authors will be grateful to any reader who may draw their attention to such imperfections as remain, and suggestions for possible improvements will be carefully noted.

In a few instances the division into chapters is arbitrary and several chapters overlap to some extent. This applies especially to the work on Gas Laws, Partial Pressures, and Combustion. Nevertheless, the divisions should prove helpful to many students, so long as the underlying common principles are not overlooked. Some students find considerable difficulty with parts of the work dealt with in chapters VIII and XI. It is recommended that these chapters should not be studied until chapters I–VII and XII have been thoroughly understood.

The authors' thanks are due to a number of colleagues who have at different times helped in shaping their outlook and to others who have read the proofs. Special mention is due to J. E. Bacon, Esq., B.Sc.(Eng.), D.I.C., A.M.I.Mech.E., who drew the diagrams and made useful contributions in regard to the subject-matter, particularly in regard to chapter XX.

W. J. P.
A. J. R.

BATTERSEA POLYTECHNIC,
LONDON, S.W.11.

CONTENTS

LIST OF PRINCIPAL SYMBOLS USED

P   Pressure, lb. per sq. in.

P_s Saturation Pressure, lb. per sq. in.

V   Volume, cu. ft. or cu. in., or specific volume, cu. ft. per lb.

t Temperature, ° F.

t_s Saturation Temperature, ° F.

T   Absolute Temperature, ° F.

C_p Specific Heat at constant pressure, heat units per lb. per deg.

C_v Specific Heat at constant volume, heat units per lb. per deg.

$C_{p\,mol}$ Volumetric or Molar Heat at constant pressure, in heat units per lb.mol per deg.

$C_{v\,mol}$ Volumetric or Molar Heat at constant volume, in heat units per lb.mol per deg.

R   Characteristic Gas Constant, in ft.lb. per lb. ° F.

R_{mol} Universal Gas Constant heat units per lb.mol degree.

n Index of Compression or Expansion.

γ Ratio of Specific Heats, $\dfrac{C_p}{C_v}$.

W, w Mass, in lb.

m Number of lb.mols.

J   Mechanical Equivalent of Heat.

H   Total Heat or Enthalpy, B.T.U. or more frequently B.T.U. per lb.

H_s Total Heat or Enthalpy under saturation conditions.

h Sensible Heat, or Total Heat of Saturated Liquid, B.T.U. or more frequently B.T.U. per lb.

L   Latent Heat, B.T.U. per lb.

x Dryness Fraction.

ϕ Entropy, usually with suffixes as defined in chapter I.

D, d Diameter.

E   Internal Energy.

Q   Finite Quantity of Heat entering or leaving a confined system.

A   Area.

g Acceleration due to Gravity.

v Velocity.

Δ A finite Change, e.g. ΔE, Change in Internal Energy.

δ A very small Change.

W.D.   Work Done.

η Efficiency.

ρ Specific Weight, lb. per cu. ft.

G   Water Potential, or Gibbs' Function, B.T.U. per lb.

p.p.   Partial Pressure.

All pressures may be taken as absolute, unless otherwise stated.

LIST OF PRINCIPAL CONSTANTS USED

These values are of sufficient accuracy for most ordinary purposes. Reference should be made to standard books of constants in exceptional cases.

Mechanical Equivalent of Heat, $J = 778$ ft.lb. per B.T.U.

Ratio of Specific Heats for Air, $\gamma = 1\cdot4$.

Characteristic Gas Constant for Air, $R = 53\cdot3$ ft.lb. per lb. per ° F.

Mean Molecular Weight of Air $= 28\cdot9$, nearly.

Universal Gas Constant, $R_{mol} = 1{,}543$ ft.lb. per lb.mol per ° F.
$\qquad\qquad\qquad\qquad = 1\cdot985$ heat units per lb.mol per deg.

Acceleration of Gravity, $g = 32\cdot2$ ft. per sec.²

Conversion Factor, $a = \dfrac{144}{778} \backsimeq \dfrac{1}{5\cdot4}$. ($a$ PV will be in B.T.U., if P is in lb. per sq. in. and V in cu. ft.)

1 in. of mercury $= 0\cdot49$ lb. per sq. in.

Absolute Zero of Temperature $= -460°$ F., i.e. T° F. $= 460 + t°$ F.

1 lb.mol of any gas occupies $358\cdot7$ cu. ft. at $14\cdot7$ lb. per sq. in. and $32°$ F.

1 horse-power hour of work (h.p.-hr.) $= 2{,}546$ B.T.U.

1 horse-power minute of work (h.p.-min.) $= 42\cdot4$ B.T.U.

1 kilo-watt hour of Work (k.W.-hr.) $= 3{,}413$ B.T.U.

Specific gravity of mercury $= 13\cdot6$.

Specific weight of fresh water at normal supply temperatures $= 62\cdot4$ lb. per cu. ft.

LIST OF SOURCES OF EXAMINATION QUESTIONS

U. Lond.	University of London.
U. Manch.	University of Manchester.
U. Dur.	University of Durham.
U. Glas.	University of Glasgow.
U. Camb.	University of Cambridge.
U. Birm.	University of Birmingham.
U. Sheff.	University of Sheffield.
U. Melb.	University of Melbourne.
U. Syd.	University of Sydney.
U. Witw.	University of the Witwatersrand (Johannesburg).
W.S.	Whitworth Scholarship.
W.S.S.	Whitworth Senior Scholarship.
U.L.C.I.	Union of Lancashire and Cheshire Institutes.
I.Mech.E.	Institution of Mechanical Engineers.
I.C.E.	Institution of Civil Engineers.
I.Chem.E.	Institution of Chemical Engineers.

CHAPTER I

REVISION OF FUNDAMENTAL KNOWLEDGE

Section A. General Thermodynamics

1. *The working substance*, or " stuff ", in a thermodynamic operation may be either a perfect gas, a gas deviating in its behaviour from the ideal characteristics, a vapour, a liquid, or a mixture of these. The basic statements given in this section will be found to apply to all these substances, the two subsequent sections being devoted to the properties of gases and vapours (and their liquids), respectively.

2. *Internal Energy or Intrinsic Energy*, E, is an inclusive term describing *all* forms of energy due to the inherent internal structure of the stuff. It can be expressed as a function of molecular energy in terms of the kinetic theory, but this approach is not usually pursued by engineers. The precise mode of calculation will be discussed later, but it should be realized that it is quoted relative to some arbitrary datum.

3. *Kinetic Energy* is the energy possessed by the stuff by virtue of the velocity v ft. per sec. of the mass as a whole, i.e. of the centre of gravity of the mass ; and for a mass of w lb. is expressed by the term $\dfrac{wv^2}{2gJ}$ B.T.U.,

or $\dfrac{v^2}{2gJ}$ B.T.U. per lb.

4. We are principally concerned with the conversion of heat energy into work. First, we may consider the stuff to be already enclosed in a container (often a cylinder) before energy conversion occurs, and to remain there after such action ceases. Such a process is said to represent a " phase " or " non-flow " type of operation. On the other hand, we may consider a " flow " type of operation where the stuff is admitted into a container, flows through it while the energy changes occur, and is then rejected from the container. It is assumed that the mass admitted per sec. is always equal to the mass discharged per sec., and that any one point in the container remains in a steady state. The product PV is then termed the *work of introduction*, being the work done to introduce a volume V into the container at the inlet, where the constant pressure P prevails. It may be more readily recognized as a quantity of work at constant pressure, if written in the form P(V − 0).

The amount of work P_1V_1 is done by the incoming stuff *on* the stuff already in the container, while similarly an amount of work P_2V_2 is done *by* the stuff in the cylinder on the stuff being discharged at some other condition of pressure and volume. We must therefore expect the term PV to occur on both sides of a general energy equation for steady flow. Such an energy equation may be written for unit mass :

$$E_1 + \frac{v_1{}^2}{2gJ} + \text{Potential Energy}_1 + \text{Quantity of Heat received} + \frac{P_1V_1}{J}$$

$$= E_2 + \frac{v_2{}^2}{2gJ} + \text{Potential Energy}_2 + \text{Shaft Work done by the stuff}$$

$$+ \frac{P_2V_2}{J} + \text{Losses.}$$

Other forms of energy, notably chemical energy, may occur. Also, one or more terms in this equation may be zero in a particular case.

In many practical problems an equation of this type applies, and it has been found convenient to introduce a single term for the sum of E and PV, terms which always occur on both sides of the equation. Thus, by definition,

Total Heat or Enthalpy = Internal Energy + Work of introduction

i.e. $H = E + a\,PV$, B.T.U. per lb. .   .   (I,1)

where P is in lb. per sq. in. and V in cu. ft. per lb., so that

$$a = \frac{144}{778} \backsimeq \frac{1}{5\cdot4}$$

If E is defined as zero at some arbitrary datum of temperature, then H will only be zero relative to the same datum if that datum is the absolute zero of temperature, in which case the work of introduction is zero ; but in many cases the work of introduction at 32° F. is of a negligible order.

A datum of − 460° F. is frequently chosen for gases (see page 12) and then H and E will be zero at − 460° F.

A datum of 32° F. is invariably chosen for steam, the saturation pressure at 32° F. being 0·089 lb. per sq. in., very nearly. Thus, for water at 32° F. and saturation conditions, from (I,1) the total heat of water, $h_{32} = 0 + \dfrac{0\cdot089 \times 0\cdot016}{5\cdot4}$, where 0·016 is the specific volume of saturated water in cu. ft. per lb. at 32° F. It can be seen, therefore, that the sensible heat of saturated water at 32° F. may be considered as zero for most practical applications.

For vapours other than steam, the datum may be chosen under conditions giving appreciable pressure energy, and h will then not be zero at the datum of E.

5. *The Law of Conservation of Energy*, when applied to a non-flow process, means that if a quantity of energy in the form of heat is supplied to a specified system, such as a boiler or engine cylinder, then such heat energy will be used either to increase the internal energy of the system by raising the temperature or by evaporating the stuff, or to do external mechanical work, or both in proportions depending on the nature of the heat addition and on the manner in which mechanical work may be performed. In all cases, it will however be true that

Heat *received* = *Increase* in Internal Energy of the stuff
+ External shaft work done *by* the stuff

i.e. $$Q = \Delta E + W.D. \qquad \qquad (I,2)$$

These three quantities will usually be in heat units.

If heat is rejected from the system or a loss of internal energy occurs, or external work is done on the stuff, then the corresponding term in equation (I,2) will be represented by a negative numerical quantity. Also, we are now dealing with a phase only, and the question of work of introduction cannot arise; cf. article 4 above.

Difficulty is sometimes experienced in appreciating why this energy equation contains only the term ΔE and not the change in total heat. The reason for this lies in the definition of E as a comprehensive function describing the internal energy as a quantity including all types of energy within the stuff, however they became manifest, e.g. temperature or pressure (cf. also article 2 above).

Great care is required to distinguish clearly between equation (I,1) which refers to *one given state* only, and equation (I,2) which describes *changes during a phase*, or a continuous operation of a given type. Also, H is the Total Heat content, as defined by (I,1), whereas Q is heat energy or caloric heat added. An addition of Q B.T.U. will not, in general, produce an equal numerical change ΔH. This will be appreciated more clearly if (I,1) and (I,2) are rewritten, so as to describe a change from one state " *a* " to another state " *b* ", the change taking place in any manner, providing only it is continuous in the mathematical sense; thus

$$\Delta H = H_b - H_a = (E_b - E_a) + a(P_b V_b - P_a V_a) \qquad (I,1a)$$

and $$Q_{a-b} = (E_b - E_a) + W.D._{a-b} \qquad (I,2a)$$

Clearly, ΔH equals Q only in the very special case when the change in the work of introduction equals the external work done, i.e. when the operation is one of constant pressure. Fig. (I,1) shows graphically the general case of equations (I,1a) and (I,2a); we have a " phase " expansion from point (*a*) to point (*b*) in any manner whatever, as shown on the P–V sketch. It will be seen graphically that $E_a + Q_{a-b} = W.D._{a-b} + E_b$, which is a restatement of (I,2a). Naturally, the actual numerical values quoted for Q and W.D. (viz. $+ 3\frac{1}{2}$ and $+ 2$) are particular values depending for their relative magnitude on the law relating P and V. The values for E, H, and PV, on the other hand, do *not* depend on the path of the P–V graph, but only on the position of points (*a*) and (*b*) on the P–V diagram. The relative magnitude of all the quoted figures is that which may attain during the expansion phase in a steam-jacketed steam engine when the graph joining (*a*) and (*b*) is hyperbolic or similar.

6. An isothermal operation is one of constant temperature.

An adiabatic operation is one during which no heat energy is received from or rejected to external systems; this means that Q in equation (I,2) will be zero.

A hyperbolic operation is one following the equation of the rectangular hyperbola, i.e. PV = constant.

A polytropic operation is one following the general law, PV^n = constant, where n is an index other than the adiabatic index, and lying usually

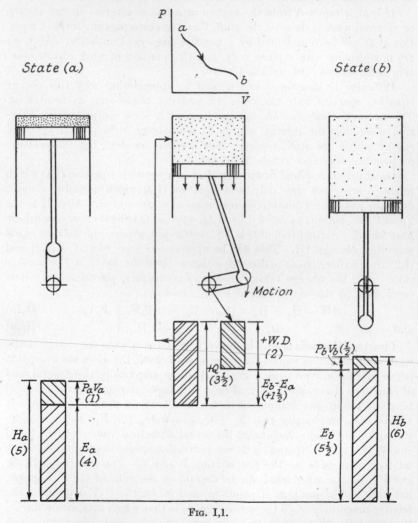

FIG. I,1.

between 1 (hyperbolic) and 1·3 or 1·4 (the adiabatic index for superheated steam or air respectively), but both lower and higher values are possible and do occur.

A throttling operation is one of constant total heat, i.e. H is constant.

The terms " constant volume " and " constant pressure " operations are self-explanatory.

7. *Entropy*, ϕ, is that thermodynamic function of a fluid which does not change during a reversible adiabatic operation.

Since the only thermodynamically reversible operations are isothermal and adiabatic, this definition is unique. In symbols,

$$\delta Q = T.\delta\phi . \quad \quad \quad \quad \quad (I,3)$$

or, if a certain function be plotted against absolute temperature then, for a reversible operation, the area under the resulting graph will represent heat energy added or rejected during that operation. The fundamental definition given in terms of reversibility clearly applies to (I,3), since an adiabatic operation implies that $\delta Q = 0$, so far as external heat energy is concerned, and therefore $\delta\phi$ must $= 0$. But in certain adiabatic operations, heat may actually be generated *within* the stuff by friction ; such an operation is still considered as adiabatic, but $\delta\phi$ is no longer zero, i.e. the operation does not take place at constant entropy (isentropically), and is not rever-
sible. These matters will be discussed more fully in the problems in which they arise. Fig. I,2 shows an iso-
thermal expansion from point 1 to point 2, the area 12651 representing Q heat units supplied to the stuff, $\phi_2 - \phi_1$ being the increase in entropy. An adiabatic isentropic expansion is shown by 1–3, the area under the curve being zero. An adiabatic non-
isentropic expansion is shown by 1–4.

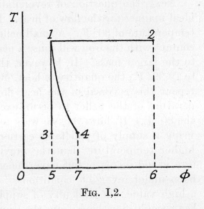

FIG. I,2.

If the path of the expansion be exactly as 1–4, a difficult matter to ascertain, then the area 1475 represents Q heat units generated within the stuff by friction, but in any case $\phi_4 - \phi_1$ is the gain in entropy.

8. The subject of Entropy always presents considerable difficulty to the student, and it is felt that a few practical illustrations may help to justify the more abstract and theoretical ideas.

The flow of heat is controlled by the temperature gradient and not by the quantity of heat. A small bullet at a temperature of 81° F. when placed in a large tank of water at 80° F. will lose heat to the water, although the heat content of the bullet is very much smaller than that of the water. The rate of heat flow will be greater if there is a greater temperature gradient. This may be likened to the case of a hydro-electric system where either the available energy is supplied by a small quantity of water at a high elevation in a mountainous district, or by a large quantity of water at a head of a few feet as in a tidal scheme. In the latter case, the *rate* of flow is so small, because of the low head, that the quantity of water must be correspondingly large, demanding very large slow-speed turbines in contrast to the small high-speed Pelton wheels of the former case. Or, consider the electrical case, when a given quantity of electrical energy may be supplied at 132,000 volts and 1 ampere, or at 2 volts when the current would need to be 66,000 amperes. These analogies must not be taken too literally, as it must always be remembered that heat is energy and is *not* the working fluid, which is only the " vehicle ".

At this point the student should think carefully on the following example. There are 20,000 B.T.U. of heat available for the production of mechanical work, and this heat is represented by either (*a*) 1,000 gallons of water at a temperature of 62° F. in an environment of 60° F. or (*b*) as 1 lb. of petrol. In (*a*) there is no practical possibility of producing mechanical work, whereas in (*b*) by releasing the same quantity of heat by combustion at a high tem-perature in a petrol engine, about 30% of the heat may be converted into useful mechanical work.

Next, the question of reversibility should be considered, as this is the ideal manner for the flow of heat. Imagine a mass of say 10 lb. of iron at a temperature of 80° F. A small pellet at a temperature of 80·01° F. put into contact with the iron will cause a heat flow, δQ, to take place from the pellet to the larger mass. If, however, the temperature of the pellet be reduced to 79·99° F., the quantity of heat, δQ, would flow back again : and we could repeat this reversal of the heat flow continuously, by adjusting the tem-perature of the pellet to be an exceedingly small amount above or below the 80° F. If, however, we were to carry on supplying heat by this means using a supply of pellets as carriers, each would have to be at a slightly higher temperature than the previous one, since the temperature of the iron would increase, but nevertheless each addition of heat δQ would have been under reversible conditions. As the temperature of the iron rises to a high value, the difficulty of supplying this heat would increase, and the heat would flow back from the iron to the environment with greater ease.

In the expression for the entropy change, $\dfrac{\delta Q}{T}$ (I,3), δQ is the small quantity of heat supplied under conditions of reversibility at an absolute temperature of T. It can be seen in an abstract fashion that in entropy we have a ratio which embraces the idea of a quantity of heat in motion and the temperature potential at which this flow is taking place. The lower the temperature at which the flow occurs, the greater the entropy change for a given quantity δQ.

Lastly, when the construction of entropy diagrams is being studied, it must be remembered that particular values of the liquid entropy refer only to the liquid under its saturation conditions, i.e. just boiling, and not to superpressure liquids (cf. section C, articles 2 and 3). Also, it is good prac-tice at this stage to gain confidence by using the diagrams for steam in this manner :—given Total Heat = 1,277·5 and Total Entropy 1·6870 ; the steam may then be found to be at a pressure of 120 lb. per sq. in., with 160° F. superheat, and so on.

9. If a working substance is expanded in a resisted manner [1] the work done during the operation is usually given by the area under the resulting P-V graph and this may be determined graphically or as the integral $\int P \, dV$, if the law relating P and V is known. For the general considerations, the term " expansion " may be taken to include negative expansion, i.e. compression.

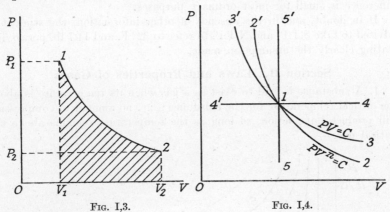

FIG. I,3.   FIG. I,4.

Let a working substance be expanded from condition " 1 " to condition " 2 ", as shown in Fig. I,3.

If PV^n = constant applies, then W.D. = $\dfrac{P_1V_1 - P_2V_2}{n - 1}$.   .   (I,4)

If PV = constant applies, then W.D. = $PV \log_e r$.   .   (I,5)

where $r = \dfrac{P_1}{P_2} = \dfrac{V_2}{V_1}$ = expansion ratio.

Fig. I,4 shows the types of expansion curves represented on a P-V diagram. It should be noted that 1-2, the general (or polytropic) law always gives a steeper slope than 1-3, the hyperbolic law, providing n is greater than 1.

It remains true that the W.D. is the area under the graphs; for a constant volume operation this must, of course, be zero, whereas for the constant pressure case the W.D. = $P(V_4 - V_1)$.

10. The terms N.T.P. (normal temperature and pressure) and S.T.P. (standard temperature and pressure) are commonly used as giving a reference datum for comparison purposes. Different authorities define these terms in various ways; one might suggest, under British climate at any rate, that " normal " temperature could be taken to refer to 60° F., and " standard " temperature to 32° F. However, no general agreement exists on these terms and many regard N.T.P. and S.T.P. as both referring to 32° F. From a student's point of view this is confusing, but with practice

---

[1] A " resisted " expansion is the normal mode of expansion in an engine cylinder, the expansion being resisted by the piston. Typical examples of unresisted or free expansions are throttling operations and expansions of the porous plug type. For discussion of a partially resisted operation, see introduction to chapter X, article 2.

it is possible to know that certain properties are customarily referred to 60° F. and others to 32° F. Thus, the calorific value of town gas is required by law to have a minimum value expressed at 60° F. ; the density of gases is usually referred to 32° F., etc. The unit of pressure in N.T.P. and S.T.P. is either 14·7 lb. per sq. in., or 30 in. Hg, or 760 mm. Hg. or 1,000 millibars. Actually, none of these agrees exactly with each other, but the difference is small for most ordinary purposes.

If in doubt, and in the absence of other information, the student is advised to take S.T.P. and N.T.P. to refer to 32° F. and 14·7 lb. per sq. in., stating clearly the assumption made.

Section B. Laws and Properties of Gases

1. A substance is said to exist as a gas when its temperature is above the critical temperature for the substance ; i.e. no amount of compression will produce liquefaction, so long as the temperature remains above the critical one.

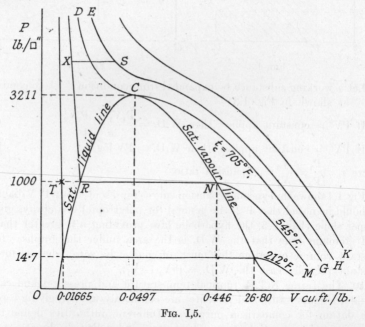

FIG. I,5.

An appreciation of this definition will be helped by a thorough study of fig. I,5, which shows the wet and dry saturation lines and a number of isothermals for H_2O. If the superheated vapour at, say, M is compressed at constant temperature the pressure will rise and it will become dry saturated at N ; then it will turn into wet vapour from N to R, the pressure and temperatures remaining constant (condensation) ; at R we shall have pure liquid and further isothermal reduction of volume will result in a rapid rise of pressure (superpressure liquid). It will be seen that for an increase of temperature over that at N, the saturation pressure rises and the latent heat decreases (see also steam tables). If the compression is now begun at G, the pressure-volume graph will be GCD, with a rapid reduction of volume in the neighbourhood of C. But no change of state will occur at all, the fluid remaining homogeneous throughout. DCG has a point of inflexion at C which is known as the critical point. For steam, the values of P_c and t_c are as marked in fig. I,5. Isothermal compression from any point to the right of GCD, such as H or K, will not produce liquefaction, and the stuff at H is then a gas. On the other hand it is conceivable to " compress " the gas at S, on HE, at constant pressure, by reducing the temperature, until the point X is reached, which represents pure liquid. No perceptible change of state takes place from S to X (i.e. no meniscus and condensation) but nevertheless a homogeneous gas at S is changed into a homogeneous liquid at X, the explanation lying in the considerable reduction in volume. It should be appreciated that in fig. I,5 the volume of water is much exaggerated in comparison with the volume of steam.

2. The specific heats C_p and C_v of a gas may be assumed to be constant under all conditions, as a first approximation. They do, however, vary with temperature, so that

$$C_p = a + k_1T + k_2T^2$$
and
$$C_v = b + k_1T + k_2T^2$$

where a, b, k are constants.

The magnitude of the terms becomes rapidly smaller and the term involving T^2 is frequently neglected.

3. The difference between the specific heats can be shown to equal the characteristic gas constant in heat units, thus

$$C_p - C_v = \frac{R}{J} \qquad . \qquad . \qquad . \qquad (I,6)$$

Note, if C_p and C_v are variable, R is still an absolute constant and equals $(a - b)J$.

$$\text{Characteristic Gas Equation, } PV = wRT \qquad . \qquad . \qquad (I,7)$$

where w is the mass in lb. (I,7) may be modified to read

$$PV = \frac{w}{\text{molecular weight}} \times (R \times \text{molecular weight}) \times T$$

i.e. $\qquad PV = mR_{mol} T \times J \qquad . \qquad . \qquad . \qquad . \qquad . \qquad . \qquad (1,7a)$

where the number of lb.mols is given by

$$m = \frac{w}{\text{molecular weight}} \qquad . \qquad . \qquad (I,8)$$

i.e. the mass of 1 lb.mol is the molecular weight of the stuff in lb. and

$$JR_{mol} = R \times \text{molecular weight} \qquad . \qquad . \qquad (I,9)$$

where R_{mol} is the universal gas constant and is equal to 1·985 Heat Units per (lb.mol × degree), being independent of the temperature units adopted.

4. It is necessary to picture clearly that a lb.mol is fundamentally a unit volume, a lb.mol of any gaseous substance occupying 358·7 cu. ft. at 14·7 lb. per sq. in. and 32° F. Many problems can be solved more readily by using the lb.mol as the unit of volume rather than the lb. as the unit of mass. It also follows that

$$C_{p\,mol} = C_p \times \text{molecular weight} \qquad . \qquad . \qquad (I,10)$$

and
$$C_{v\,mol} = C_v \times \text{molecular weight} \qquad . \qquad . \qquad (I,11)$$

and
$$C_{p\,mol} - C_{v\,mol} = R_{mol}, \text{ in heat units} \qquad . \qquad . \qquad (I,6a)$$

where $C_{p\,mol}$ and $C_{v\,mol}$ are referred to as the volumetric or molar specific heats and are measured in heat units per (lb.mol × degree). One of their advantages lies in the fact that the molar heats for all gases, having an equal number of atoms in their molecules, will be the same. Some confusion is caused by the use of volumetric heats expressed not per lb.mol, but per standard cu. ft. (S.C.F.) ; these would be given by $\dfrac{C_{mol}}{358\cdot7}$, in which case the relative magnitude would be sufficient indication of the unit, but this is not so when $\dfrac{C_{mol} \times 778}{358\cdot7}$ is used, as this is the volumetric heat in ft.lb. per (S.C.F. × ° F.), and these units should be expressly stated. In the following chapters the symbols C_p and C_v (without dimensions) can be taken to indicate heat units per (lb. mass × degree), and the symbols $C_{p\,mol}$ and $C_{v\,mol}$ (or volumetric heats) can be assumed to refer to heat units per (lb.mol × degree). Any other meaning will be expressly stated.

5. Most students will know the usual form of Avagadro's Law or Hypothesis, which states that equal volumes of different gases contain the same number of molecules, at the same pressure and temperature. It follows immediately that the mass per unit volume of any gas is proportional to the molecular weight of the gas, or for any two gases

$$\frac{\rho_1}{\rho_2} = \frac{\text{molecular weight of 1}}{\text{molecular weight of 2}} \qquad . \qquad . \qquad (I,12)$$

provided the temperature and pressure are equal.

6. If a mixture of gases (or of gases and vapours) is contained in a vessel of fixed volume, then it can be shown from the kinetic theory that each stuff occupies the *whole* volume, providing no chemical action occurs. The total pressure, as registered by a pressure gauge attached to the vessel, will then be the sum of the separate or partial pressures which each stuff would exert if occupying the whole volume alone. This statement is known as Dalton's Law of Partial Pressures. The temperature of the mixture will be the same as the temperature of each constituent part. From equation (I,7a) and (I,7) for any two gases,

$$\frac{P_1 V_1}{P_2 V_2} = \frac{m_1 R_{mol} T_1 J}{m_2 R_{mol} T_2 J} = \frac{w_1 R_1 T_1}{w_2 R_2 T_2}$$

Now, $V_1 = V_2$, and $T_1 = T_2$,

$$\frac{P_1}{P_2} = \frac{m_1}{m_2} = \frac{w_1 R_1}{w_2 R_2} \qquad . \qquad . \qquad . \qquad . \qquad (I,13)$$

i.e. the partial pressures are proportional to the number of lb.mols.

7. If a gas expands under adiabatic isentropic conditions in a resisted manner the law of expansion is $PV^\gamma = $ constant ; it can be shown that the index must be equal to the ratio of the specific heats, i.e.

$$\gamma = \frac{C_p}{C_v} \qquad . \qquad . \qquad . \qquad . \qquad . \qquad (I,14)$$

It should be noted that the symbol γ is conventionally used for the adiabatic index of gases only. Vapours, such as steam, also have adiabatic indices but they are liable to a great deal more variation than for gases. The symbol n is used for vapours to indicate mean values of polytropic and isentropic indices over a given range (cf. also chapter I, section C, article 11).

8. Boyle's Law,

$$PV = \text{constant} \qquad . \qquad . \qquad . \qquad . \qquad (I,15)$$

which implies isothermal conditions for *a gas only*.

9. It should be noted that (I,7) always applies to changes of a gas, and that either $PV = $ constant, or $PV^n = $ constant *may* apply. Since R is an absolute constant, (I,7) may be written, for a fixed quantity of stuff,

$$\frac{P_1 V_1}{T_1} = \frac{P_2 V_2}{T_2} \qquad . \qquad . \qquad . \qquad . \qquad (I,16)$$

If this holds in conjunction with $PV^n = $ constant, i.e.

$$P_1 V_1{}^n = P_2 V_2{}^n,$$

then the following may be deduced by elimination :

$$\frac{T_2}{T_1} = \left[\frac{V_1}{V_2}\right]^{n-1} \qquad . \qquad . \qquad . \qquad . \qquad (I,17)$$

and

$$\frac{T_2}{T_1} = \left[\frac{P_2}{P_1}\right]^{\frac{n-1}{n}} \qquad . \qquad . \qquad . \qquad . \qquad (I,18)$$

These relations may be put into words as an aid to memory :

$$\frac{\text{Final Temperature}}{\text{Initial Temperature}} = \left[\frac{\text{Initial Volume}}{\text{Final Volume}}\right]^{n-1} = \left[\frac{\text{Final Pressure}}{\text{Initial Pressure}}\right]^{\frac{n-1}{n}}$$

i.e. Ratio of Temperatures = Inverse Ratio of Volumes to the power $(n - 1)$

$$= \text{Ratio of Pressures to the power} \left(\frac{n-1}{n}\right).$$

10. Joule's Law of Internal Energy states that this function depends on the temperature only and leads to the statement, true for gases only :

$$E = wC_vT \qquad . \qquad . \qquad . \qquad . \qquad (I,19)$$

reckoned in this case from the absolute zero of temperature. Since equation (I,1) still applies,

$$H = wC_vT + PV, \text{ neglecting the conversion factor.}$$

Together with (I,7) and (I,6) this leads to

$$H = wC_pT \qquad . \qquad . \qquad . \qquad . \qquad (I,20)$$

11. Equation (I,3) can be used to calculate the change of entropy of a gas by using the equation already given. Thus, for a change from $P_1V_1T_1$ to $P_2V_2T_2$ we get, for constant C_p and C_v,

$$\phi_2 - \phi_1 = wC_v \log_e \frac{P_2}{P_1} + wC_p \log_e \frac{V_2}{V_1} \qquad . \qquad . \qquad (I,21)$$

or, if $C_p = a + kT$ and $C_v = b + kT$, we get

$$\phi_2 - \phi_1 = wb \log_e \frac{T_2}{T_1} + wk(T_2 - T_1) + w(a - b) \log_e \frac{V_2}{V_1}. \qquad (I,21a)$$

12. From the conservation of energy equation (I,2) in conjunction with the gas laws, for a polytropic operation *only*

$$Q = \frac{\gamma - n}{\gamma - 1} \int \frac{P \, dV}{J} \qquad . \qquad . \qquad . \qquad . \qquad (I,22)$$

where $\int P \, dV$ is, of course, the work done in ft.lb.

13. It has been shown by Carnot that the efficiency of a thermodynamic cycle reaches an optimum value when the cycle consists entirely of reversible operations, i.e. adiabatic and isothermal ones. Hence, the

$$\text{Carnot } \eta = \frac{T_1 - T_2}{T_1} \qquad . \qquad . \qquad . \qquad . \qquad (I,23)$$

for an engine cycle working between a highest temperature T_1 and a lowest temperature T_2; while there are cycles, such as the Stirling and the ideal Regenerative cycles, which have theoretical efficiencies equal to the Carnot efficiency, none can have a higher efficiency.

14. In the theoretical treatment of efficiencies, the practical aspects are often overlooked. This is especially so in connection with the Carnot cycle. The student is advised to plot out the pressure-volume diagram for 1 lb. of air on this cycle between temperature limits of say 600° F. abs. and 4,000° F. abs. resulting in an indicator diagram rather like a thin crescent, involving very high pressures, very large volumes, and a low m.e.p. Such an engine could be built, but it would be so large, have so small power and present such mechanical difficulties that it would not be an economic proposition. In practice, we are concerned with the overall economic

efficiency in which the theoretical efficiency of the cycle may be completely obscured by considerations of space, availability, speed, auxiliary gear required, safety, reliability and initial cost.

Also in connection with cycles, it must be realized that the working fluid is passed from state to state, always being returned to the original state after completion of the various phases in regular order. Consider 1 lb. of air at 30 lb. per sq. in. and 60° F. Allow this air to expand isothermally to 15 lb. per sq. in., supplying heat to keep the temperature constant at 60° F. The work done by the air is equal to the heat supplied and at first sight it would appear that we have 100% conversion of heat into work. This is only *one phase* of a cycle, and we could not repeat the process unless we had inexhaustible supplies of air at 30 lb. per sq. in. In order to complete the cycle, we should need to pass the air through other phases to restore the air to its original condition of 30 lb. per sq. in. and the efficiency of the cycle, whatever it may be, could not exceed the Carnot efficiency.

15. The thermal efficiency of any cycle, ideal or actual, may be found as the ratio $\dfrac{\text{work done}}{\text{heat supplied}}$.

In ideal cycles *only*, the work done is usually found as the difference between the heat supplied and the heat rejected. This is only possible because in these cases the expansions and compressions are adiabatic.

16. It will be clear from article 2, this section, that if C_p and C_v are taken to be variable, i.e. functions of temperature, then γ will also be a function of temperature. The adiabatic index is thus not an absolute constant for a gas, as is the characteristic constant, R.

If a change in Internal Energy is calculated for a gas with variable specific heats, we shall have to write down the normal relation (I,19) in terms of a small change, and then carry out an integration. Thus,

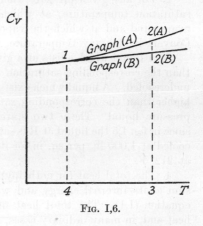

FIG. I,6.

$$dE = wC_v\, dT = w(a + k_1 T + k_2 T^2)dT.$$

Integrating,

$$E_2 - E_1 = w\left[aT + \frac{k_1}{2}T^2 + \frac{k_2}{3}T^3\right]_{T_1}^{T_2}$$

$$= w\left\{a(T_2 - T_1) + \frac{k_1}{2}(T_2{}^2 - T_1{}^2) + \frac{k_2}{3}(T_2{}^3 - T_1{}^3)\right\}.$$

Thus, the change in E must be found by integration, i.e. as the area 1–2A–3–4 under the graph (A) in fig. I,6. If, however, C_v is taken as

$(a + k_1\text{T})$ only, graph (B) will result and the " mean " value of C_v over the temperature range T_1 to T_2 may be used to find E ; for, neglecting the term involving k_2,

$$\text{E}_2 - \text{E}_1 = w\left\{a(\text{T}_2 - \text{T}_1) + \frac{k_1}{2}(\text{T}_2{}^2 - \text{T}_1{}^2)\right\}$$

$$= w(\text{T}_2 - \text{T}_1)\left\{a + k_1\left(\frac{\text{T}_2 + \text{T}_1}{2}\right)\right\}$$

$$= w(\text{T}_2 - \text{T}_1) \times \text{C}_v \text{ mean}$$

and this is equal to the area 1–2B–3–4 in fig. I,6.

This simplification must however be used to find $\varDelta$E only. In the case of $\varDelta\phi$, when the specific heats are variable in *any* manner, an integration must be carried out without exception.

Section C.   Properties of Vapours and their Liquids
(with special reference to steam and water)

1. A substance is said to exist as a vapour when its temperature is below the critical temperature, i.e. liquefaction at constant temperature is possible by compression (cf. fig. I,5).

2. For any given pressure, there is one definite temperature, called the saturation temperature, at which a liquid may be partially or wholly evaporated and at which the vapour may exist in contact with its liquid. Conversely, for any temperature, there is a definite saturation pressure.

3. A liquid which exists at a given pressure and at a temperature lower than the corresponding saturation temperature is said to be supercooled or undercooled. A liquid which exists at a given temperature and at a pressure higher than the corresponding saturation pressure is said to be a super-pressure liquid. These two statements refer to the same phenomenon since in fig. I,5 the liquid at R is saturated ; at T it may be said to be super-cooled at 1,000 lb. per sq. in. or it may be said to be superpressure liquid at 212° F.

4. The total heat (or enthalpy) of any liquid or vapour is given as the sum of its internal energy and work of introduction in accordance with equation (I,1). The total heat of a liquid is referred to as its sensible heat and, in many ordinary cases, such as for water, will be approximately equal to the internal energy of the liquid, the volume of the liquid and hence its PV term being small. If a liquid is partially evaporated by the addition of latent heat, the resulting vapour is said to be wet, and the dryness fraction is defined as

$$x = \frac{\text{H} - h}{\text{L}}$$

where H = total heat or enthalpy of the wet vapour
   h = sensible heat or enthalpy of the liquid
   L = latent heat of evaporation.

The dryness fraction is thus the fraction of latent heat possessed by the vapour and can never exceed 1, numerically. When $x = 1$, $H = H_s$, the total heat of dry saturated vapour. Further heating of dry saturated steam at constant pressure will produce a rise in temperature, i.e. a superheated vapour, and since the specific heat of most vapours varies considerably, except over small ranges of temperature, the total heat cannot easily be calculated. The total heat of superheated vapour will be referred to as H_{sup}, and is usually obtained from tables.

5. We thus have two possible equations for the total heat of a vapour :

$$H = E + a\,PV \qquad . \qquad . \qquad . \qquad . \quad (I,1)$$

and

$$H = h + xL \qquad . \qquad . \qquad . \qquad . \qquad (I,24)$$

or

$$H = H_{sup} \qquad . \qquad . \qquad . \qquad . \qquad (I,24a)$$

one of the latter two being frequently used to find H, and (I,1) being then used to find E.

6. The entropy of boiling water will be denoted by ϕ_w, that for dry saturated steam by ϕ_s, and that for superheated steam by ϕ_{sup}. By analogy with total heat quantities, we define the " latent entropy " as

$$\phi_L = \phi_s - \phi_w = \frac{L}{T} \qquad . \qquad . \qquad . \qquad (I,25)$$

so that the entropy of wet vapour will be given by

$$\phi = \phi_w + x\phi_L \qquad . \qquad . \qquad . \qquad (I,26)$$

Again, ϕ_{sup} is usually obtained from tables.

It is possible, by going back to the definition of entropy, equation (I,3), to express $\delta Q = ws\,\delta T$ for a constant pressure operation, where s is the specific heat at constant pressure of the fluid. (I,3) then becomes $ws\,\delta T = T\,\delta\phi$, which gives on integration,

$$\phi_2 - \phi_1 = s\,\log_e \frac{T_2}{T_1} \qquad . \qquad . \qquad . \qquad (I,27)$$

In the case of boiling water, and for a datum as defined in article 7 below, this can be written

$$\phi_w = s\,\log_e \frac{T}{492} \qquad . \qquad . \qquad . \qquad (I,28)$$

or for a vapour,

$$\phi_{sup} - \phi_s = C_p\,\log_e \frac{T_{sup}}{T_{sat}} \qquad . \qquad . \qquad (I,29)$$

where T_{sup} and T_{sat} are the superheat and saturation temperatures in ° F. abs. respectively. It must be stressed that (I,28) and (I,29) are only applicable when it is reasonable to assume s or C_p to be constant over the range of temperatures used ; whenever possible, reference should be made to tables.

7. Both entropy and internal energy have a numerical value only relative to some more or less arbitrary datum. The datum is selected according to convenience and is laid down by the compiler of the particular

set of tables which may be in use. In the case of the steam tables used throughout this book (*Abridged Callendar Steam Tables*), the datum is at 32° F., at which h, E, and ϕ are all zero (cf. article 4, section A).

In the case of other vapours, notably refrigeration vapours, other data are chosen, such as — 40 degrees which is the same on the Centigrade and Fahrenheit scales. Reference to data other than 32° F. will be found in the text.

8. The volume of liquids and vapours is usually found from tables. For steam, in particular, we follow Callendar's procedure and determine the volume of water from the relation given on page 1 of the steam tables. Thus,

$$V_w = 0.01602 + 0.000023 \text{ G, cu. ft. per lb.} \qquad . \qquad \text{(I,30)}$$

where G is the water potential, or Gibbs' Function, or Thermodynamic Potential (see article 10 below).

The volume of dry saturated steam V_s is tabulated in Table I of the steam tables. Then the volume of wet steam will be

$$V = xV_s + (1 - x)V_w$$

or very nearly

$$V = xV_s \qquad . \qquad . \qquad . \qquad . \qquad . \qquad \text{(I,31)}$$

the term $(1 - x)V_w$ usually being too small in the case of steam to influence xV_s which is governed by the accuracy of the tabulated values of V_s.

The volume of superheated steam is calculated from the formula

$$V_{sup} = \frac{1.253(H_{sup} - 835)}{P} \text{ cu. ft. per lb.} \qquad . \qquad \text{(I,32)}$$

given on the last page of the steam tables. N.B.—P is in lb. per sq. in., and no conversion factor is needed.

9. Fig. I,7 shows a diagram of absolute temperature plotted against entropy, for H_2O. Note that the liquid line intersects the temperature axis at 492° F. in accordance with our datum. The diagram is approximately to scale, except for the constant pressure lines for water which are shown as diverging from the liquid saturation curve to a greater extent than they actually do. For most practical purposes these " whiskers " coincide with the saturation curve. Constant Quality, or Dryness lines and constant volume lines are also indicated.

10. The Gibbs' Function G[1] which was used to calculate the specific volume of water (equ. I,30) can be represented graphically on a T-ϕ chart. Thus in fig. I,8, G for water at the state point A will be the shaded area OFA intercepted by the liquid saturation line and the T-axis. The values of G are thus seen to be a function of temperature, and they will be

---

[1] G is used as a positive number by Engineers. The original definition of this function was given by Willard Gibbs as $\zeta = H - T\phi$, so that strictly $\zeta = - G$. This original definition is still used in Chemical Thermodynamics and Chemical Engineers especially should note the difference of definition.

found in Table I of the steam tables. Thus, V_w (equ. I,30) is a function of temperature only, the very small compressibility, or Bulk Modulus effect being usually neglected in Thermodynamics.

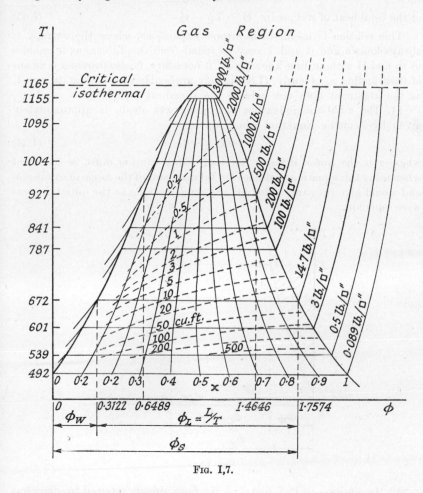

FIG. I,7.

The function G is also useful in another way. Let the water at A be evaporated completely, giving state point B. From the geometry of fig. I,8

area EOAD $= h_A$, the pressure energy of water being negligible under
saturation conditions (cf. article 4, section A)

area EOABC $= h + L$

$$T\phi_s - G = h + L = H_s.$$

C

If the evaporation were only carried as far as K, where

$$EM = \phi = \phi_w + x\phi_L,$$

then $$T\phi - G = h + xL$$

or the total heat of wet steam, $H = T\phi - G$.   .   .   .   (I,33)

This relation is useful in isentropic expansions, where the entropy is always known and G and T may be found from the Tables, as it enables us to find H without first knowing x; if necessary, it also provides a means of then finding x. Clearly, (I,33) is only applicable up to the state $x = 1$, as the argument does not hold in the superheat region.

11. The adiabatic index for expanding wet steam is approximately given by Zeuner's Equation which states

$$n = 1 \cdot 035 + 0 \cdot 1x$$.   .   .   .   (I,34)

where x is the *initial* dryness fraction. Some caution must be exercised when using this equation as it does not take account of the range of expansion and would give the same value for any range, so long as the initial dryness were common.

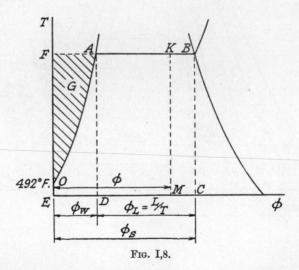

Fig. I,8.

12. In addition to P–V and T–ϕ diagrams already referred to, diagrams of H–ϕ (Total Heat–Entropy) are used a great deal and the student should possess a printed H–ϕ chart for steam (*Total Heat Entropy Chart for Steam*, 1939, Fahrenheit Units, Edward Arnold & Co.) as reference to this will frequently be made. Diagrams of Pressure–Total Heat, and of Total Heat–Entropy in non-rectangular co-ordinates are also useful and they will be discussed in the appropriate chapter.

13. In the preceding articles, reference has been made to " operations ", changing the pressure, volume, temperature, internal energy, etc. from

some state " 1 " to some other state " 2 ". Equations such as (I,1a) refer to the changes during such an " operation " or " *phase* ". In general, the working fluid in a heat engine will pass through a number of such phases in cyclic order ; hence an engine is said to work on a " cycle " which consists of a number of " phases ".

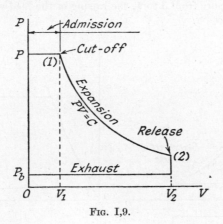

FIG. I,9.

Fig. I,9 shows the hypothetical indicator diagram for a simple single-acting steam engine, assuming hyperbolic expansion and neglecting clearance volume.

Net W.D. in cycle = W.D. during admission + W.D. during

$$\text{expansion} + \text{W.D. during exhaust} = P_1 V_1 + P_1 V_1 \log_e \frac{V_2}{V_1} - P_b V_2$$

and mean effective pressure,

$$\text{m.e.p.} = \frac{\text{W.D. in cycle}}{\text{Stroke Volume}} = \frac{\text{area of diagram}}{\text{length of diagram}}$$

$$\text{m.e.p.} = \frac{P_1(1 + \log_e r)}{r} - P_b \quad . \quad . \quad . \quad . \quad (I,35)$$

where $r = \dfrac{V_2}{V_1} = $ expansion ratio.

The hypothetical diagram of fig. 9 is essentially artificial, in that it makes a great many assumptions which are subsequently rectified by introducing a diagram factor k, such that

$$k = \frac{\text{actual m.e.p.}}{\text{hypothetical m.e.p.}} \quad . \quad . \quad . \quad (I,36)$$

The hyperbolic mode of expansion is only possible if heat energy can flow into the steam during the expansion stroke. This cycle shows the state of affairs within the engine cylinder only.

Against this, we have the " Flow " or " thermodynamic " cycle, shown in fig. I,10, which is also known as the Rankine Cycle. This is the thermodynamic cycle, because it depicts not only an isentropic expansion in the engine or turbine from 1 to 2, but also the condensation, without undercooling, in the condenser from 2 to 3, the raising of the feed water pressure to the boiler pressure from 3 to 4, the raising of the feed water temperature

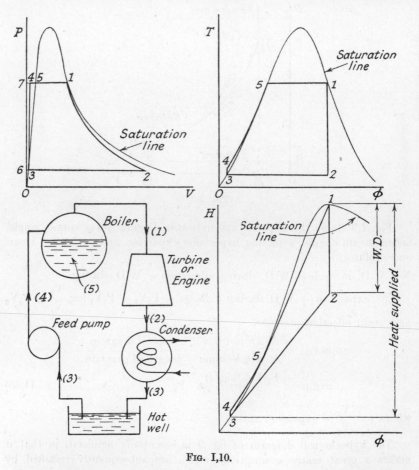

FIG. I,10.

to the saturation temperature corresponding to the boiler pressure from 4 to 5, and the evaporation of the water from 5 to 1. The point 1 may be in the wet region, on the vapour saturation curve, or in the superheat region. Neglecting the relatively small amount of P–V area 3674, which is shown to an exaggerated scale in fig. I,10, the work done in the whole flow cycle 12671, from the P–V diagram is

$$\text{W.D.} = P_1 V_1 + \text{W.D. during phase (1-2)} - P_2 V_2.$$

But the phase expansion 1-2 takes place at constant entropy under adiabatic conditions, so from (I,2)

$$Q = 0 = \varDelta E + \text{W.D.}$$

i.e. $\text{W.D.}_{1-2} = -\varDelta E = E_1 - E_2$

and whole cycle $\text{W.D.} = P_1 V_1 + (E_1 - E_2) - P_2 V_2$

$$= (E_1 + P_1 V_1) - (E_2 + P_2 V_2)$$

$$\text{W.D.} = H_1 - H_2 \quad . \quad . \quad . \quad . \quad . \quad (I,37)$$

It cannot be overemphasized that $H_1 - H_2$, or the heat drop through the actual engine or turbine, is the work done in the *whole* cycle, the expansion phase being resisted and taking place without loss.

Neglecting the feed pump work, we have

$$\text{Rankine } \eta = \frac{\text{work done}}{\text{heat supplied}} = \frac{H_1 - H_2}{H_1 - h_2} \quad . \quad . \quad . \quad (I,38)$$

h_2 being the sensible heat of saturated liquid at the condenser pressure which heat is returned to the boiler. N.B. $h_2 = h_3$.

The stage 4-5, fig. I,10, may take place in an economizer, etc. as an integral part of the boiler, or may be partially carried out in special feed heaters between the feed pump and the boiler, or more commonly between the hot well and the feed pump, the necessary heat being frequently supplied by bleeding live steam from the boiler or turbine.

The work done in the flow-cycle, which has been shown to be equal to the isentropic heat drop 1-2, can also be expressed in terms of pressures and volumes, thus :

$$\text{Isentropic Heat Drop} = \text{W.D.} = P_1 V_1 + \frac{P_1 V_1 - P_2 V_2}{n - 1} - P_2 V_2$$

$$= \frac{n}{n-1}(P_1 V_1 - P_2 V_2)$$

$$= \frac{n}{n-1} P_1 V_1 \left[1 - \left(\frac{P_2}{P_1} \right)^{\frac{n-1}{n}} \right] \quad . \quad . \quad (I,39)$$

The expressions (I,37) and (I,39) have their use for different applications which will be discussed later in the relevant chapters, together with the limitations in their application.

14. By considering a Carnot cycle working over a small temperature range δT, it may be shown that for any vapour

$$V = J \frac{xL}{T} \frac{dT}{dP}, \text{ very nearly} \quad . \quad . \quad . \quad (I,40)$$

where V is the specific volume of the vapour at the temperature T. This relation is known as Clapeyron's equation.

CHAPTER II

GAS LAWS

1. *Prove that the index γ in PV^γ = c for the adiabatic expansion of a gas is the ratio of the specific heats at constant pressure and constant volume. A certain gas occupies 4 cu. ft. at 15 lb. per sq. in. and 68° F. It is compressed adiabatically to a pressure of 100 lb. per sq. in. Find the new temperature, the new volume and the change in internal energy of the gas, given that the density is 0·0868 lb. per cu. ft. at N.T.P. and C_v = 0·175.*
(U. Lond.)

The characteristic gas equation is PV = RT, per lb. of gas.
Differentiating implicitly,

$$P \, dV + V \, dP = R \, dT.$$

Substituting from (I,6),
$$= JC_v^{\cdot}\left(\frac{C_p}{C_v} - 1\right)dT.$$

$$C_v \, dT = \frac{P \, dV + V \, dP}{J(\gamma - 1)}, \text{ where } \gamma = \frac{C_p}{C_v}.$$

But $C_v \, dT$ is the change in internal energy, per lb. of gas,
∴ from the conservation of energy equation (I,2), where Q = 0 for an adiabatic operation,

$$0 = \frac{P \, dV + V \, dP}{J(\gamma - 1)} + \frac{P \, dV}{J}, \text{ all in heat units,}$$

$$-(\gamma - 1)P \, dV = P \, dV + V \, dP$$
$$-\gamma P \, dV = V \, dP.$$

Separating the variables, $-\gamma\dfrac{dV}{V} = \dfrac{dP}{P}.$

Integrating, $-\gamma \log_e V = \log_e P - \log_e$ (constant).

∴ PV^γ = Constant. Q.E.D.

The density of a gas is usually referred to 32° F., so that by assigning this meaning to normal temperature from (I,7)

$$R = \frac{14·7 \times 144 \times 1}{0·0868 \times 492} = 49·55 \text{ ft.lb. per lb. } ° F.$$

By (I,6) $C_p - 0·1750 = \dfrac{49·55}{778}$

$$C_p = 0·1750 + 0·0637 = 0·2387$$

$$\therefore \gamma = \frac{0·2387}{0·1750} = 1·364.$$

Applying (I,18), $\qquad T_2 = 528\left(\dfrac{100}{15}\right)^{\frac{1\cdot364-1}{1\cdot364}}$

$\qquad\qquad\qquad\qquad = 528(6\cdot667)^{0\cdot267}.$

By slide rule evaluation, $\qquad = 528 \times 1\cdot660 = 877°$ F. abs.

$\qquad\qquad\qquad\qquad\qquad\qquad\qquad \underline{t_2 = 417°\ \text{F.}}\quad$ Ans.

Again, $\qquad P_2V_2{}^\gamma = P_1V_1{}^\gamma$

$\qquad\qquad\left(\dfrac{V_2}{V_1}\right)^\gamma = \dfrac{15}{100}$

$\qquad\qquad V_2 = 4\left(\dfrac{1}{6\cdot667}\right)^{\frac{1}{1\cdot364}} = 4 \times \dfrac{1}{4\cdot01}.$

$\qquad\qquad\qquad\qquad \underline{V_2 = 1\cdot0\ \text{cu. ft.}}\ \text{very nearly.}\quad$ Ans.

or, since $\dfrac{P_1V_1}{T_1} = \dfrac{P_2V_2}{T_2},\quad \dfrac{100 \times V_2}{876\cdot5} = \dfrac{4 \times 15}{528},\quad \therefore\ V_2 = 1\cdot0$ very nearly.

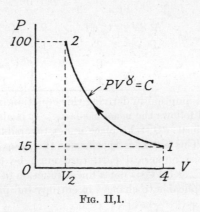

Fig. II,1.

From (I,19) $\quad E_2 - E_1 = wC_v(T_2 - T_1).$

In order to evaluate this, we must first find the mass of gas present, by applying the characteristic equation; thus

$$w = \frac{15 \times 144 \times 4}{49\cdot55 \times 528} = 0\cdot330\ \text{lb.},$$

whence $\qquad \Delta E = 0\cdot330 \times 0\cdot175 \times (416\cdot5 - 68).$

$\qquad\qquad\qquad \underline{\Delta E = +\ 20\cdot1\ \text{B.T.U.}},\ \text{i.e. an increase.}\quad$ Ans.

It should be noted that this question refers only to changes during " phase " or " non-flow " types of processes, as shown in fig. II,1.

2. *Show that, for a substance the equation of state of which is $PV = RT$, the entropy is given by*

$$\phi - \phi_0 = \frac{R}{J} \log \frac{V}{V_0} + \int_{T_0}^{T} \frac{C_v dT}{T}$$

State your assumptions and define the symbols.

For air, $R = 53 \cdot 5$ ft. per ° F. abs. $C_v = 0 \cdot 171 + (3 \cdot 3 \times 10^{-9})T^2$ B.T.U. per lb. ° F., where T is in ° F. abs.

Taking $\phi = 0$ at $32°$ F. and $14 \cdot 7$ lb. per sq. in., find ϕ at $1{,}040°$ F. and 500 lb. per sq. in. (U. Dur.)

The general approach to all entropy relations of this type is to recall the definition of $\delta\phi$ in equation (I,3), i.e. $dQ = T \, d\phi$, and then to express dQ in terms of a change in internal energy and work done (I,2).

Thus,
$$dQ = dE + \frac{P \, dV}{J}.$$

By (I,19) and dividing by T,

$$\frac{dQ}{T} = \frac{P \, dV}{JT} + \frac{C_v \, dT}{T} \quad \text{per lb.},$$

i.e.
$$d\phi = \frac{R}{J} \frac{dV}{V} + \frac{C_v \, dT}{T}, \quad \therefore \ \frac{P}{T} = \frac{R}{V}.$$

Integrating,
$$\phi - \phi_0 = \frac{R}{J} \log_e \frac{V}{V_0} + \int_{T_0}^{T} \frac{C_v \, dT}{T} \quad \text{per lb.} \quad \text{Q.E.D.}$$

The principal assumption in deriving this equation is that the substance is a perfect gas and follows the usual gas laws. It is also assumed that the small additions of heat, dQ, take place under reversible conditions, otherwise $dQ \neq T \, d\phi$. This excludes specifically the cases of fluid friction.

In evaluating the numerical part, care must be taken not to use a " mean " value of C_v as (a) C_v is not a linear function of T and (b) " mean " values are never applicable to changes in entropy (cf. page 14).

$$\phi = \frac{R}{J} \log_e \left(\frac{P_0}{P} \frac{T}{T_0} \right) + \int_{492}^{1{,}500} \left[\frac{0 \cdot 171}{T} + (3 \cdot 3 \times 10^{-9})T \right] dT$$

$$= \frac{53 \cdot 5}{778} \log_e \left(\frac{14 \cdot 7}{500} \times \frac{1{,}500}{492} \right) + 0 \cdot 171 \log_e \frac{1{,}500}{492} + \frac{3 \cdot 3 \times 10^{-9}}{2} (1{,}500^2 - 492^2)$$

$$= - \frac{53 \cdot 5}{778} \log_e 11 \cdot 17 + 0 \cdot 171 \log_e 3 \cdot 05 + \frac{1 \cdot 65}{10^9} \times 1{,}992 \times 1{,}008$$

$$= - 0 \cdot 166 + 0 \cdot 191 + 0 \cdot 0033.$$

$$\underline{\phi = + 0 \cdot 028.} \quad \text{Ans.}$$

3. *One pound of air is compressed according to the law* $PV^{1.25} = const.$
*from a pressure of 15 lb. per sq. in. and a temperature of 15° C. to a pressure
of 240 lb. per sq. in. Calculate the temperature at the end of the compression,
the heat received or rejected by the air during the process and the change of
entropy. Sketch the operation on an entropy–temperature diagram.*

Specific heat at constant pressure = 0·240
Specific heat at constant volume = 0·171

(*I.C.E.*)

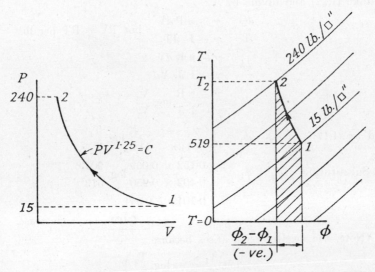

Fig. II,2.

$$T_1 = \left(15 \times \frac{9}{5} + 32\right) + 460 = 519° \text{ F. abs.}$$

From (I,18)

$$T_2 = 519\left(\frac{240}{15}\right)^{\frac{1.25-1}{1.25}} = 519 \times 16^{\frac{1}{5}}.$$

$$\underline{T_2 = 904° \text{ F. abs.}} \quad \text{Ans.}$$

Now, $\quad \dfrac{R}{J} = C_p - C_v = 0\cdot069 \quad$ and $\quad \gamma = \dfrac{C_p}{C_v} = 1\cdot402.$

From (I,4) $\quad$ W.D. $= \dfrac{P_1V_1 - P_2V_2}{J(n-1)}$ heat units

and from (I,7) $\quad -\dfrac{R}{J} \cdot \dfrac{T_1 - T_2}{n-1}$ B.T.U. per lb.

$$= \frac{0\cdot069}{0\cdot25}(519 - 904).$$

W.D. $= -106\cdot2$ B.T.U. per lb., i.e. work done *on* the gas.

$\therefore$ By (I,22) $Q = -106 \cdot 2 \times \dfrac{1 \cdot 402 - 1 \cdot 250}{0 \cdot 402}.$

$$Q = -40 \cdot 2 \text{ B.T.U. per lb.}\quad\text{Ans.}$$

This amount of heat *rejected* is shown as the hatched area on the T-ϕ diagram, fig. II,2.

There are several ways of finding $\Delta\phi$; e.g. equation (I,21) may be rewritten in terms of temperatures and pressures (which are all known) or take (I,22) and divide by T :

$$\frac{dQ}{T} = \frac{\gamma - n}{\gamma - 1}\frac{P\, dV}{JT},\quad\text{but PV = RT per lb.}$$

$$\therefore d\phi = \frac{\gamma - n}{\gamma - 1}\frac{R}{J}\frac{dV}{V}$$

$$\phi_2 - \phi_1 = \frac{\gamma - n}{\gamma - 1}\frac{R}{J}\log_e\frac{V_2}{V_1}$$

and by (I,17) $\phi_2 - \phi_1 = \dfrac{\gamma - n}{(\gamma - 1)(n - 1)}\dfrac{R}{J}\log_e\dfrac{T_1}{T_2}.$

Substituting, $\phi_2 - \phi_1 = -\dfrac{0 \cdot 152 \times 0 \cdot 069}{0 \cdot 402 \times 0 \cdot 250}\log_e\dfrac{904}{519}$

$$= -0 \cdot 1042 \times 0 \cdot 554.$$

$$= -0 \cdot 058,\text{ i.e. a decrease.}\quad\text{Ans.}$$

(Note, the negative sign arises because

$$\log_e\frac{T_1}{T_2} = -\log_e\frac{T_2}{T_1}\Big)$$

---

4. *A cylinder contains 4 cu. ft. of a gas at 15 lb. per sq. in. and 90° C. (194° F.). The gas is compressed to a volume of 1 cu. ft., the final pressure being 85 lb. per sq. in. Determine :*

(a) *the weight of gas in the cylinder ;*
(b) *the value of the index " n " for the compression ;*
(c) *the increase in internal energy of the gas ;*
(d) *the heat received or rejected by the gas during the compression.*

If, after the above compression, the gas is to be cooled at constant pressure to its original temperature of 90° C. (194° F.), find the further work of compression required.

$\gamma = 1 \cdot 4,\ R = 100$ *ft.lb. per lb. per ° C. or 55·6 ft.lb. per lb. per ° F.*

(*U.L.C.I.*)

The known data are :

$V_1 = 4$ cu. ft., $P_1 = 15$ lb. per sq. in., $T_1 = 194 + 460 = 654°$ F. abs., $V_2 = 1$ cu. ft., $P_2 = 85$ lb. per sq. in.

(a)
$$PV = wRT.$$
$$w = \frac{15 \times 144 \times 4}{55 \cdot 6 \times 654} = 0 \cdot 238 \text{ lb.} \quad \text{Ans.}$$

(b)
$$P_1 V_1{}^n = P_2 V_2{}^n$$
$$\left(\frac{4}{1}\right)^n = \frac{85}{15}.$$

$$n = 1 \cdot 250. \quad \text{Ans.}$$

(c)
$$\varDelta E = wC_v(T_2 - T_1).$$

Now by (I,17)
$$T_2 = 654 \times \left(\frac{4}{1}\right)^{1 \cdot 250 - 1}.$$

$$T_2 = 654 \times 1 \cdot 414 = 925° \text{ F. abs.}$$

and by (I,6) and (I,14)
$$C_v = \frac{R}{J(\gamma - 1)} = \frac{55 \cdot 6}{778 \times 0 \cdot 4} = 0 \cdot 1787$$

$$\therefore E_2 - E_1 = 0 \cdot 238 \times 0 \cdot 1787(925 - 654)$$
$$E_2 - E_1 = 11 \cdot 53 \text{ B.T.U., i.e. an increase.} \quad \text{Ans.}$$

(d) We shall now need to find the work done on the gas during the compression.

$$\text{W.D.} = \frac{144}{1 \cdot 250 - 1}(15 \times 4 - 85 \times 1), \text{ by (I,4)}$$

$$= -144 \times 4 \times 25$$
$$= -14{,}400 \text{ ft.lb.} = -18 \cdot 51 \text{ B.T.U.}$$

Either by (I,2)

$$Q = +11 \cdot 53 - 18 \cdot 51$$

$$\underline{Q = -6 \cdot 98 \text{ B.T.U.} \quad \text{Ans.}}$$

Or by (I,22)

$$Q = \frac{1 \cdot 4 - 1 \cdot 25}{0 \cdot 4}(-18 \cdot 51)$$

$$\underline{Q = -6 \cdot 94 \text{ B.T.U.} \quad \text{Ans.}}$$

i.e. heat is rejected by the gas (as would be expected in a compression where $n < \gamma$). The slight difference in the answers is due to slide rule inaccuracy.

(e) Further work done at constant pressure is

$$= P(V_3 - V_2) = wR(T_3 - T_2)$$
$$= 0 \cdot 238 \times 55 \cdot 6 \times (654 - 925)$$

$$= -3{,}580 \text{ ft.lb.} = \underline{-4 \cdot 62 \text{ B.T.U.},}$$

i.e. work done *on* the gas. Ans.

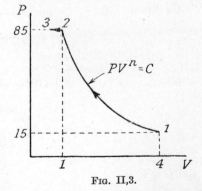

Fig. II,3.

5. *Establish the relationship that exists between the specific heats of a gas and the universal gas constant.*

Discuss the basis on which the characteristic equation $PV = RT$ is founded. State what the various symbols in the following equations represent :

$$PV = CwT \ ; \ \ PV = \frac{RwT}{m} \ ; \ \ PV^\gamma = constant.$$

The initial volume of 0·4 lb. of gas was 5·38 cu. ft. at a temperature of 15° C. and a pressure of 15 lb. per sq. in. After adiabatic compression to 2 cu. ft. the pressure was found to be 60·9 lb. per sq. in.

Find : (a) *The constant for this gas ;* (b) *The molecular weight of this gas ;* (c) *The ratio of the specific heats ;* (d) *The specific heat at constant pressure ;* (e) *The specific heat at constant volume.*

(U.L.C.I.)

The symbols used in this question are slightly different from the ones used in these pages and as defined in chapter I.

The proof will be found in any first-year textbook on Heat Engines.

In $PV = CwT$, C is the characteristic gas constant in ft.lb. per lb. ° F., P is the pressure in lb. per sq. ft., V is the volume in cu. ft., w is the mass in lb., and T is the absolute temperature in ° F.

In $PV = \dfrac{RwT}{m}$, R is the universal gas constant in ft.lb. per lb.mol ° F., m is the molecular weight of the gas, and the other symbols have the same meaning as above. N.B. $\dfrac{w}{m} =$ number of lb.mols.

Now, $V_1 = 5\cdot38$ in.ft., $T_1 = \left(\dfrac{15 \times 9}{5} + 32 \right) + 460 = 519°$ F. abs.

$P_1 = 15$ lb. per sq. in., $V_2 = 2$ cu. ft., $P_2 = 60\cdot9$ lb. per sq. in.

(a) $PV = wCT$, i.e. $15 \times 144 \times 5\cdot38 = 0\cdot4 \times 519 \times C.$
characteristic constant, $\underline{C = 56\cdot0 \text{ ft.lb. per lb. ° F.}}$ Ans.

(b) From (I,9)   molecular weight $= \dfrac{1\cdot985 \times 778}{56\cdot0} = \underline{27\cdot6}.$ Ans.

(c) $P_1 V_1{}^\gamma = P_2 V_2{}^\gamma, \ \therefore \left(\dfrac{5\cdot38}{2} \right)^\gamma = \dfrac{60\cdot9}{15} \ \ \underline{\gamma = 1\cdot418}.$ Ans.

(d) $\dfrac{C_p}{C_v} = 1\cdot418$ and $C_p - C_v = \dfrac{56\cdot0}{778}.$

$\therefore C_p = \dfrac{56\cdot0}{778 \left(1 - \dfrac{1}{1\cdot418} \right)} = \dfrac{56\cdot0}{778 \times 0\cdot295} = \underline{0\cdot244}.$ Ans.

(e) $C_v = \dfrac{0\cdot244}{1\cdot418} = \underline{0\cdot1725}.$ Ans.

6. *Derive the formula* $T^b V^{a-b} e^{ST} = constant$ *for the adiabatic expansion of a gas, if* $C_p = a + ST$ *and* $C_v = b + ST$, *where a, b and S are constants and T is in* ° *F. abs.*

Find the work done if a quantity of gas weighing 2 lb. and originally occupying 2 cu. ft. at 600 lb. per sq. in., expands adiabatically until the temperature is 500° F., given that $a = 0\cdot227$, $b = 0\cdot157$, *and* $S = 0\cdot000025$.

(*U. Lond.*)

Since the expansion is adiabatic, the starting point will be to put $Q = 0$ in (I,2) which becomes, in terms of small quantities,

$$0 = C_v \, dT + \frac{P \, dV}{J} = (b + ST)dT + \frac{RT}{JV}dV, \quad \text{from (I,7)}.$$

But $\dfrac{R}{J} = a - b$ (cf. corollary to I,6), hence, dividing through by T,

$$0 = b\frac{dT}{T} + S \, dT + (a - b)\frac{dV}{V}.$$

Integrating,   constant $= b \log_e T + ST + (a - b) \log_e V$

or $T^b V^{a-b} e^{ST} = \text{constant}.$ Ans.

In many cases of adiabatic operations, particularly when γ is not constant, it is best to find the phase work by applying (I,2),

i.e.   W.D. $= - \Delta E = - (E_2 - E_1).$

Now, the characteristic equation gives us T_1 :

$$600 \times 144 \times 2 = 2 \times 54\cdot5 \times T_1$$

$$T_1 = 1585° \text{ F. abs.}$$

[R $= 778(a - b) = 778 (0\cdot227 - 0\cdot157) = 54\cdot5$ ft.lb. per lb. ° F.]

and $T_2 = 960°$ F. abs. is given.

$$\therefore \text{ W.D.} = - \int_{1,585}^{960} 2C_v \, dT, \quad \because \ w = 2 \text{ lb.}$$

$$= 2\int_{960}^{1,585} (0\cdot157 + 0\cdot000025T)dT$$

$$= 2\left[0\cdot157 \, T + \frac{0\cdot000025}{2} \, T^2 \right]_{960}^{1,585}$$

W.D. $= 236$ B.T.U.   Ans.

This is an example involving a change in internal energy in terms of linearly variable specific heats, and therefore it would be permissible to use " mean " specific heats, as explained on page 14.

7. *One mol of a mixture of octane vapour and air is compressed adiabatically through a volume compression ratio 6 : 1, the mean value of γ being 1·33. The initial temperature and pressure of the mixture are 200° F. and 14·0 lb. per sq. in. At the end of compression the mixture burns at constant volume, the heat released being 32,400 B.T.U. per mol of mixture, and after combustion there is an increase of $7\frac{1}{2}\%$ in the number of molecules.*

Using the mean volumetric heats given below, estimate the temperature and pressure of the products of combustion, assuming no loss of heat to the surroundings.

Mean volumetric heats C_v per mol of products, between the datum temperature of 200° F. and a temperature $t°$ F.:

$t°$ F					1,000	2,000	3,000	4,000	5,000
C_v					5·79	6·19	6·62	6·91	7·11

(*U. Lond.*)

Let points 1, 2, 3 refer to commencement of compression, end of compression, and end of combustion respectively.

By (I,17) $T_2 = 660 \times 6^{0·33} = 1,190°$ F. abs.

also, $P_2 = 14 \times 6^{1·33} = 152$ lb. per sq. in.

By (I,4) and (I,7a)

$$\text{W.D. on gas during compression} = \frac{R_{mol}(T_2 - T_1)}{\gamma - 1}$$

$$= \frac{1·985 \times 530}{0·33} = 3,190 \text{ B.T.U. per lb.mol.}$$

(This is negative work done *by* the gas.)

Note especially that 200° F. is quoted as datum, i.e. $E_1 = 0$.

By (I,2), since the compression is adiabatic, $Q_{1-2} = 0$

           $\therefore$ $E_2 - E_1 = -$ W.D.

i.e. $E_2 = + 3,190$ B.T.U. per mol of mixture.

During constant volume combustion no external work is done,

$\therefore$ by (I,2) $E_3 - E_2 = Q$

                  $E_3 = 3,190 + 32,400$

                       $= 35,600$ B.T.U. per mol of original mixture.

We now have, after combustion, by (I,19) $E_3 = 1·075 \times C_v \times (t_3 - 200)$, reckoned from the datum of 200° F. where t_3 is in ° F., *not* absolute. We thus have to find a value for t_3 such that the last equation gives E_3 as 35,600 B.T.U. approx. Since C_v itself depends on t_3 and no simple law of variation for C_v is available, we must solve by trial.

   Say, $t_3 = 4,000$, then $E_3 = 1·075 \times 6·91 \times (4,000 - 200)$

                              $= 28,200$, i.e. an error of $- 7,400$,

   say, $t_3 = 5,000$, then $E_3 = 1·075 \times 7·11 \times 4,800$

                              $= 36,700$, i.e. an error of $+ 1,100$,

$\therefore$ t_3 lies between 4,000 and 5,000° F. and is nearer 5,000° F.

say, $t_3 = 4,800$, then $E_3 = 1\cdot075 \times 7\cdot08 \times 4,600$
$$= 35,000, \text{ i.e, an error of } - 600,$$

where the value of $7\cdot08$ is read off a graph obtained by plotting the given values of C_v against t.   (It is left as an exercise for the student to verify this.)   If the error varied linearly, which it does not strictly do, t_3 would

now be $4,800 + 200 \times \dfrac{600}{1,700} = 4,870°$ F.,

say, $t_3 = 4,870$, then from the same graph $C_v \eqsim 7\cdot09$

$E_3 \eqsim 1\cdot075 \times 7\cdot09 \times 4,670$
$E_3 \eqsim 35,600$ B.T.U. per mol of original mixture,

$$\therefore \underline{t_3 = 4,870°\text{ F.}}\quad \text{Ans.}$$

$$\therefore P_3 = P_2 \times \frac{m_3}{m_2} \times \frac{T_3}{T_2}, \text{ from (I,7a)}$$

$$= 152 \times \frac{1\cdot075}{1} \times \frac{5,330}{1,190} = \underline{732 \text{ lb. per sq. in.}}\quad \text{Ans.}$$

N.B.   This example should be studied in conjunction with example No. 12 on page 38.

8. *Deduce an expression for the change in entropy of 1 lb. of gas in terms of the temperatures T_1 and T_2 before and after compression, if the law of compression is $PV^n = $ constant, and the specific heats are of the form*

$$C_p = a + sT \text{ and } C_v = b + sT.$$

The compression ratio of an engine is 11 to 1, and the initial temperature and pressure are 260° F. and 14·2 lb. per sq. in., and the total volume is 51·4 cu. in.   At the end of compression the temperature is 1,020° F.   The values of the constants for the specific heats are : $a = 0\cdot227$, $b = 0\cdot161$ and $s = 0\cdot000025$, T being the absolute temperature.

Find : (a) *the weight of charge undergoing compression, the final pressure, and the index of compression ;* (b) *the change of entropy per lb. of charge ;* (c) *the change in internal energy per lb. of charge.*   (*U. Lond.*)

By (I,2), $dQ = dE + \dfrac{P\,dV}{J}$.

Dividing through by T, $d\phi = \dfrac{C_v\,dT}{T} + \dfrac{P\,dV}{JT}$, per lb.

Substituting for C_v, $d\phi = b\dfrac{dT}{T} + s\,dT + \dfrac{P\,dV}{JT}$.   .   .   (i)

But (I,7) gives $P\,dV + V\,dP = R\,dT$.   .   .   .   (ii)

and $PV^n = c$ gives $nP\,dV = -V\,dP$.   .   (iii)

(ii) and (iii) give $P\,dV - nP\,dV = R\,dT$

i.e.
$$P \, dV = \frac{R \, dT}{1 - n}.$$

Substituting in (i), $\quad d\phi = b\frac{dT}{T} + s \, dT + \frac{R}{J(1 - n)} \frac{dT}{T}$

$$= \left[b - \frac{R}{J(n - 1)} \right]\frac{dT}{T} + s \, dT.$$

Integrating, $\quad \phi_2 - \phi_1 = \left(b - \frac{R}{J} \frac{1}{n - 1} \right) \log_e \frac{T_2}{T_1} + s(T_2 - T_1)$

or $\quad\quad \phi_2 - \phi_1 = \left(b - \frac{a - b}{n - 1} \right) \log_e \frac{T_2}{T_1} + s(T_2 - T_1).$ Q.E.D.

[Note, this is equivalent to the equation quoted as (I,21a).]

(a) $\quad\quad\quad\quad\quad\quad\quad \dfrac{R}{J} = a - b = 0.066$

$$\therefore R = 51.35 \text{ ft.lb. per. lb } ° F.$$
$$PV = wRT$$

$$\therefore 14.2 \times 51.4 \times \frac{1}{12} = w \times 51.35 \times 720$$

$$\underline{w = 0.00164 \text{ lb.}} \quad \text{Ans.}$$

$$\frac{P_1 V_1}{T_1} = \frac{P_2 V_2}{T_2}$$

$$\therefore P_2 = 14.2 \times 11 \times \frac{1,480}{720}$$

$$\underline{P_2 = 322 \text{ lb. per sq. in.}} \quad \text{Ans.}$$

And by (I,17) $\quad\quad \dfrac{1,480}{720} = 11^{n-1} \quad\quad\quad \underline{n = 1.30.} \quad \text{Ans.}$

(b) By substitution in the expression proved above

per lb., $\phi_2 - \phi_1 = \left(0.161 - \dfrac{0.066}{0.30} \right) \log_e \dfrac{1,480}{720} + 0.000025(1,480 - 720)$

$$= (- 0.059 \times 2.3 \times 0.3129) + 0.019$$

$$= \underline{- 0.0236}, \text{ i.e. a decrease.} \quad \text{Ans.}$$

(c) per lb., $E_2 - E_1 = (T_2 - T_1) \times C_{v \text{ mean}} \quad \text{or} \quad \displaystyle\int_{T_1}^{T_2} (b + sT)dT$

$$= (1,480 - 720)\left(0.161 + 0.000025 \times \frac{1,480 + 720}{2} \right)$$

$$= \underline{+ 143.1 \text{ B.T.U.}}, \text{ i.e. a gain.} \quad \text{Ans.}$$

9. *Show that the rate of heat reception or rejection per unit change of volume when a gas is compressed or expanded is given by $\dfrac{\gamma - n}{\gamma - 1} P$ if the specific heats remain constant.*

In an oil engine, the compression curve has a mean value of 1·35 for the index of compression between the values of 20 and 25 lb. per sq. in. The mean rate of piston displacement between these points is 87 cu. ft. per minute. Find the rate of heat rejection per second over the range, if $\gamma = 1·4$.

How would you expect the value of n to change as the compression proceeds? Give your reasons.

(*U. Lond.*)

From (I,2)
$$dQ = C_v \, dT + \frac{P \, dV}{J} \qquad . \qquad . \qquad . \qquad \text{(i)}$$

From (I,7), differentiating implicitly,
$$P \, dV + V \, dP = R \, dT \qquad . \qquad . \qquad . \qquad \text{(ii)}$$

Also,
$$PV^n = \text{constant}$$

Differentiating,
$$PnV^{n-1} \, dV + V^n \, dP = 0.$$

Dividing through by V^{n-1},
$$Pn \, dV = - V \, dP \qquad . \qquad . \qquad . \qquad \text{(iii)}$$

Substituting from (iii) in (ii),
$$dT = \frac{1}{R}(P \, dV - nP \, dV)$$

$\therefore$ in (i)
$$dQ = \frac{C_v}{R}P \, dV(1 - n) + \frac{P \, dV}{J}.$$

But
$$C_v = \frac{R}{J(\gamma - 1)} \quad \text{by (I,6) and (I,14)},$$

$$\therefore J \times dQ = \frac{1 - n}{\gamma - 1}P \, dV + P \, dV.$$

$$J\frac{dQ}{dV} = P\left(\frac{1 - n}{\gamma - 1} + 1\right) = \frac{\gamma - n}{\gamma - 1}P. \quad \text{Q.E.D.}$$

Also,
$$\frac{dQ}{dt} = \frac{dQ}{dV}\frac{dV}{dt}$$

$$\therefore \frac{dQ}{dt} = \left(\frac{1·4 - 1·35}{0·4} \times \frac{22·5 \times 144}{778}\right)\left(\frac{87}{60}\right)$$

$$= 0·757 \text{ B.T.U. per sec. Ans.}$$

The value of n would be expected to decrease as the compression proceeds owing to the higher temperatures which are likely to occur. At first this will be partially balanced by an increase in piston speed tending to

D

raise n, also by the increased density and the smaller cylinder area from which losses may occur. The net effect on n will generally be to decrease towards the end of the compression.

10. *The expansion of a perfect gas is so controlled that the pressure changes according to the law* $P = aV + b$, *where a and b are constants and V is the*

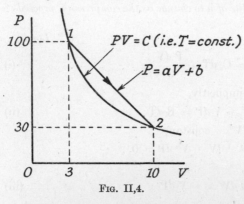

volume. *The mass of the gas is 1·5 lb., and the initial and final pressures are 100 and 30 lb. per sq. in. and the corresponding volumes are 3 and 10 cu. ft. The characteristic gas constant is 48·2 ft.lb. F. units, and γ is 1·39. Find (a) the change in entropy per lb. during the expansion, (b) the maximum value of the internal energy per lb. reckoned from 32° F., (c) the net heat removed or added during the process.* (U. Lond.)

FIG. II,4.

The P–V diagram (for the phase considered) is a straight line, fig. II,4, such that

$$100 = 3a + b$$
$$30 = 10a + b$$

whence, $a = -10$ and $b = 130.$

(a) Applying equation (I,2) to a small change and dividing through by T,

$$\frac{dQ}{T} = \frac{dE}{T} + \frac{P\,dV}{T};$$

substituting from (I,19) and (I,7),

$$\frac{dQ}{T} = C_v \frac{dT}{T} + \frac{R}{J} \frac{dV}{V} \quad \text{per lb. of gas.}$$

By (I,3) and integrating,

$$\phi_2 - \phi_1 = C_v \log_e \frac{T_2}{T_1} + \frac{R}{J} \log_e \frac{V_2}{V_1}.$$

But the data of the question tell us that $P_1V_1 = P_2V_2$, which means that $T_1 = T_2$, for a perfect gas,

$$\therefore \text{ per lb. } \phi_2 - \phi_1 = \frac{48·2}{778} \log_e \frac{10}{3} = +0·0745, \text{ i.e. an increase. Ans.}$$

(b) Although $P_1V_1 = P_2V_2$, i.e. $T_1 = T_2$, it is not true that the temperature of the gas remains constant throughout, as such a path would be represented by a hyperbola $PV = C$ and not a straight line $P = aV + b$. It follows that the temperature will vary as a function of P (or V) where

$$P = aV + b = a\frac{wRT}{P} + b, \text{ from (I,7)}$$

or $$P^2 - bP = awRT.$$

Differentiating implicitly,

$$2P\,dP - b\,dP = awR\,dT$$

$$\frac{dT}{dP} = \frac{2P - b}{awR} = 0, \text{ if } P = \frac{b}{2} = \underline{65 \text{ lb. per sq. in.}}$$

i.e. $\underline{V = 6\cdot5 \text{ cu. ft.}}$

It will be clear by inspection that $(65 \times 6\cdot5)$ is greater than any other PV product on the expansion line and we have thus found the condition for maximum temperature.

Thus $$T_{max.} = \frac{65 \times 144 \times 6\cdot5}{1\cdot5 \times 48\cdot2} = 841\cdot5° \text{ F. abs.}$$

But from (I,14) and (I,6)

$$C_v = \frac{R}{J(\gamma - 1)} = \frac{48\cdot2}{778 \times 0\cdot39}$$

$$C_v = 0\cdot1588$$

By (I,19) $$E = 0\cdot1588(841\cdot5 - 492).$$

$$\underline{E = 55\cdot5 \text{ B.T.U. per lb.,}} \text{ reckoned from } 32° \text{ F. \quad Ans.}$$

(c) By (I,2) $$Q = \Delta E + \text{W.D.}$$

As we are here concerned with the *net* Q between the initial and final state points, $\Delta E = 0$, and the work done is the area under the P–V diagram ; thus

$$Q = 0 + \frac{65 \times 144 \times 7}{778} = \underline{+ 84\cdot2 \text{ B.T.U.} \quad \text{Ans.}}$$

It is worth noting that the heat flowing into the gas during the first portion of the expansion (until $T = 841\cdot5°$ F.) will be greater than $84\cdot2$ B.T.U. due to the increase in internal energy, but for the remainder of the operation heat is rejected again, giving the *net* heat added as $84\cdot2$ B.T.U. The student is advised to check this by finding Q separately for the two parts of the expansion.

11. *Show that when a perfect gas changes from a state represented by $P_1 V_1 T_1$ to another state represented by $P_2 V_2 T_2$, the increase of entropy per unit mass is given by*

$$K_v \log \frac{P_2}{P_1} + K_p \log \frac{V_2}{V_1}.$$

Find the value of n so that the gain of entropy during the heating of the gas at constant volume between temperatures T_1 and T_2 will be the same as that during an expansion according to the law $PV^n = \text{constant}$ between the same temperatures. Show also that the heat supplied per unit mass of gas will be the same in each case. (*U. Camb.*)

The symbols K_v and K_p are used in this question instead of C_v and C_p.

Now, from (I,2) $$\frac{dQ}{T} = \frac{C_v \, dT}{T} + \frac{P \, dV}{JT}$$

and from (I,3) and (I,7) $$d\phi = C_v \frac{dT}{T} + \frac{R}{J} \frac{dV}{V}.$$

Integrating and substituting from (I,6),

$$\phi_2 - \phi_1 = C_v \log_e \frac{T_2}{T_1} + (C_p - C_v) \log_e \frac{V_2}{V_1}.$$

But $$\frac{T_2}{T_1} = \frac{P_2}{P_1} \frac{V_2}{V_1}$$

$$\therefore \ \phi_2 - \phi_1 = C_v \log_e \frac{P_2}{P_1} + C_p \log_e \frac{V_2}{V_1} \text{ per lb.} \quad \text{Q.E.D.}$$

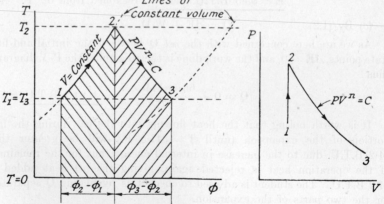

Shaded areas = Heat added

FIG. II,5.

The diagram, fig. II,5, refers to the second part of this question. Note,

$T_1 = T_3$ and $T_2 > T_1$. It follows from the above, at constant volume,

$$\phi_2 - \phi_1 = C_v \log_e \frac{T_2}{T_1} \qquad . \qquad . \qquad . \qquad . \qquad \text{(i)}$$

Now, if $PV^n = C$, we use equations (I,17) and (I,18), viz.

$$\frac{T_2}{T_3} = \left(\frac{P_2}{P_3}\right)^{\frac{n-1}{n}} \text{ and } \frac{T_2}{T_3} = \left(\frac{V_3}{V_2}\right)^{n-1}$$

But we have proved, using appropriate suffices, that

$$\phi_3 - \phi_2 = C_v \log_e \frac{P_3}{P_2} + C_p \log_e \frac{V_3}{V_2}$$

$$\therefore \phi_3 - \phi_2 = C_v \frac{n}{n-1} \log_e \frac{T_3}{T_2} + C_p \frac{1}{n-1} \log_e \frac{T_2}{T_3}$$

$$= \frac{1}{n-1} \log_e \frac{T_2}{T_3} \Big[C_p - nC_v \Big] \qquad . \qquad . \qquad . \qquad \text{(ii)}$$

Equating (i) and (ii) and remembering that $T_3 = T_1$,

$$(n-1)C_v = C_p - nC_v \text{ i.e.} \qquad n = \frac{C_p + C_v}{2C_v}$$

$$n = \tfrac{1}{2}(\gamma + 1). \quad \text{Ans.}$$

At constant volume, $\quad Q_{1-2} = C_v(T_2 - T_1)$ per lb. $\quad . \qquad . \qquad .$ (iii)

But, from (I,2) $\qquad Q_{2-3} = (E_3 - E_2) + \text{W.D.}_{2-3}$

Now, $\text{W.D.}_{2-3} = \dfrac{P_2 V_2 - P_3 V_3}{J(n-1)} \text{ or } \dfrac{R(T_2 - T_3)}{J(n-1)}$ per lb., from (I,7)

$$\therefore Q_{2-3} = C_v(T_3 - T_2) + (C_p - C_v)\left(\frac{T_2 - T_3}{n-1}\right)$$

$$= (T_2 - T_3)\left[\frac{C_p - C_v}{n-1} - C_v\right]$$

where $n = \dfrac{\gamma+1}{2}$, as proved above, and $T_3 = T_1$,

$$\therefore Q_{2-3} = (T_2 - T_1)\left(2\frac{C_p - C_v}{\gamma - 1} - C_v\right)$$

$$= (T_2 - T_1)\left(\frac{C_p - C_v}{\gamma - 1}\right), \quad \because \gamma C_v = C_p$$

$$= C_v(T_2 - T_1)\left(\frac{\gamma - 1}{\gamma - 1}\right)$$

which is identical with (iii) above, $\qquad$ i.e. $Q_{1-2} = Q_{2-3}$. Ans.

The student is advised to study carefully the temperature–entropy diagram, fig. II,5, together with the P–V diagram.

12. (a) *A gas-engine mixture, at 210° F. and 14·7 lb. per sq. in., is compressed adiabatically, the compression ratio being 5 to 1. If the index of adiabatic compression is taken at 1·38, show that the final compression temperature is 1,235° F. abs. Determine, also, the change in internal energy during compression per standard cubic foot of the mixture.*

(b) *Assuming the true volumetric heat of a mixture, consisting of 9 volumes of air to 1 of gas, is (4·95 + 0·00066T) B.T.U. per lb.mol, where T is the temperature F. abs., and the temperature at the end of compression is 1,235° F. abs., show that the temperature at the end of constant-volume combustion is about 4,000° F. abs. The gas has a calorific value of 500 B.T.U. per standard cubic foot, and there is a 3% contraction in volume due to combustion.*

(1 lb.mol = 358 standard cubic feet.)

(*U. Dur.*)

(*a*) By (I,17) $T_2 = 670 \times 5^{0.38} = 670 \times 1.844$

$$= 1,235° \text{ F. abs.} \quad \text{Ans.}$$

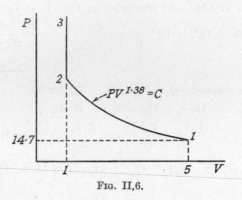

FIG. II,6.

Now, (I,6a) gives $1.985 = C_{p \text{ mol}} - C_{v \text{ mol}}$

and the adiabatic index, $1.38 = \dfrac{C_{p \text{ mol}}}{C_{v \text{ mol}}}$

$$\therefore C_{v \text{ mol}} = \frac{1.985}{0.38} = 5.22, \text{ between points 1 and 2.}$$

By (I,19) $\Delta E = wC_v\Delta T$, where w is the mass in lb. and C_v is expressed per lb. of mass. Alternatively,

$$\Delta E = mC_{v \text{ mol}} \ \Delta T, \text{ where } m \text{ is the number of lb.mols.}$$

$\therefore E_2 - E_1 = 5.22 \times (1,235 - 670) = 2,950$ B.T.U. per lb.mol

and one lb.mol of any gas occupies 358 S.C.F.

$$\therefore E_2 - E_1 = \frac{2,950}{358} = 8.24 \text{ B.T.U. per S.C.F.} \quad \text{Ans.}$$

(b) Since the air-fuel ratio by volume is 9 : 1, it will be easiest to assume that there are 10 lb.mols of mixture and thus 1 lb.mol of fuel. Hence, per 10 lb.mols of original mixture

$$\text{heat added, } Q_{2-3} = 500 \times 358 = 179,000 \text{ B.T.U.}$$

Equation (I,2) enables us to write down the change in E from 2 to 3 since no external work is done at constant vol.

i.e. $E_3 - E_2 = 179,000$ B.T.U. per 10 lb.mols of original mixture.

But from (I,19) $\qquad E_3 - E_2 = \displaystyle\int_{T_2}^{T_3} mC_v \, dT,$

and it was shown on pages 13 and 14 that we may use a " mean " value of C_v in place of the integration when C_v is a linear function of temperature. If the temperature at 3 is about 4,000° F. abs. then the mean value of C_v from T_2 to T_3 is

$$C_{v \text{ mean}} = \frac{(4 \cdot 95 + 0 \cdot 00066 \times 4,000) + (4 \cdot 95 + 0 \cdot 00066 \times 1,235)}{2}$$

$$= \frac{9 \cdot 90 + 3 \cdot 45}{2} = 6 \cdot 68.$$

Also, the 10 lb.mols of original mixture have now contracted to 9·7 lb.mols

$$\therefore \; E_3 - E_2 = 9 \cdot 7 \times 6 \cdot 68 \times (4,000 - 1,235)$$
$$= 179,000 \text{ B.T.U. per 10 lb.mols of original mixture,}$$

and as this value is the same as the value calculated from the quantity of heat liberated, we have shown that

$$\underline{T_3 = 4,000° \text{ F. abs.}} \qquad \text{Ans.}$$

In order to avoid confusion the following points should be carefully noted :

(i) the number of molecules of an air-fuel mixture may be increased or decreased due to combustion, depending on the type of fuel;

(ii) when there is a molecular decrease or increase, the heat actually liberated is always based on the mols of fuel present *before* the molecular change occurred, i.e. on the mols of *original* mixture ;

(iii) when there is a molecular decrease, as in this question, the available internal energy is shared amongst fewer molecules, so that the (kinetic) energy per molecule is increased. This results in a higher temperature of the mixture after combustion than would have resulted had the contraction been neglected. The converse is true in the case of molecular increases ;

(iv) when the value of C_v is given as a linear function of temperature, it is frequently expressed as a mean value over a stated temperature range, e.g. $C_v = a + k(t - 212)$ or $C_v = a + k(t - 32)$, where t is the temperature in ° F. This point is illustrated in example No. 7 on page 30.

13. *A quantity of gas at 300° F. expands from 0·37 cu. ft. to 2·16 cu. ft., according to the law $PV^n =$ constant. The initial pressure is 200 lb. per sq. in. and the final pressure 14·3 lb. per sq. in. The value of the specific heat at constant volume is 0·179 at 300° F., and at this temperature the value of γ is 1·39. The specific heats at constant pressure and constant volume are of the form $a + 0·000025T$ and $b + 0·000025T$ respectively, where T is the absolute temperature.*

Find : (a) *the work done by the gas during the expansion ;* (b) *the change in internal energy ;* (c) *the heat received or rejected during the process.* (U. Lond.)

Since $PV^n =$ constant,

$$200 \times 0·37^n = 14·3 \times 2·16^n$$

$$\left(\frac{2·16}{0·37}\right)^n = \frac{200}{14·3}, \text{ i.e. } 5·83^n = 14.0$$

whence, $n = 1·497$.

This tells us that the expansion is such that $n > \gamma$, i.e. the expansion curve is steeper than adiabatic on the P–V diagram and, of course, much steeper than isothermal. It should also be clear from (I,22) that the answer to (c) will be negative, i.e. heat rejected by gas. (Note, this corresponds to a loss of entropy on the T–ϕ diagram.) Fig. II,7 illustrates these points.

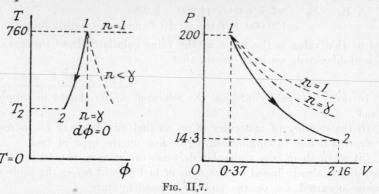

Fig. II,7.

(a) From (I,4) **W.D.** $= \dfrac{144}{0·497}(200 \times 0·37 - 14·3 \times 2·16).$

$$\text{W.D.} = 12,490 \text{ ft.lb.} = \underline{16·1 \text{ B.T.U.}} \quad \text{Ans.}$$

(b) $\qquad\qquad C_v = 0·179 = b + 0·000025 \times 760$

$$\therefore b = 0·160.$$

And $\qquad\qquad C_p = \gamma C_r = 1·39 \times 0·179 = 0·2488$

$$R = 778(C_p - C_v) = 778(0·2488 - 0·179) = 54·3 \text{ ft.lb. °F. units.}$$

Weight of gas present,

$$w = \frac{PV}{RT} = \frac{200 \times 144 \times 0 \cdot 37}{54 \cdot 3 \times 760} = 0 \cdot 2585 \text{ lb.}$$

and

$$T_2 = T_1 \frac{P_2 V_2}{P_1 V_1} = \frac{760 \times 14 \cdot 3 \times 2 \cdot 16}{200 \times 0 \cdot 37} = 317 \cdot 4° \text{ F. abs.}$$

$$\therefore \Delta E = w(T_2 - T_1)C_{v \text{ mean}} \qquad \text{or} = \int_{T_1}^{T_2} w(b + 0 \cdot 000025T)dT$$

$$= - 0 \cdot 2585 \times 442 \cdot 6 \times \left(0 \cdot 160 + 0 \cdot 000025 \times \frac{760 + 317 \cdot 4}{2} \right)$$

$$= - 0 \cdot 2585(70 \cdot 8 + 5 \cdot 96)$$

$$\underline{\Delta E = - 19 \cdot 8 \text{ B.T.U.}}, \text{ i.e. a loss. Ans.}$$

(c) By (I,2)

$$Q = 16 \cdot 1 + (- 19 \cdot 8) = \underline{- 3 \cdot 7 \text{ B.T.U.}}, \text{ i.e. heat rejected. Ans.}$$

EXAMPLES

1. State the First and Second Laws of Thermodynamics.

A quantity of air occupying a volume of 0·2 cu. ft. at a pressure of 480 lb. per sq. in. expands, fully resisted, according to the law $PV^{1 \cdot 25} = $ constant until its absolute temperature is halved. Find its final pressure and volume, and the work done and heat received during the expansion.

$K_p = 0 \cdot 24$, $K_v = 0 \cdot 171$. (*U. Camb.*)

[15 lb. per sq. in. ; 3·2 cu. ft. ; 27,650 ft.lb. ; 13·6 B.T.U.]

2. Prove that (for any heat engine process when a gas is the working substance) the change in internal energy is given by $\dfrac{1}{J(\gamma - 1)} (P_2 V_2 - P_1 V_1)$ and the change in total heat by $\dfrac{\gamma}{J(\gamma - 1)} (P_2 V_2 - P_1 V_1)$. Calculate these quantities for $\frac{1}{2}$ lb. of air expanding according to the law $PV^{1 \cdot 2} = c$ from 100 lb. per sq. in. abs. 500° F., to 10 lb. per sq. in. abs. What will be the work done by the air during the expansion ?

$C_p = 0 \cdot 240$, $C_v = 0 \cdot 171$. (*I.Mech.E.*)

[Proofs follow from (I,19) and (I,1) with (I,6), (I,14) and (I,7) ; $\Delta E = 26 \cdot 1$ B.T.U. ; $\Delta H = 36 \cdot 7$ B.T.U. ; W.D. from (I,4) = 52·8 B.T.U.]

3. One lb. air at a pressure of 550 lb./in.² abs. and a temperature of 1,000° F. is contained in a cylinder fitted with a piston. Heat is supplied to the air at constant pressure until the air has doubled its volume. It then expands according to the law $PV^{1 \cdot 35} = $ constant until the volume is ten times the initial value. Calculate :

(a) The initial volume of the air, (b) the volume and temperature after heating, (c) the volume, temperature and pressure after expansion, and (d) the total work done by the air on the piston.

Take R for air as 53·3 ft.lb./lb. × ° F. (*U. Glas.*)

[(a) 0·983 cu. ft. ; (b) 1·966 cu. ft., 2,460° F. ; (c) 9·83 cu. ft. 1,200° F., 62·5 lb. per sq. in. ; (d) 270,000 ft.lb. for heating *and* expansion.]

4. A quantity of gas is expanded from a pressure of 28 lb. per sq. in. to 12 lb. per sq. in., the relationship between the pressure and volume at any point being given by $V = \sqrt{60 - 2P}$, where V is in cu. ft. and P in lb. per sq. in. The initial temperature is 171° F., $C_p = 0.240$, $C_v = 0.171$. Estimate the quantity of heat which enters or leaves the gas during the process, stating the direction.

(*U. Lond.*)

$[w = 0.238$ lb. ; $P = 30 - \dfrac{V^2}{2}$,   hence   W.D. $= \displaystyle\int P\, dV = 15.79$ B.T.U. ;

$\varDelta T = 181°$ F. ; $\varDelta E = 7.37$ B.T.U. ; by (I,2) $\underline{Q = 23.16 \text{ B.T.U.}}$ entering the gas.]

5. A quantity of gas having a mean molecular weight of 36·2 is compressed according to the law $PV^n = $ constant, the initial pressure and volume being 15 lb. per sq. in. and 3·5 cu. ft. respectively. The temperature at the start of compression is 65° F., and at the end is 240° F. The amount of heat rejected during the compression is 3·62 B.T.U.

If the specific heat of the gas at constant pressure is 0·22 per lb., calculate :
(*a*) The final pressure, (*b*) the change in entropy.   (*U. Lond.*)

$[R = 42.67$; $C_v = 0.165$; $\gamma = 1.331$; $w = 0.3375$ lb. from (I,7) ; from (I,22) and by using (I,4) with (I,7), $n = 1.242$; from (I,18) $\underline{P_2 = 65.4 \text{ lb. per sq. in.}}$; $\underline{\phi_2 - \phi_1 = -0.0061}$ from (I,21).]

6. Show that when 1 lb. of a perfect gas is expanded through a volume ratio of r, the law of expansion being $PV^n = $ constant, the change in entropy is given by $(C_p - nC_v) \log_e r$.

A gas has a molecular weight of 32 and is compressed from an initial pressure and temperature of 15 lb. per sq. in. and 85° F. to a final temperature of 235° F. If the decrease in entropy during the process is 0·01 units per lb., find the final pressure, given that $C_v\cdot = 017$.   (*U. Lond.*)

[The proof follows the same method as example No. 11 above ; $C_p = 0.232$; use (I,21) and replace $\dfrac{V_2}{V_1}$ from (I,7) in terms of temperatures and pressures ; it is not justifiable to assume $PV^n = $ constant in second part ; (I,21) solves for $\log_e \dfrac{P_2}{P_1}$; $\underline{P_2 = 43.8 \text{ lb. per sq. in.}}$]

7. If, during the working stroke of an internal combustion engine using air as the working substance, the air receives heat as the volume increases in such a manner that $\dfrac{dQ}{dV} = $ constant, show that the law of the expansion is

$$(P - a)V^{\gamma} = \text{constant},$$

where a is a constant.

If at two points in the stroke where the pressures are 500 and 100 lb. per sq. in. respectively, the volumes per lb. air are 3·0 and 9·76 cu. ft. respectively, find the value of a and the heat received by the air per lb.

For air : $\gamma = 1.40$, $R = 96$ ft.lb. Centigrade units.   (*U. Camb.*)

[Start from $dQ = dE + P\, dV$; use (I,19) and (I,7) to express $\dfrac{dQ}{dV}$ in terms of P, V and γ ; $\dfrac{dQ}{dV} = $ constant enables the variables to be separated and both sides can be integrated. Alternatively $\dfrac{d^2Q}{dV^2}$ must be zero here and this results in a second order homogeneous differential equation, giving the required solution ; $\underline{a = 5.1}$; $T_1 = 4{,}050°$ F. abs. ; $T_2 = 2{,}638°$ F. abs. ; $\varDelta E = -242$ B.T.U. per lb. ; $\displaystyle\int P\, dV = +264.8$ B.T.U. per lb. ; $\underline{Q = +22.8 \text{ B.T.U. per lb.}}$]

CHAPTER III

AIR COMPRESSORS

Introduction

1. The following is a brief summary of some of the salient points which may arise in problems. Fig. III,1(a) shows the cycle for a single-stage reciprocating compressor, the clearance volume being neglected. It will be readily seen from fig. III,1(a) that the area of the diagram, i.e. the work done on the compressor per cycle (or per stroke, if single-acting)

$$\text{W.D.} = \frac{n}{n-1}(P_2V_2 - P_1V_1) \text{ ft.lb.} \qquad . \qquad . \quad \text{(III,1)}$$

or by (I,7)
$$\text{W.D.} = \frac{n}{n-1}wR(T_2 - T_1) \text{ ft.lb.} \qquad . \qquad . \quad \text{(III,2)}$$

where w lb. are dealt with per cycle;

or again, by (I,18)
$$\text{W.D.} = \frac{n}{n-1}wRT_1\left\{\left(\frac{P_2}{P_1}\right)^{\frac{n-1}{n}} - 1\right\} \qquad . \qquad . \quad \text{(III,3)}$$

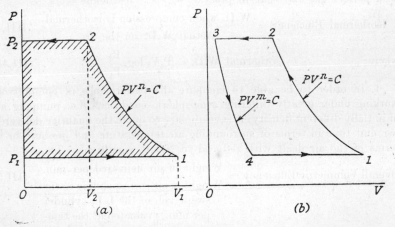

FIG. III,1.

2. If clearance is allowed for, the theoretical indicator diagram will be as in fig. III,1(b), where the indices m and n may or may not be equal. V_3 is the clearance volume, $V_1 - V_3$ the stroke volume. The weight of air delivered per cycle will be the weight in the cylinder at the time of suction valve closure, w_1, *less* the weight left in the cylinder when delivery ceases, w_3;

43

i.e.   weight delivered per cycle $= (w_1 - w_3)$ lb.

Care must be taken to avoid any statement to the effect that the temperature at point (1) is equal to the surrounding air temperature, when clearance is taken into account. For the weight of air trapped in the cylinder at (3) will expand to (4), where

$$T_4 = T_3\left(\frac{P_4}{P_3}\right)^{\frac{m-1}{m}} \qquad \cdot \qquad \cdot \qquad \cdot \qquad \text{(I,18)}$$

and T_4 may be well below intake air temperature. T_1 can be calculated, assuming perfect mixing and neglecting all heat interchanges between the mixing air and the cylinder walls. In actual fact, this heat interchange is appreciable, and the value of T_1 thus calculated is likely to be inaccurate.

Similar remarks apply to the temperature at (3), fig. III,1(a), which is usually taken as equal to the temperature at (2); this neglects the considerable heat interchange during delivery and cannot give exact results. It is outside the scope of this book to estimate the amount of heat interchanged between points (2) and (3), and points (4) and (1).

3. The area of the diagram, fig. III,1(a), will be smallest, and hence the work done a minimum, when the law of the compression is PV = constant, i.e. isothermal compression, as we always assume that air behaves as a perfect gas and that in practice $n > 1$. We define

$$\text{Isothermal Efficiency} = \frac{\text{W.D. when compression is isothermal}}{\text{Actual W.D. on the air}} \qquad \text{(III,4)}$$

where   isothermal W.D. $= P_1V_1 \log_e \dfrac{P_2}{P_1}$ $\qquad \cdot \qquad$ (III,4a)

4. In order to be able to compare the performance of compressors working under greatly differing atmospheric conditions (i.e. pumping air of initially different density) it is customary to quote the quantity delivered per unit time in terms of surrounding air temperature and pressure or in terms of the air dealt with reduced to N.T.P. conditions. Thus,

$$\text{Overall Volumetric Efficiency} = \frac{\text{Weight of air delivered per min.}}{\substack{\text{Weight of air corresponding to the} \\ \text{swept vol. of the L.P. cylinder} \\ \text{per min., evaluated at the tem-} \\ \text{perature and pressure of the} \\ \text{environment}}} \qquad \text{(III,5)}$$

Alternatively,

$$\text{Overall Volumetric Efficiency} = \frac{\substack{\text{Volume of free air delivered per} \\ \text{min. (i.e. at environment tem-} \\ \text{perature and pressure)}}}{\text{Swept vol. of L.P. cylinder per min.}} \qquad \text{(III,5a)}$$

It will be apparent that this definition of volumetric efficiency is not an absolute value depending as it does on the particular climatic conditions in which the machine is used. Thus, the overall volumetric efficiency may decrease considerably if the compressor is used in an aeroplane in flight instead of at sea level. This qualification of the definition (III,5) does not detract from its importance, so long as it is clearly understood that the overall volumetric efficiency is being discussed.

If we desire to quote a value for the volumetric efficiency which is independent of the environment in which the compressor is used, i.e. a value which describes the performance of the machine itself as a criterion of the quality of its design and manufacture, then we define

$$\text{Absolute Volumetric Efficiency} = \frac{\text{Weight of air delivered per min.}}{\begin{array}{c}\text{Weight of air corresponding to}\\ \text{the swept vol. of the L.P.}\\ \text{cylinder per min. evaluated at}\\ \text{N.T.P.}\end{array}} \quad \text{(III,6)}$$

Alternatively,

$$\text{Absolute Volumetric Efficiency} = \frac{\begin{array}{c}\text{Vol. of air delivered per min. at}\\ \text{N.T.P.}\end{array}}{\begin{array}{c}\text{Swept vol. of L.P. cylinder per}\\ \text{min.}\end{array}} \quad \text{(III,6}a\text{)}$$

N.T.P. is usually taken as 60° F. and 14·7 lb. per sq. in. in this connection. The *overall* volumetric efficiency is the one in most common use, although the qualifying word " overall " is frequently omitted. It is the more realistic of the two terms from the point of view of a practical engineer, but the absolute value should not be too lightly discarded since no machine can be expected to give satisfactory service, except when operating under the proper design conditions.

5. For multi-stage machines, neglecting clearance, it can be shown that the net work done, for given equal values of n for all stages and for fixed suction and delivery pressures, will be a minimum provided the intermediate pressures are in geometric progression and intercoolers are so arranged as to cool the air to its intake temperature after each stage. Applying this to a two-stage compressor, we get by reference to fig. III,2, if n, P_1 and P_2 are fixed, for minimum total work

$$\frac{P_i}{P_1} = \frac{P_2}{P_i}, \quad \text{or} \quad P_i = \sqrt{P_1 P_2} \quad . \quad . \quad . \quad \text{(III,7)}$$

and this will make the work per stage equal, so that

$$\text{Total W.D.} = \frac{2n}{n-1} w R T_1 \left\{ \left(\frac{P_2}{P_1} \right)^{\frac{n-1}{2n}} - 1 \right\} . \quad . \quad \text{(III,8)}$$

If w is the weight per cycle, (III,8) will give the W.D. per cycle; whereas if w is the weight per min., (III,8) will give the W.D. per min. Equation (III,8) can readily be extended to cover the case of more than two, say x stages. Then, $\dfrac{2n}{n-1}$ will be replaced by $\dfrac{xn}{n-1}$ and similarly $\dfrac{n-1}{2n}$ should read $\dfrac{n-1}{xn}$, while $\dfrac{P_2}{P_1}$ will always refer to delivery and suction pressures.

It is essential to remember that (III,7) only applies if

(a) the intercooling is " perfect ", i.e. $T_A = T_B$ in fig. III,2, whence $P_A V_A = P_B P_B$,

(b) n is the same for both stages, and

(c) clearance is neglected.

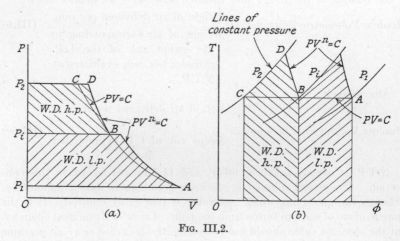

Fig. III,2.

If intercooling is not " perfect ", we must always work from first principles, using the gas laws. But it can be shown that (III,8) does apply if clearance is taken into account, providing w is taken as the actual weight dealt with—e.g. $(w_1 - w_3)$ lb. in fig. III,1(b), page 43—and the compression and expansion indices are equal.

6. When clearance is neglected, the quantity of heat rejected by the air per stage to the cooling water will be

$$\left[\frac{\gamma - n}{\gamma - 1} \times \text{Compression Phase Work}\right] + [wC_p(T_2 - T_1)]$$

the first term deriving from (I,22) and the second term being the heat given up in an intercooler or after-cooler where $(T_2 - T_1)$ is the fall in air temperature through the cooler. It can be shown that the sum of these two terms is equal to the total stage W.D. on the compressor (cf. III,2), a fact which becomes clear on reference to the T-ϕ diagram, fig. III,2(b).

7. The heat carried away by the compressed air at a temperature T_2 (suction at T_1) will be

$$wC_p(T_2 - T_1) \quad . \qquad . \qquad . \qquad . \quad \text{(III,9)}$$

this quantity being, of course, its total heat reckoned from free air conditions.

It follows then, that for an uncooled adiabatic reciprocating compressor, where the only external heat (or work) quantities arising are the W.D. on the air and the heat carried away by it, we have

$$\text{W.D. per min.} = C_p(T_2 - T_1) \text{ per lb. of air per min.} \qquad \text{(III,10)}$$

This is important in rotary compressors where adiabatic compression is considered the ideal performance, and (III,10) will thus represent the minimum (isentropic) work required to drive such an *uncooled* machine. Actually the compression index n is usually greater than γ (cf. fig. III,3)

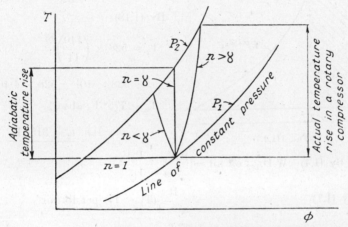

FIG. III,3.

in rotary compressors, and the actual work required will therefore be greater than that given by (III,10).

Definition :

Adiabatic Temperature Efficiency of rotary compressors

$$= \frac{\text{Adiabatic isentropic Temperature Rise}}{\text{Actual Temperature Rise}} \qquad \text{. (III,11)}$$

(cf. also introduction to chapter X, page 162).

8. All expressions for W.D. above (art. 1–7) refer to the work actually done or required to be done on the air, and the horse-power derived from these expressions will be referred to as the indicated or air horse-power.

It is clear that the work input at the shaft of a compressor will need to be greater, the difference

$$\left.\begin{array}{c}\text{Air}\\ \text{Indicated}\end{array}\right\}\text{horse-power} - \left.\begin{array}{c}\text{Shaft}\\ \text{Brake}\end{array}\right\}\text{horse-power} = \text{Friction horse-power}$$

and $$\text{Mechanical Efficiency} = \frac{\text{Shaft (Brake) h.p.}}{\text{Air (Indicated) h.p.}} \qquad \text{. (III,12)}$$

1. *An air compressor takes in air at 14 lb. per sq. in., 20° C., compresses it according to the law $PV^{1.2} = constant$, and delivers it to a receiver at a constant pressure of 140 lb. per sq. in.*

Find the temperature at the end of compression. Calculate per lb. of air (i) the work done and the heat rejected during compression, and (ii) the work done during delivery.

$$(R = 53.3, \ \gamma = 1.4.) \qquad (U. \ Camb.)$$

$$20° \text{ C.} = 20 \times \frac{9}{5} + 32 = 68° \text{ F.}$$

By (I,18)

$$T_2 = 528 \times \left(\frac{140}{14}\right)^{\frac{0.2}{1.2}}$$

$$= 528 \times 10^{\frac{1}{6}} = 528 \times 1.468$$

$$T_2 = 775° \text{ F. abs.}$$

FIG. III,4.

i.e. $\underline{t_2 = 315° \text{ F.}}$ Ans.

(i) By (I,4)   W.D.$_{1-2}$ *on* air $= \dfrac{P_2V_2 - P_1V_1}{n - 1}$

and by (I,7) $= \dfrac{R}{n - 1}(T_2 - T_1)$ per lb. air

i.e.   W.D.$_{1-2}$ *on* air $= \dfrac{53.3}{0.2}(775 - 528)$

$$= \underline{65,900 \text{ ft.lb. per lb. air.}} \quad \text{Ans.}$$

(Note, this is only the compression phase work done, not the work done in the whole cycle.)

By (I,22) $Q = \dfrac{1.4 - 1.2}{0.4} \times \left(-\dfrac{65,900}{778}\right)$

$$= -\frac{1}{2} \times \frac{65,900}{778} = \underline{-42.3 \text{ B.T.U. per lb. air.}} \quad \text{Ans.}$$

i.e. 42.3 B.T.U. are rejected.

It would be possible to calculate ΔE from (I,19) and substituting in (I,2), taking care to watch the signs. The student is advised to do this and thus check the last answer.

(ii) The W.D. during delivery is given by the shaded rectangle, and equals

$$P_2V_2 \text{ ft.lb.}$$

i.e. RT_2 ft.lb. per lb. air

i.e. $53.3 \times 775 = \underline{41,300 \text{ ft.lb. per lb. air.}}$ Ans.

It should be pointed out that 41,300 ft.lb. represent the absolute work done during delivery, as shown by the shaded area, fig. III,4. The actual W.D. will depend upon the pressure acting on the other side of the piston which in turn depends on whether this is a single- or double-acting machine.

2. *A single-stage, double-acting air compressor is required to deal with 600 cu. ft. of air per min., measured at 14·7 lb. per sq. in. and 60° F. The pressure and temperature at the end of suction are 13·8 lb. per sq. in. and 90° F. ; the delivery pressure, 90 lb. per sq. in. ; the speed, 500 r.p.m. Assuming a clearance volume 5% of the stroke volume, laws of compression and expansion $PV^{1\cdot32} = constant$, calculate the necessary stroke volume. Also find the temperature of the air delivered and the i.h.p. of the compressor. (R = 53·3.)*

(I.Mech.E.)

Note the difference between suction conditions and free air conditions.

Let stroke vol. = 100, then $V_3 = 5$ and $V_1 = 105$.

Weight dealt with

$$= \frac{600 \times 14\cdot7 \times 144}{53\cdot3 \times 520}$$

$$= 45\cdot8 \text{ lb. per min.}$$

$$T_2 = 550 \times \left(\frac{90}{13\cdot8}\right)^{\frac{0\cdot32}{1\cdot32}}, \text{ by (I,18)}$$

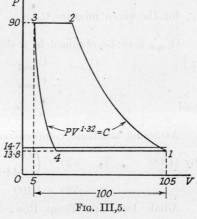

FIG. III,5.

$$= 550 \times 6\cdot52^{\frac{1}{4\cdot12}} = 550 \times 1\cdot577 = 868° \text{ F. abs.}$$

$$\underline{T_2 = T_3 = 868° \text{ F. abs.}} \quad \textbf{Ans.}$$

Assuming the temp. during delivery to remain constant,

Weight compressed $= 2(w_1 - w_3)$ lb. per rev.

$$= 2 \times \frac{144}{53\cdot3}\left(\frac{13\cdot8 \times 105}{550} - \frac{90 \times 5}{867}\right) \text{ by (I,7)}$$

$$= 11\cdot4 \text{ lb. per rev. for a stroke vol. of 100 cu. ft.}$$

$$\therefore \underline{\text{Actual Stroke Volume} = \frac{100 \times 45\cdot8}{11\cdot4 \times 500} = 0\cdot805 \text{ cu. ft.}} \quad \textbf{Ans.}$$

By (III,2) i.h.p. $= \frac{1\cdot32}{0\cdot32} \times 45\cdot8 \times 53\cdot3(868 - 550) \times \frac{1}{33,000}$.

$$\underline{\text{i.h.p.} = 96\cdot7.} \quad \textbf{Ans.}$$

A.T.E.

E

3. *A turbo-compressor takes 20,000 cu. ft. of natural gas per min. at atmospheric pressure with a composition of 17% of ethane and 83% of methane by volume, and compresses it to 10 lb. per sq. in. (gauge). What horse-power is required if the adiabatic efficiency of the compressor is 65% ?*

$$\text{For ethane} \quad C_p = 0\text{·}397 \text{ and } C_v = 0\text{·}325.$$
$$\text{For methane} \quad C_p = 0\text{·}593 \text{ and } C_v = 0\text{·}450. \quad (I.Chem.E.)$$

It is necessary, in the first instance, to find the value of the adiabatic index, γ, for the mixture.

Now ethane has a chemical formula C_2H_6, i.e. a mol. wt. of 30 and methane ,, ,,   ,,   ,, CH_4, ,, ,, ,, ,, ,, 16

$\therefore$ by (I,10) for ethane, $C_{p\,mol} = 0\text{·}397 \times 30 = 11\text{·}91$

and for methane, $C_{p\,mol} = 0\text{·}593 \times 16 = 9\text{·}49$

$\therefore$ for the given mixture $C_{p\,mol} = \dfrac{(11\text{·}91 \times 17) + (9\text{·}49 \times 83)}{17 + 83} = 9\text{·}904.$

$C_{v\,mol}$ may be obtained in a similar manner ; or since

$$C_{p\,mol} - C_{v\,mol} = R_{mol}$$
$$\therefore C_{v\,mol} = 9\text{·}904 - 1\text{·}985 = 7\text{·}919$$

and
$$\gamma = \frac{9\text{·}904}{7\text{·}919} = 1\text{·}250.$$

Assuming adiabatic compression and $T_1 = 460 + 60 = 520°$ F. abs.

by (I,18) $T_2 = 520 \times \left(\dfrac{14\text{·}7 + 10}{14\text{·}7}\right)^{\frac{0\text{·}25}{1\text{·}25}} = 520 \times 1\text{·}68^{\frac{1}{5}}$

$$= 520 \times 1\text{·}109$$

Adiab. Isentropic Temp. Rise $= 520 \times 1\text{·}109 - 520 = 520 \times 0\text{·}109 = 57°$ F.

by (III,11)   Actual Temp. Rise $= \dfrac{57}{0\text{·}65} = 87°$ F.

Mean mol. wt. of mixture $= \dfrac{(17 \times 30) + (83 \times 16)}{100} = 18\text{·}38$

$\therefore C_p$ for mixture $= \dfrac{9\text{·}904}{18\text{·}38} = 0\text{·}539$

and by (I,9) R ,,   ,, $= \dfrac{1\text{·}985 \times 778}{18\text{·}38} = 84\text{·}0$ ft.lb. per lb. ° F.

Mass of gas dealt with $= \dfrac{PV}{RT} = \dfrac{14\text{·}7 \times 144 \times 20,000}{84\text{·}0 \times 520} = 969$ lb. per min.

Using (III,10) and making the relevant assumptions,

$$\text{h.p.} = \frac{969 \times 0\text{·}539 \times 87 \times 778}{33,000} = \underline{1,070} \quad \text{Ans.}$$

4. *Under what circumstances would you recommend the use of multi-stage compressors ? Explain the underlying principle by means of pressure–volume and temperature–entropy diagrams.*

A three-stage compressor compresses hydrogen from 15 lb. per sq. in. abs. to 500 lb. per sq. in. abs. and delivers it at this pressure to a receiver. The initial temperature is 15° C. The law of compression is $PV^{1.25} = $ constant, and is the same for each stage. Assuming equal stage pressure ratios, perfect intercooling, and that the effect of cylinder clearance and valve resistance, etc. may be ignored, determine the theoretical h.p. required to deliver 500 cu. ft. per min. measured at the given suction conditions. (I.Chem.E.)

Multi-stage compressors invariably employ intercoolers between the stages ; this reduces the air temperature considerably, which results in a proportionate saving of work, i.e. an increase of the isothermal efficiency. " Perfect " intercoolers are assumed to cool the air back to its initial temperature at the beginning of compression and fig. III,6 illustrates this point. Multi-stage compression would be advisable in cases where the overall pressure ratio exceeds, say, 5. Apart from the above thermodynamic advantage, there are a number of purely mechanical advantages, such as reduction in the size of flywheel required due to a smoother torque diagram, better lubrication due to lower working temperatures, and reduced leakage losses.

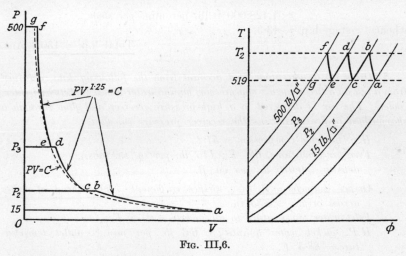

FIG. III,6.

Now

$$T_1 = 460 + \left(15 \times \frac{9}{5} + 32\right) = 519° \text{ F. abs.}$$

Equal Stage Pressure Ratios, $\dfrac{P_2}{15} = \dfrac{P_3}{P_2} = \dfrac{500}{P_3}$

i.e. $P_2 = \sqrt[3]{15^2 \times 500}$ and $P_3 = \sqrt[3]{15 \times 500^2}$.

We could evaluate these pressures, but it is not really necessary to do so ; as $n = 1\cdot25$ in all cylinders and intercooling is perfect, the temperature of the gas is equal on leaving each stage, and bearing in mind that the pressure ratios are equal, by (I,18)

$$T_2 = 519 \times \left(\frac{500}{15}\right)^{\frac{0\cdot25}{1\cdot25}} \times \frac{1}{3}$$

$$= 519 \times (33\cdot33)^{\cdot\frac{1}{5}} = 519 \times 1\cdot263 = 656° \text{ F}.$$

By (I,9), for hydrogen,

$$R = \frac{1\cdot985 \times 778}{2} = 772 \text{ ft.lb. per lb. } ° \text{ F}.$$

By (I,7)   Weight dealt with $= \dfrac{15 \times 144 \times 500}{772 \times 519}$

$$= 2\cdot69 \text{ lb. per min.}$$

∴ from (III,2) with the work shared equally between the cylinders, common value of n, and equal temperature rise

$$\text{W.D.} = \frac{1\cdot25}{0\cdot25} \times 2\cdot69 \times 772 \times (656 - 519)$$

$$= 1,428,000 \text{ ft.lb. per min. } per \ stage,$$
whence,   stage h.p. $= 43\cdot3$.

∴ Total h.p. $= 130$.   Ans.

---

5. *Draw up a percentage heat account from the following data, obtained from a test on a two-stage air compressor, having water-cooled jackets and intercooler. The air is delivered to a high-pressure receiver and flow through a sharp-edged orifice maintains the receiver pressure constant.*

H.p. to drive compressor = 51·2.

Free air conditions, 60° F., 14·7 lb. per sq. in. (abs.),
density = 0·076 lb. per cu. ft.

Orifice diameter = 3 in. ; orifice coefficient = 0·6 ; head of water across orifice = 5·35 in.

Inlet water temperature to all jackets = 47·5° F.

H.P. jacket water quantity = 6·3 lb. per min. ; outlet temperature = 88·5° F.

L.P. jacket water quantity = 5·7 lb. per min. ; outlet temperature = 100° F.

Intercooler jacket water quantity = 13·3 lb. per min. ; outlet water temperature = 96·5° F.

Air delivery temperature = 226° F. ; sp. ht. of air = 0·24.

(U. Manch.)

It is known that in air consumption. measurements of this type, the compressibility effects may be ignored, provided the pressure difference across the orifice is limited to about 5 in. of water.[1] Applying this assumption, we have

$$\text{Air velocity through orifice} = \sqrt{2g\frac{h}{12}\frac{\rho_w}{\rho_a}} = v \text{ ft. per sec.}$$

where h = pressure difference in inches of water

ρ_w, ρ_a = density of water and air respectively.

If C = orifice coefficient of discharge, and a = orifice area in sq. ft., then Mass flow of air through orifice = $Cav\rho_a$ lb. per sec.

i.e. $$w = Ca\sqrt{2g\frac{h}{12}\rho_w\rho_a} = Ca\sqrt{\frac{2gH}{V_a}}$$

where H is the pressure difference across the orifice in lb. per sq. ft., and $V_a = \dfrac{1}{\rho_a}$.

In this example, $W = 0.6 \times \dfrac{\pi}{4} \times \left(\dfrac{1}{4}\right)^2 \times \sqrt{\dfrac{64.4}{12} \times 5.35 \times 62.4 \times 0.076}$

$$= 0.0295 \times \sqrt{136} = 0.345 \text{ lb. per sec.}$$

$$= 20.65 \text{ lb. per min. (assuming } \rho_w=62.4 \text{ lb. per cu. ft.).}$$

Heat equivalent of h.p. input $= 51.2 \times \dfrac{33,000}{778} = 51.2 \times 42.4$

$$= 2,170 \text{ B.T.U. per min.}$$

Heat carried away by air

$$= 20.65 \times 0.24 \times (226 - 60) = 823 \text{ B.T.U. per min.}$$

Heat to L.P. jacket water $= 5.7 \times (100 - 47.5) = 299$ B.T.U. per min.
Heat to intercooler water $= 13.3 \times (96.5 - 47.5) = 651$ B.T.U. per min.
Heat to H.P. jacket water $= 6.3 \times (88.5 - 47.5) = 258$ B.T.U. per min.

Arranging this information in the. form of a heat balance, we get

SUPPLIED	DISCHARGED		
As horse-power 2,170 B.T.U. per min.	To heat in air 823 B.T.U. per min.	=	37·9%
	,, L.P. water 299 ,, ,, ,,	=	13·8%
	,, I.C. water 651 ,, ,, ,,	=	30·0%
	,, H.P. water 258 ,, ,, ,,	=	11·9%
	Miscellaneous 139 ,, ,, ,,	=	6·4%
2,170 B.T.U. per min.	2,170 B.T.U. per min.	=	100·0%

[1] This problem is discussed more fully on pages 98 and 99.

The " miscellaneous " term of 139 B.T.U. per min. represents radiation and convection losses from the plant. It is not quite clear whether the 51·2 h.p. input represents the shaft (or brake) horse-power or the air (or indicated) horse-power. In the former case, which appears more likely, the miscellaneous term would also include *some* of the friction losses, the bulk of which reappear as heat in the cylinder jacket water.

6. *Derive an expression for the minimum work required to compress and deliver 1 lb. of air in a two-stage compressor. State carefully the assumptions made.*

A three-stage compressor delivers air at 1,000 lb. per sq. in. The index of compression is 1·2 throughout, and the usual assumptions may be made regarding the temperature and pressure in the intercoolers. Estimate the minimum work required to deal with 1 lb. of air from an atmospheric pressure of 14·7 lb. per sq. in., given $\gamma = 1·4$ and the temperature at the start of compression 85° F.

Find also the heat abstracted per lb. in each intercooler.

(*U. Lond.*)

The first part of the question will be familiar to many students and it will only be briefly outlined

$$\text{Total W.D.} = \frac{n}{n-1}P_1V_1\left\{\left[\left(\frac{P_i}{P_1}\right)^{\frac{n-1}{n}} - 1\right] + \left[\left(\frac{P_d}{P_i}\right)^{\frac{n-1}{n}} - 1\right]\right\}$$

cf. equation (III,3) and note $P_iV_3 = P_1V_1$.

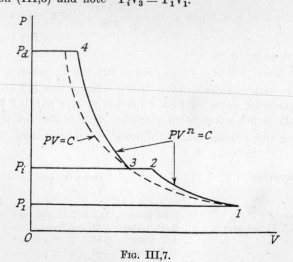

Fig. III,7.

This work will be a minimum when { } is a minimum, i.e. for a given compressor and fixed values of P_1, P_2 and n when

$$\frac{d}{dP_i}\{\quad\} = 0$$

i.e. $\left(\dfrac{1}{P_1}\right)^{\frac{n-1}{n}}\left(\dfrac{n-1}{n}\right)(P_i)^{-\frac{1}{n}} + (P_d)^{\frac{n-1}{n}}\left(\dfrac{1-n}{n}\right)P_i^{\frac{1-2n}{n}} = 0$

$$\therefore\ P_i^{\frac{2n-2}{n}} = (P_1P_d)^{\frac{n-1}{n}}$$

or $P_i = \sqrt{P_1P_d}$ . . . . (III,7)

Hence,   Min. W.D. $= \dfrac{2n}{n-1}P_1V_1\left[\left(\dfrac{P_d}{P_1}\right)^{\frac{n-1}{2n}} - 1\right]$ . . (III,8)

Q.E.D.

The assumptions may be summarized thus :

(a) clearance is neglected,
(b) n in $PV^n = C$ is the same for both cylinders,
(c) intercooling is perfect, i.e. $T_1 = T_3$, i.e. $P_1V_1 = P_3V_3$,
(d) no pressure drop through intercooler,
(e) suction and delivery at constant pressure with perfect valve action.

Now, for a three-stage machine, by induction,

$$\text{Min. W.D.} = \frac{3n}{n-1}\,wRT_1\left[\left(\frac{P_2}{P_1}\right)^{\frac{n-1}{3n}} - 1\right]$$

i.e. $= \dfrac{3 \times 1\cdot2}{0\cdot2} \times 53\cdot3 \times 545\left[\left(\dfrac{1{,}000}{14\cdot7}\right)^{\frac{0\cdot2}{3\cdot6}} - 1\right]$

$= 18 \times 53\cdot3 \times 545 \times 0\cdot263$

$= 138{,}000$ ft.lb. per lb. air.   Ans.

Now, $C_p = \dfrac{R}{J}\dfrac{\gamma}{\gamma-1}$, by (I,6) and (I,14)

i.e. $C_p = \dfrac{53\cdot3}{778} \times \dfrac{1\cdot4}{0\cdot4} = 0\cdot240$

and by (I,18) $\dfrac{T_2}{T_1} = \left(\dfrac{1{,}000}{14\cdot7}\right)^{\frac{0\cdot2}{3\cdot6}} = 1\cdot263$, as before,

where T_2 is the air temperature at the end of compression in *each* stage. Since the pressure ratios and n are equal in the stages and intercooling is perfect, the temperature of the air will be the same on entering each intercooler, i.e.

$$T_2 = T_1 \times 1\cdot263 = 545 \times 1\cdot263$$

$\therefore$ Heat to coolant in *each* intercooler

$= C_p(T_2 - T_1) = 0\cdot24 \times 545 \times 0\cdot263$

$= 34\cdot4$ B.T.U. per lb.   Ans.

7. *In an air compressor, show that the cylinder clearance does not affect the theoretical work needed to compress and deliver 1 lb. of air, provided that the delivery and suction pressures remain constant and that the indices of compression and expansion have the same value.*

A two-stage compressor delivering air at 250 lb. per sq. in. has the clearance volume of the low-pressure cylinder 4% of the swept volume. The atmospheric conditions are 14·5 lb. per sq. in. and 65° F., and at the start of compression the pressure in the cylinder is 14·2 lb. per sq. in. The temperature at the start of compression in each stage is 92° F., and the intercooler pressure is 58 lb. per sq. in. The law of compression and expansion for both stages is $PV^{1\cdot 25} =$ constant.

Find : (a) *the volumetric efficiency ;*

(b) *the work required per lb. of air delivered by the compressor ;*

(c) *the overall efficiency of compression referred to isothermal compression from atmospheric temperature and pressure.*

$$(R = 53\cdot 3.)$$ (*U. Lond.*)

Referring to fig. III,8,

$$\text{Net W.D.} = \frac{n}{n-1}\Big[(P_2V_2 - P_1V_1) - (P_3V_3 - P_4V_4)\Big], \text{ (cf. III,1)}$$

$$= \frac{n}{n-1}R\Big[w_1(T_2 - T_1) - w_3(T_3 - T_4)\Big],$$

because $PV = wRT$, $w_1 = w_2$, $w_3 = w_4$.

But it is usual to assume that delivery takes place at constant temperature, i.e. $T_3 = T_2$. Hence if n is the same for both curves and with delivery and suction pressures remaining constant $T_4 = T_1$,

$$\therefore \text{ W.D.} = \frac{n}{n-1}R\,(T_2 - T_1)(w_1 - w_3) \text{ per cycle.}$$

But weight delivered $= w_1 - w_3$ lb. per cycle.

$$\therefore \text{ W.D.} = \frac{n}{n-1}R\,(T_2 - T_1) \text{ per lb. air.}$$

which is independent of the clearance volume. The student is asked to note that the result is restricted to cases where the above assumptions hold.

Let $V_1 - V_3 = 100$ in fig. III,9, then $V_3 = 4$, and $V_1 = 104$.

$$T_1 = T_5 = 552° \text{ F. abs.}$$

$$P_1V_1^{\,n} = P_2V_2^{\,n}$$

$$\therefore\ V_2 = 104 \times \left(\frac{14\cdot 2}{58}\right)^{\frac{1}{1\cdot 25}} = \frac{104}{3\cdot 082} = 33\cdot 75$$

and by (I,18) $$T_2 = 552 \times \left(\frac{58}{14\cdot 2}\right)^{\frac{0\cdot 25}{1\cdot 25}} = 552 \times 1\cdot 325 = 731\cdot 3° \text{ F. abs.}$$

(*a*)   Vol. delivered $= V_2 - V_3 = 29\cdot 75$, measured at 58 lb. per sq. in. and 731·3° F.

$$\frac{P_1 V_1}{T_1} = \frac{P_2 V_2}{T_2}$$

$\therefore$ Vol. of free air delivered $= 29 \cdot 75 \times \dfrac{58}{14 \cdot 5} \times \dfrac{525}{731 \cdot 3} = 85 \cdot 5$

i.e. <u>Overall Volumetric Efficiency</u> $= \dfrac{85 \cdot 5}{\text{swept volume}} \times 100\% = \underline{85 \cdot 5\%}$ Ans.

(b) Using the relation proved in the first part of this question,

L.P. cylinder, W.D. per lb. air $= \dfrac{1 \cdot 25 \times 53 \cdot 3}{0 \cdot 25}(731 \cdot 3 - 552)$

$$= 47{,}800 \text{ ft.lb.}$$

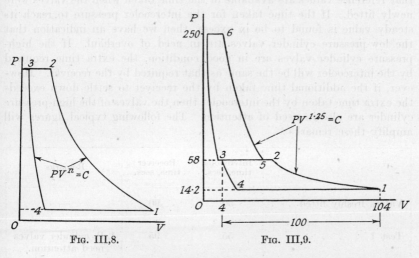

Fig. III,8.   Fig. III,9.

A similar relation will hold for the H.P. cylinder, and as $T_1 = T_5$,

by (I,18) $\qquad T_6 = 552 \times \left(\dfrac{250}{58}\right)^{\frac{0 \cdot 25}{1 \cdot 25}} = 552 \times 1 \cdot 340.$

Hence, H.P. cylinder, W.D. per lb. air

$$= \frac{1 \cdot 25 \times 53 \cdot 3}{0 \cdot 25} \times 552 \times 0 \cdot 340 = 50{,}100 \text{ ft.lb.}$$

Total W.D. per lb. air $= 47{,}800 + 50{,}100 = \underline{97{,}900 \text{ ft.lb.}}$ Ans.

(c)   Isothermal W.D. per lb. air $= RT \log_e \dfrac{250}{14 \cdot 5}$ (cf. III,4a)

$$= 53 \cdot 3 \times 525 \times \log_e 17 \cdot 24$$
$$= 79{,}680 \text{ ft.lb.}$$

By (III,4)   <u>Isothermal Efficiency</u> $= \dfrac{79{,}680}{97{,}900} = \underline{81 \cdot 5\%}$ Ans.

8. *A compound air compressor is connected to a receiver, previously emptied. Explain how the efficiency of working of the compressor valves may be checked, without taking indicator cards, during the process of charging the receiver.*

Two single-stage compressors work between the same pressure limits, the one having zero clearance and the other a definite clearance.

Prove that if they take in equal volumes they will also discharge equal volumes and that the work done according to the cards will be the same for both if n in $PV^n = c$ is the same for all curves. (*U. Lond.*)

The test referred to is a simple one and consists in noting the time taken, from the instant of starting the compressor, for both the intercooler and receiver pressures to attain their normal steady values. It is assumed that reference values are available of the time taken when the valves were newly fitted. If the time taken for the intercooler pressure to reach its steady value is found to be in excess, then we have an indication that the low-pressure cylinder valves are in need of overhaul. If the high-pressure cylinder valves are in good condition, the extra time required by the intercooler will be the same as that required by the receiver. However, if the additional time taken by the receiver to settle down exceeds the extra time taken by the intercooler then the valves of the high-pressure cylinder are also in need of attention. The following typical figures will amplify these remarks :

	Intercooler time, secs.	Receiver time, secs.	Remarks
Valves freshly fitted . .	50	90	—
Test 1	55	95	L.P. cylinder valves need attention.
Test 2	50	95	H.P. cylinder valves need attention.
Test 3	55	100	Both sets of valves need attention.

Referring to fig. III,10, the volume of air taken in, allowing for clearance, is $V_1 - V_4$, and therefore the stroke volume of the compressor with zero clearance must be $V_1 - V_4$, as shown. Let P_D and P_S be the common delivery and suction pressures respectively.

Now, working from first principles,

Zero Clearance Compressor,

$$\text{W.D.} = P_D V_5 + \frac{P_D V_5 - P_S(V_1 - V_4)}{n - 1} - P_S(V_1 - V_4)$$

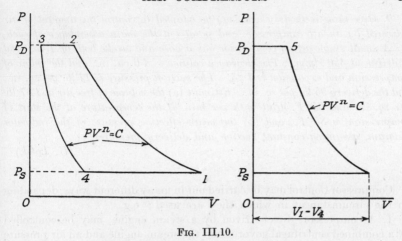

FIG. III,10.

$$= \frac{n}{n-1}\Big[[P_D V_5 - P_S(V_1 - V_4)]\Big] \quad . \quad . \quad . \quad \text{(i)}$$

In the other case,

$$\text{W.D.} = \frac{n}{n-1}\Big[(P_D V_2 - P_S V_1) - (P_D V_3 - P_S V_4)\Big]$$

$$= \frac{n}{n-1}\Big[P_D(V_2 - V_3) - P_S(V_1 - V_4)\Big] \quad . \quad . \quad \text{(ii)}$$

Now, $\qquad\qquad \left.\begin{array}{l}P_D V_2{}^n = P_S V_1{}^n \\ P_D V_3{}^n = P_S V_4{}^n\end{array}\right\}$ i.e. $\dfrac{V_2}{V_3} = \dfrac{V_1}{V_4}$

and,

an obvious fact in the case of equal indices. Hence, also

$$\frac{V_2 - V_3}{V_3} = \frac{V_1 - V_4}{V_4}$$

or $\qquad\qquad\qquad \dfrac{P_D(V_2 - V_3)^n}{P_D V_3{}^n} = \dfrac{P_S(V_1 - V_4)^n}{P_S V_4{}^n}$

the denominators of which are equal; $\therefore$ the numerators must be equal,
i.e. $\qquad\qquad\qquad\quad \left.\begin{array}{l}P_D(V_2 - V_3)^n = P_S(V_1 - V_4)^n \\ P_D V_5{}^n = P_S(V_1 - V_4)^n\end{array}\right\}$

But, in any case, $\qquad\qquad$

$$\therefore \; \underline{V_5 = V_2 - V_3.} \quad \text{Q.E.D.}$$

i.e. the two compressors discharge equal volumes.

By making the substitution $V_5 = V_2 - V_3$ in equation (i) above, it is clear that (i) and (ii) are identical, i.e. the work done per card will be identical in the two cases.

9. *Give three methods which may be adopted to control the amount of air delivered by an air compressor, and point out the main advantages of each.*

A small single-acting compressor has a bore and stroke both of 4 in., and is driven at 350 r.p.m. The clearance volume is 4·6 cu. in., and the index of compression and expansion is 1·23. The suction pressure is 14 lb. per sq. in., and the delivery 95 lb. per sq. in. Estimate (a) *the volume of free air at 14·7 lb. per sq. in. and 65° F. dealt with per min. if the temperature at the start of compression is 85° F., and* (b) *the mean effective pressure of the indicator diagram, assuming constant suction and delivery pressures.*

(U. Lond.)

Compressor Control may be carried out in many different ways, depending on the circumstances in which they are used ; e.g.

1. A compressor, direct driven by a steam engine, may be controlled by a combined centrifugal governor on the steam engine and an air-pressure regulator, the control consisting in an adjustment of the speed to suit the load. The mechanism operates either the steam throttle or varies the cut-off. This is suitable where the prime mover may be run at reduced speeds without too great a drop in efficiency.

2. Where the drive is by means of electrical motors it will usually be necessary to keep the speed constant (it may be inevitable with synchronous motors), and then some unloading device may be used to blow low-pressure air off to the atmosphere. By artificially obstructing the low-pressure intake and thus lowering the intake pressure in addition to the mass aspired, the temperature of delivery may be raised to a dangerous value due to the higher pressure ratio, and this method is therefore not to be recommended.

3. A method, commendable because it affords some control over the volumetric efficiency, is to provide variable clearance control. This is achieved by having air pockets adjacent to the cylinder, which are brought into communication with the cylinder by automatically operated valves.

4. With mechanically operated valves it is usual to hold the suction valve open for part of the compression stroke.

In many cases a combination of these, and other, controls may actually be used.

$$\text{Cyl. vol.} = \frac{\pi}{4} \times 16 \times 4 = 50\cdot25 \text{ cu. in.} \quad \therefore V_1 = 54\cdot85 \text{ cu. in.}$$

$$P_2 V_2{}^n = P_1 V_1{}^n \quad \therefore V_2 = 54\cdot85 \times \left(\frac{14}{95}\right)^{\frac{1}{1\cdot23}} = 11\cdot56 \text{ cu. in.}$$

$$\frac{P_1 V_1}{T_1} = \frac{P_2 V_2}{T_2}$$

$$\therefore T_2 = 545 \times \frac{95}{14} \times \frac{11\cdot56}{54\cdot85} = 780° \text{ F. abs.}$$

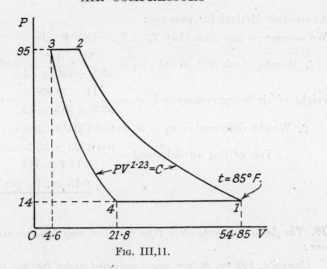

FIG. III,11.

$$P_3V_3{}^n = P_4V_4{}^n$$

$$\therefore \ V_4 = 4{\cdot}6 \times \left(\frac{95}{14}\right)^{\frac{1}{1{\cdot}23}} = 21{\cdot}8 \ \text{cu. in.}$$

(a) Vol. delivered per min. $= 350(11{\cdot}56 - 4{\cdot}6)$ cu. in.

$$= 1{\cdot}41 \ \text{cu. ft. at } 780° \ \text{F. and } 95 \ \text{lb. per sq. in.}$$

(This assumes that the temperature remains constant from 2 to 3.)

$\therefore$ Vol. of free air at $14{\cdot}7$ lb. per sq. in. and $525°$ F.

$$= 1{\cdot}41 \times \frac{95}{14{\cdot}7} \times \frac{525}{780} = \underline{6{\cdot}13 \ \text{cu. ft. per min.}} \quad \text{Ans.}$$

(b) W.D. per cycle $= \dfrac{n}{n-1}[(P_2V_2 - P_1V_1) - (P_3V_3 - P_4V_4)]$

$$= \frac{n}{n-1}[P_2(V_2 - V_3) - P_1(V_1 - V_4)]$$

$$= \frac{1{\cdot}23}{0{\cdot}23}[(95 \times 6{\cdot}96) - (14 \times 33{\cdot}05)] \ \text{in. lb.}$$

$$= 1{,}065 \ \text{in. lb.}$$

Now, m.e.p. $= \dfrac{\text{Area of Diagram}}{\text{Length of Diagram}}$

$$= \frac{1{,}065}{50{\cdot}25} = \underline{21{\cdot}2 \ \text{lb. per sq. in.}} \quad \text{Ans.}$$

Alternative Method for part (a) :

We assume in any case that $T_2 = T_3 = 780°$ F. abs.

$\therefore$ Weight of air left in cyl., $w_3 = \dfrac{95 \times 4 \cdot 6}{53 \cdot 3 \times 780 \times 12} = 0 \cdot 000877$ lb.

Weight of air being compressed, $w_1 = \dfrac{14 \times 54 \cdot 85}{53 \cdot 3 \times 545 \times 12} = 0 \cdot 00220$ lb.

$\therefore$ Weight delivered $= w_1 - w_3 = 0 \cdot 001323$ lb. per cycle.

Vol. of *free* air delivered $= \dfrac{0 \cdot 001323 \times 53 \cdot 3 \times 525}{14 \cdot 7 \times 144} \times 350$

$\underline{\underline{= 6 \cdot 13 \text{ cu. ft. per min.}}}$ Ans.

10. *The following particulars refer to a two-stage single-acting air compressor :*

> *Capacity, 150 cu. ft. per min., measured under free air conditions of 60° F. at a pressure of 14·7 lb. per sq. in.*
> *Delivery pressure 250 lb. per sq. in.*
> *Pressure during suction stroke, 14 lb. per sq. in.*
> *Temperature at start of compression in each stage, 85° F.*
> *Clearance volume of low-pressure cylinder, 6%.*
> *Index of compression and expansion, 1·25 throughout.*
> *Speed, 120 r.p.m.*

Assuming that the intercooler pressure is chosen so that theoretically the work is shared equally between the two cylinders, find (a) *the indicated horsepower, and* (b) *the dimensions of the low-pressure cylinder if the bore is equal to the stroke.*

$$(R = 53 \cdot 3.)$$

(U. Lond.)

Care should be taken not to confuse the actual suction conditions (14 lb. per sq. in. and 85° F.) with the free air conditions (14·7 lb. per sq. in. and 60° F.).

(a)   Mass of air dealt with $= \dfrac{14 \cdot 7 \times 144 \times 150}{53 \cdot 3 \times 520}$

$= 11 \cdot 5$ lb. per min.

Now $P_i = \sqrt{14 \times 250}$, by (III,7), but it is not really necessary to evaluate this as we can find T_B directly, viz.

$$T_B = 545 \left(\frac{250}{14} \right)^{\frac{0 \cdot 25}{1 \cdot 25} \times \frac{1}{2}}$$

by using (I,18) in conjunction with (III,7). Alternatively P_i may be evaluated, viz. 59·1 lb. per sq. in., and then

$$T_B = 545\left(\frac{59\cdot1}{14}\right)^{\frac{0\cdot25}{1\cdot25}} = 545 \times 1\cdot335 = 728° \text{ F. abs.}$$

By (III,2) and remembering that the work is shared equally between the cylinders,

$$\text{Total W.D. per lb. air} = 2 \times \frac{1\cdot25}{0\cdot25} \times 53\cdot3(728 - 545)$$

$$= 97,500 \text{ ft.lb.}$$

$$\therefore \underline{\text{i.h.p.}} = \frac{97,500 \times 11\cdot5}{33,000} = \underline{33\cdot9}. \text{ Ans.}$$

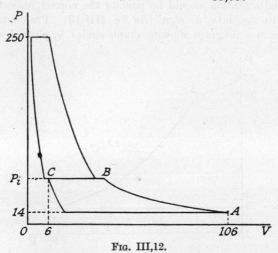

FIG. III,12.

(b) Mass of air dealt with per stroke, for a single-acting compressor

$$= w_A - w_C$$

$$= \frac{144}{53\cdot3}\left(\frac{14 \times 106}{545} - \frac{59\cdot1 \times 6}{728}\right)$$

$$= 6\cdot06 \text{ lb. per 100 cu. ft. stroke volume}$$

and assuming that the temperature remains constant during delivery, i.e. from B to C, actual swept vol. per min. $= \frac{100}{6\cdot06} \times 11\cdot5 = 190$ cu. ft.

whence, $190 = \frac{\pi}{4}d^2 \times d \times 120$, the bore being equal to the stroke

$$d^3 = \frac{19}{3\pi} \qquad\qquad \underline{d = 1\cdot264 \text{ ft.} = 15\cdot3 \text{ ins.}} \text{ Ans.}$$

11. *A single-acting air compressor is connected to a receiver which feeds a pipe-line. The compressor, which runs at 300 r.p.m., has a stroke volume of 2·5 cu. ft. and takes in its charge at 13 lb. per sq. in. and 80° F., compression following $PV^{1·2}$ = constant. Assuming that the piston has simple harmonic motion and that the temperature in the receiver remains constant at 70° F., while the mass of air per sec. passing from the receiver to the pipe-line is also constant, find the necessary volume of receiver, if the pressure is to be kept within the limits of 78 and 82 lb. per sq. in. Neglect the clearance volume of the compressor.*

$$(R = 53·3.)$$

(U. Lond.)

This is a question which illustrates an important point in air-compressor work. Special attention should be paid to the correct indicator diagram appropriate to the data, as shown in fig. (III,13). Projected below the P–V diagram, is a diagram showing crank angles, θ, plotted on a base of

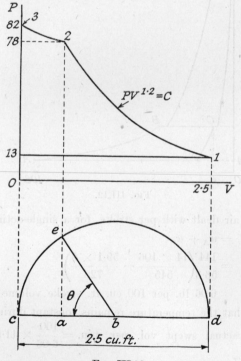

FIG. III,13.

stroke volume, the piston having S.H.M. $cd = 2·5$ cu. ft.; "e" is the point corresponding to point 2 on the P–V diagram, the commencement of delivery, and "a" is the projection of e on to cd; hence $V_2 = ac$ and is the volume swept during the delivery period 2–3, while θ is the corresponding crank angle turned through.

Now, $\qquad P_1V_1{}^n = P_2V_2{}^n$

$$\therefore V_2 = 2 \cdot 5 \times \left(\frac{13}{78}\right)^{\frac{1}{1 \cdot 2}} = 0 \cdot 562 \text{ cu. ft.}$$

and, $\qquad ab = bc - ac$

i.e. $\qquad ab = 1 \cdot 25 - 0 \cdot 562 = 0 \cdot 688 \text{ cu. ft.}$

and $\qquad \cos \theta = \dfrac{0 \cdot 688}{1 \cdot 25} = 0 \cdot 551.$

$$\theta = 56° \, 36'.$$

$\therefore$ Time taken for crank to turn θ degrees, i.e. for piston to move from 2 to 3, i.e. deliver one cylinder charge,

$$t = \frac{56 \cdot 6 \times 2\pi}{180} \times \frac{60}{300 \times 2\pi} = 0 \cdot 03145 \text{ sec.}$$

Now, $PV = wRT$,

$\therefore$ Mass of air compressed per cycle $= w_1 = \dfrac{13 \times 144 \times 2 \cdot 5}{53 \cdot 3 \times 540} = 0 \cdot 1626 \text{ lb.}$

$\therefore$ Mass delivered to receiver per sec. $= 0 \cdot 1626 \times \dfrac{300}{60} = 0 \cdot 813 \text{ lb.}$

But as the mass of air passing from the receiver to the pipe line is constant, $0 \cdot 813$ lb. per sec. must also leave the receiver. Therefore, $0 \cdot 813 \times 0 \cdot 03145 = 0 \cdot 0256$ lb. air per cycle are leaving the receiver during the delivery period.

Mass of air in receiver at start of delivery, by (I,7)

$$w_2 = \frac{144 \times 78 \times V}{53 \cdot 3 \times 530} = 0 \cdot 398V \text{ lb.}$$

where V is the volume of the receiver.

Similarly, mass of air in receiver at end of delivery,

$$w_3 = \frac{144 \times 82 \times V}{53 \cdot 3 \times 530} = 0 \cdot 418V \text{ lb.}$$

Hence,

| Mass in receiver at start of delivery | + Mass delivered to receiver per cycle | − Mass passing from receiver during delivery | = Mass in receiver at end of delivery |

i.e. $\qquad 0 \cdot 398V + 0 \cdot 1626 - 0 \cdot 0256 = 0 \cdot 418V$

$$\therefore V = \frac{0 \cdot 1370}{0 \cdot 020} = \underline{6 \cdot 85 \text{ cu. ft.}} \quad \text{Ans.}$$

1. An engine receives compressed air at 100 lb. per sq. in. absolute pressure and at a temperature of 25° C. The expansion line of the indicator diagram is given by $PV^{1 \cdot 35}$ = a constant. The expansion goes on until a pressure of 17 lb. per sq. in. absolute is reached when the air is exhausted at that pressure. Calculate :

(a) The temperature at the end of the expansion, and (b) the number of lb. of air used per i.h.p.-hr. (*W.S.S.*)

[Neglect clearance; $t_2 = -120°$ F. ; W.D. per lb. air = 40,700 ft.lb. ; lb. per i.h.p.-hr. = 48·5.]

2. A single-stage single-acting air compressor has a clearance volume equal to 7·5% of the swept volume. The pressure during suction remains constant at 14·3 lb. per sq. in. and the temperature at commencement of compression is 85° F. The delivery pressure is constant at 95 lb. per sq. in., and the compression follows the law $PV^{1 \cdot 25}$ = constant. Find :

(a) The bore and the stroke necessary to deliver 3,000 cu. ft. of free air per hr., the atmospheric conditions being 14·7 lb. per sq. in. and 60° F. ; (b) the horse-power required to drive the compressor if the mechanical efficiency is 87%. The bore/stroke ratio is 1·2, and the speed is 250 r.p.m. (*U. Lond.*)

[Weight dealt with = 229 lb. per hr. ; temp. after compression = 796° F. abs. ; per 100 cu. ft. of stroke volume : 5·20 lb. delivered per cycle ; Stroke Volume = 0·294 cu. ft. ; D = 0·766 ft. ; L = 0·638 ft. ; h.p. = 8·90.]

3. An air motor is to have four single-acting cylinders and be supplied with compressed air at 80 lb. per sq. in. gauge and 75° F. The clearance will be 5% of the stroke volume. Cut off is to occur at 0·5 of the stroke and expansion will follow the law $PV^{1 \cdot 3} = c$ to the end of the stroke. Exhaust will take place to atmosphere and compression, commencing at 95% of the return stroke, will follow the law $PV^{1 \cdot 35} = c$.

Assuming a stroke-bore ratio of 1·25, find the cylinder bore and stroke of the motor if it is to develop 3·5 b.h.p. at 300 r.p.m., the mechanical efficiency being 80%. Atmospheric pressure = 14·7 lb. per sq. in. abs. (*U. Witw.*)

[P at release = 40·8, P at end of compression = 37·5 lb. per sq. in. ; m.e.p. of diagram = 63 lb. per sq. in. ; available i.h.p. per cylinder = $0·0468D^3$; D = 2·86 in. ; L = 3·57 in.]

4. Derive an expression, in terms of initial and final pressures and the volume of air drawn in per stroke, for the minimum work done in the two-stage compression of air. Assume adiabatic compression and perfect cooling of the air between stages. Neglect clearance. All steps in the analysis must be clearly shown.

The L.P. piston of a two-stage, double-acting air compressor running at 120 r.p.m. is 30 in. in diameter and has a stroke of 12 in. Air is compressed adiabatically in the L.P. cylinder to 25 lb. per sq. in. gauge, delivered to an intercooler where it is cooled at constant pressure to 78° F. and then compressed to 85 lb. per sq. in. gauge in the H.P. cylinder. Determine the required horse-power of an electric motor to drive the compressor if the mechanical efficiency of the compressor is 88% and of the motor 86%.

Assume a volumetric efficiency for the compressor of 81·5% and atmospheric pressure and temperature as 12 lb. per sq. in. abs. and 60° F. respectively.

(*U. Witw.*)

[Assume R = 53·3, $\gamma = 1·4$; vol. dealt with = 4·0 cu. ft. per cycle at 12 lb. per sq. in. and 60° F. $\equiv$ 59·8 lb. per min. ; temp. rise L.P. = 198° F. ; ditto H.P. = 171° F. ; h.p. = 165.]

5. Air is compressed in a two-stage compressor, with intercooling to the suction temperature, from 14 to 90 lb./in.^{2} The index of compression is 1·32, and the capacity of the compressor 1,500 cu. ft. per min.

The compressed air passes through a long air main to a reheater immediately adjacent to an air motor. There is a pressure loss of 5 lb./in.^{2} and a leakage loss of 6% in the air main.

The air enters the heater at 70° F. and leaves at 220° F., the efficiency of the reheater being 70%.

The air is used non-expansively in the air motor. Find the overall efficiency of the system assuming the mechanical efficiencies of the motor and compressor are 90%. The air enters the compressor at 60° F.

[Take R = 54 F.P.F., and C_p = 0·24.]   (*U. Sheff.*)

[Assumptions : Capacity quoted relative to free air at 14·7 lb. per sq. in. and 60° F. ; air motor exhausts slightly above atmospheric pressure, say at 15 lb. per sq. in.

Weight compressed = 113 lb./min. ; compressor b.h.p. = 223 ; heat supplied to reheater = 5,460 B.T.U./min. $\equiv$ 128·2 h.p. ; motor b.h.p. = 87·4 ; η = 24·8%.]

6. In a three-stage air compressor running at 240 r.p.m. with the cylinders arranged as in the diagram, fig. III, 14, 400 cu. ft. of free air are to be compressed per minute. The pressure at suction in the L.P. cylinder is 14 lb. per sq. in., temperature 90° F., and the final delivery pressure 1,000 lb. per sq. in. The clearances are 4, 7 and 10% of the displacement volumes for the L.P., I.P. and H.P. cylinders respectively. Assuming perfect intercooling, stage pressures in geometrical progression, $PV^{1·3}$ = constant for compression and expansion curves, and stroke = diameter of low-pressure cylinder, calculate suitable diameters for the cylinders.

N.B.—Free air is air at 14·7 lb. per sq. in. and 60° F.   (*U. Lond.*)

[w = 30·55 lb. per min. ; P_2 = 58·1, P_3 = 241 lb. per sq. in. ; temperature after compression in *each* cylinder = 765° F. abs. ; per 100 cu. ft. of L.P. stroke volume : 6·33 lb. are dealt with per cycle and V_1 = 2·01 cu. ft. ; per 100 cu. ft. of I.P. stroke volume : 24·56 lb. are dealt with per cycle and

FIG. III,14.

V_2 = 0·518 cu. ft. ; ditto H.P. : 94·9 lb. per cycle and V_3 = 0·134 cu. ft. ; stroke = d_1 = 16·8 in. ; d_2 = 14·65 in. ; d_3 = 4·2 in.]

7. A two-stage air compressor delivers 5,000 cu. t. of free air per hr. The pressure and temperature in the cylinder at the start of compression are 14·2 lb. per sq. in. and 93° F. The diameter of the low-pressure cylinder is twice that of the high-pressure cylinder. The air enters the high-pressure cylinder at a temperature of 105° F. and is then compressed to 250 lb. per sq. in., the law of compression being $PV^{1·22}$ = constant for both stages.

Neglecting the effects of clearance, estimate :

(*a*) the intercooler pressure ; (*b*) the air horse-power required ; (*c*) the ratio of cylinder diameters for minimum work, making the usual assumptions regarding the intercooler conditions.

The free air conditions are 14·65 lb. per sq. in. and 63° F.   (*U. Lond.*)

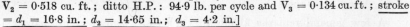

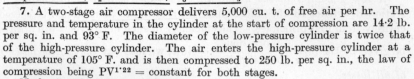

[(*a*) 58 lb. per sq. in.   (*b*) Wt. per min., 6·32 lb. ; W.D. per lb. L.P., 46,800 ft.lb. ; ditto H.P., 50,250 ; horse-power, 18·6.   (*c*) Ideal intercooler pressure, 59·5 lb. per sq. in. ; ratio of diameters, 2·05.]

CHAPTER IV

AIR-STANDARD CYCLES

Introduction

Most students will be familiar with the fundamental types of air-standard cycles which form the reference basis for the actual performance of internal combustion engines. Fig. IV,1 shows the four principal ideal cycles which may be summarized as follows :

(a) The constant volume or Otto cycle for spark ignition (gas and petrol) engines.

(b) The Diesel cycle, sometimes referred to as the constant pressure cycle—a misleading term. Very few engines, except large marine engines, are left today which employ this cycle.

(c) The dual-combustion, or semi-Diesel, or compression-ignition, or mixed cycle is the ideal cycle for many types of compression-ignition (C.I.) engines which are not infrequently called " Diesel " engines, although " semi-Diesel " engines is a more correct term. It should be more widely realized, however, that many modern C.I. engines approximate as closely to the constant volume cycle as do the petrol or gas engine.

(d) The (true) constant pressure or Joule cycle which has recently assumed great practical importance as the ideal cycle for gas turbine units. It will thus be seen that the term " constant pressure " cycle should be reserved for this cycle and should not be used to describe the Diesel cycle.

Whereas the four phases of the cycles (a)–(c) all occur within an engine cylinder, it should be noted that in the case of (d) the four phases all take place in different components of the plant. This matter is explained in more detail in chapter X.

A few general remarks about **air** cycles are contained in chapter I, section B, articles 13–15. Most questions relating to them should be solved entirely from first principles. The efficiency of such ideal cycles will always be given by the ratio $\dfrac{\text{Work done}}{\text{Heat supplied}}$. Now, we may say that in the *absence of all losses*,

$$\text{Work done} = \text{Heat supplied} - \text{Heat rejected}.$$

$$\therefore \text{ Air-standard Efficiency} = 1 - \frac{\text{Heat rejected}}{\text{Heat supplied}} \qquad . \quad \text{(IV,1)}$$

A number of air-standard cycles other than (a)–(d) above occur ; some

68

have a practical basis such as the Atkinson and Stirling cycles. Other cycles are found on examination papers, the object being to test the student's knowledge of fundamental principles and his ability to apply such principles to non-standard cases.

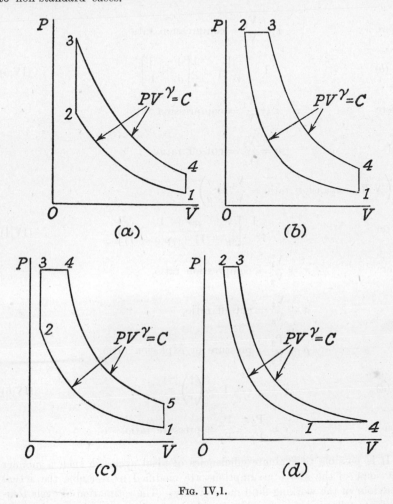

Fig. IV,1.

In the simplest approach to ideal cycles, it is usually assumed that the specific heats of the fluid are those for air, that the process of combustion does not affect their values, that they are constant throughout, i.e. independent of temperature, and that the weight of the charge is unaffected by any injected fuel. When an " air-standard efficiency " is quoted, these assumptions are always implicitly made.

It can be shown that the four cycles described above have air-standard efficiencies as follows:

(a)
$$1 - \frac{1}{r^{\gamma-1}}$$.   .   .   .   . (IV,2)

where
$$r = \frac{V_1}{V_2} = \text{compression ratio.}$$

(b)
$$1 - \frac{1}{r^{\gamma-1}} \times \frac{1}{\gamma}\left[\frac{a^\gamma - 1}{a - 1}\right]$$.   .   . (IV,3)

where
$$r = \frac{V_1}{V_2} = \text{compression ratio,}$$

and
$$a = \frac{V_3}{V_2} = \text{cut-off ratio.}$$

$$\left(N.B., \text{ expansion ratio} = \frac{V_4}{V_3} = \frac{r}{a}\right)$$

(c)
$$1 - \frac{1}{r^{\gamma-1}}\left[\frac{\rho a^\gamma - 1}{(\rho - 1) + \gamma\rho(a - 1)}\right]$$.   .   . (IV,4)

where
$$r = \frac{V_1}{V_2} = \text{compression ratio,}$$

$$a = \frac{V_4}{V_3} = \text{cut-off ratio,}$$

$$\rho = \frac{P_3}{P_2} = \text{pressure or explosion ratio.}$$

(d)
$$1 - \left(\frac{1}{r}\right)^{\frac{\gamma-1}{\gamma}}$$.   .   . (IV,5)

where
$$r = \frac{P_2}{P_1} = \frac{P_3}{P_4} = \text{pressure ratio.}$$

It is possible to evaluate efficiencies of ideal cycles in such a manner that some of the above assumptions are modified to resemble the actual behaviour of the working fluid more closely. The estimation of cycle temperatures, allowing for variable specific heats, molecular contraction, the changes in the specific heats due to combustion, dissociation, and the increase in the weight of the charge if fuel is injected is a matter of some difficulty and can, in general, only be solved by trial and error, and by the use of some empirical relations. Such investigations are outside the scope of this book, and are only of interest to post-graduate and research students.

1. *In the constant volume cycle the temperatures at the beginning and end of the compression are 43° C. and 323° C. respectively. Determine the air-standard efficiency and the compression ratio. Assume* $\gamma = 1\cdot4$.

A petrol engine, with the above compression ratio, develops 30 i.h.p. and consumes 1·63 gal. of fuel per hour. The specific gravity of the fuel is 0·78 and its calorific value is 10,500 C.H.U. per lb. Determine the indicated thermal efficiency and the relative efficiency of this engine.

(1 gal. of water weighs 10 lb.)

(U.L.C.I.)

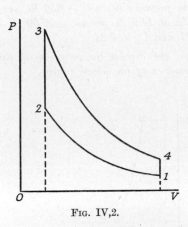

FIG. IV,2.

$$t_1 = (43 \times 1\cdot8) + 32 = 109\cdot4° \text{ F.} \;; \quad T_1 = 570° \text{ F. abs. nearly}$$
$$t_2 = (322 \times 1\cdot8) + 32 = 613° \text{ F.} \;; \quad T_2 = 1{,}073° \text{ F. abs.}$$

By (I,17)
$$\frac{1{,}073}{570} = \left(\frac{V_1}{V_2}\right)^{0\cdot4}$$

i.e.
Compression ratio $r = \dfrac{V_1}{V_2} = (1\cdot882)^{2\cdot5} = \underline{4\cdot85}$ Ans.

By (IV,2)
Air-standard $\eta = 1 - \left(\dfrac{1}{4\cdot85}\right)^{0\cdot4}$

$$= 1 - \frac{1}{1\cdot882} = \frac{0\cdot882}{1\cdot882} = \underline{46\cdot9\%}. \quad \text{Ans.}$$

Now, Calorific Value $= 10{,}500 \times 1\cdot8 = 18{,}900$ B.T.U. per lb.
Fuel consumption $= 1\cdot63 \times 0\cdot78 \times 10 = 12\cdot7$ lb. per hr.

$$\underline{\text{Indicated Thermal } \eta} = \frac{30 \times 2{,}546}{12\cdot7 \times 18{,}900} \times 100 = \underline{31\cdot8\%}. \quad \text{Ans.}$$

$$\underline{\text{Relative } \eta} = \frac{31\cdot8}{46\cdot9} \times 100 = \underline{68\%}. \quad \text{Ans.}$$

2. *The following question has been taken from a treatise on Applied Thermodynamics :*

A compression-ignition engine working on the composite cycle takes in two-thirds of its total heat supply at constant volume and one-third at constant pressure.

Calculate :

    (a) *the temperatures at the five cardinal points of the cycle ;*
    (b) *the ideal thermal efficiency of the cycle.*

Given : Compression ratio = 13 : 1.
        Maximum pressure in cycle = 650 lb. per in.
        Air intake at 14·7 lb. per in. and 60° F.
        $C_v = 0·17$ *and* $C_p = 0·24$.

Solve the problems, and discuss the propriety of applying the method of solution to the performance of an actual engine.   (U. Manch.)

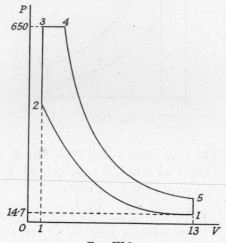

Fig. IV,3.

$$T_1 = 520° \text{ F.} ; \quad \gamma = \frac{0·24}{0·17} = 1·41.$$

(a) By (I,17) $T_2 = T_1\left(\dfrac{V_1}{V_2}\right)^{\gamma-1}.$

$$T_2 = 520 \times 13^{0·41} = 520 \times 2·86.$$

$$\underline{T_2 = 1,487° \text{ F. abs.}} \quad \text{Ans.}$$

$$P_2 V_2^\gamma = P_1 V_1^\gamma$$

$$\therefore P_2 = 14 \cdot 7 \times 13^{1 \cdot 41} = 14 \cdot 7 \times 37 \cdot 1 = 546 \text{ lb. per sq. in.}$$

$$\therefore T_3 = T_2 \frac{P_3}{P_2} = 1{,}487 \times \frac{650}{546}.$$

$$T_3 = 1{,}769° \text{ F. abs.} \quad \text{Ans.}$$

or by (I,16)
$$T_3 = T_1 \frac{P_3 V_3}{P_1 V_1} = \frac{520 \times 650 \times 1}{14 \cdot 7 \times 13}$$

$$= 1{,}769° \text{ F. abs.}$$

Heat added at constant volume $\quad Q_{2-3} = C_v(T_3 - T_2)$ per lb. air,
i.e. $\quad Q_{2-3} = 0 \cdot 17(1{,}769 - 1{,}487) = 48$ B.T.U. per lb. air,

$$\therefore Q_{3-4} = \tfrac{1}{2} \times 48 = 24 \text{ B.T.U. per lb. air}$$

because Q_{2-3} is $\tfrac{2}{3}$ of the total heat supplied,
i.e.
$$24 = C_p(T_4 - T_3).$$

$$T_4 = \frac{24}{0 \cdot 24} + 1{,}769 = \underline{1{,}869° \text{ F. abs.}} \quad \text{Ans.}$$

and
$$V_4 = V_3 \frac{T_4}{T_3} = 1 \times \frac{1{,}869}{1{,}769} = 1 \cdot 056.$$

Again, by (I,17) $\quad T_5 = T_4 \left(\frac{V_4}{V_5}\right)^{\gamma - 1} = 1{,}869 \times \left(\frac{1 \cdot 056}{13}\right)^{0 \cdot 41}.$

$$T_5 = 1{,}869 \times \left(\frac{1}{12 \cdot 3}\right)^{0 \cdot 41} = \frac{1{,}869}{2 \cdot 80} = \underline{668° \text{ F. abs.}} \quad \text{Ans.}$$

(b) $\qquad \eta = 1 - \dfrac{\text{Heat rejected}}{\text{Heat supplied}}, \text{ by (IV,1)}$

$$= 1 - \frac{C_v(T_5 - T_1)}{C_v(T_3 - T_2) + C_p(T_4 - T_3)}$$

$$= 1 - \frac{668 - 520}{(1{,}769 - 1{,}487) + 1 \cdot 41(1{,}869 - 1{,}769)}$$

$$= 1 - \frac{148}{282 + 141} = 1 - 0 \cdot 35.$$

$$\eta = 65\%. \quad \text{Ans.}$$

The last part of the question is answered elsewhere in this chapter, notably on pages 70 and 87.

3. *Show that for a perfect gas the work done by a constant pressure expansion from any point on one given isothermal to another given isothermal is constant.*

Deduce the maximum theoretical efficiency which can be obtained from a cycle comprising two constant pressure lines and two isothermal lines. What practical condition would have to be obtained before this maximum theoretical efficiency could be reached? (W.S.)

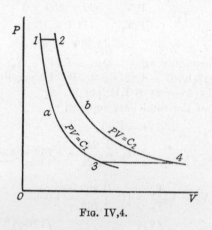

FIG. IV,4.

Let $1a3$ and $2b4$ be the two isothermals, and let 1–2, 3–4 be the two constant pressure expansions.

$$\text{W.D.}_{1-2} = P_1(V_2 - V_1) = R(T_2 - T_1) \text{ per lb.}$$
$$\text{W.D.}_{3-4} = P_3(V_4 - V_3) = R(T_4 - T_3) \text{ per lb.}$$

But for isothermals, $T_2 = T_4$ and $T_1 = T_3$,

$$\therefore \underline{\text{W.D.}_{1-2} = R(T_4 - T_3) \text{ per lb.} = \text{W.D.}_{3-4}}. \quad \text{Ans.}$$

Let 1243 be the cycle referred to.

By (IV,1),
$$\eta = 1 - \frac{\text{Heat rejected}}{\text{Heat received}}.$$

Bearing in mind that the heat rejected or received is numerically equal to the W.D. in an isothermal operation [cf. (I,2) where $\Delta E = 0$ when $T = \text{constant}$].

$$\text{Heat rejected} = C_p(T_4 - T_3) + \text{W.D.}_{3-1}$$

$$= C_p(T_4 - T_3) + \frac{R}{J}T_3 \log_e \frac{P_1}{P_3}, \text{ per lb.}$$

$$\text{Heat received} = C_p(T_2 - T_1) + \frac{R}{J}T_2 \log_e \frac{P_2}{P_4}, \text{ per lb.}$$

$$\eta = 1 - \frac{C_p(T_4 - T_3) + \dfrac{R}{J}T_3 \log_e \dfrac{P_1}{P_3}}{C_p(T_2 - T_1) + \dfrac{R}{J}T_2 \log_e \dfrac{P_2}{P_4}}$$

$$= 1 - \frac{1 + \dfrac{C_p - C_v}{C_p} \dfrac{T_3}{T_4 - T_3} \log_e r}{1 + \dfrac{C_p - C_v}{C_p} \dfrac{T_2}{T_4 - T_3} \log_e r}, \text{ where } r = \frac{P_1}{P_3} = \frac{P_2}{P_4}$$

$$= 1 - \frac{1 + \dfrac{T_3}{T_4 - T_3} \log_e r^{\frac{\gamma-1}{\gamma}}}{1 + \dfrac{T_2}{T_4 - T_3} \log_e r^{\frac{\gamma-1}{\gamma}}}$$

$$= \frac{1 + \dfrac{T_2}{T_4 - T_3} \log_e a - 1 - \dfrac{T_3}{T_4 - T_3} \log_e a}{1 + \dfrac{T_2}{T_4 - T_3} \log_e a}, \text{ where } a = \left(\frac{P_1}{P_3}\right)^{\frac{\gamma-1}{\gamma}}$$

$$= \frac{(T_2 - T_3) \log_e a}{T_2(1 + \log_e a) - T_3}. \quad \text{Ans.}$$

The practical difficulties in any air cycle involving isothermal operations lie in the fact that a piston engine would have to have an extremely low piston speed, and a cylinder made of a perfect heat conductor. Attempts have been made to use heat regenerators (e.g. the Stirling Cycle), but again they must be made of material of infinitely good conductivity. If the cycle were to take place entirely in an engine cylinder, the slow speed required for the isothermal expansion would make a constant pressure heat addition extremely difficult.

4. *Describe the ideal air cycle for the Diesel engine receiving heat at constant pressure and rejecting heat at constant volume. Show that the efficiency of this cycle is less than that of the constant volume cycle for the same compression ratio, and also show that the efficiency decreases as the amount of heat received is increased.*

Find the ideal efficiency of a Diesel engine having a compression ratio of 10 to 1, if the temperature at the start of compression is 140° F., and at the end of combustion is 2,200° F.

$$(\gamma = 1.4.)$$

(U. Lond.)

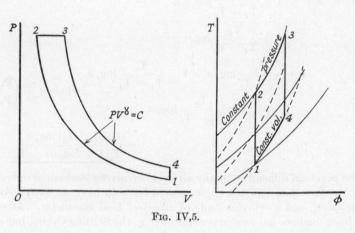

FIG. IV,5.

The description of the ideal cycle is best done by reference to P–V and T–ϕ diagrams, as shown, and it is left to the student to justify these diagrams.

Referring to the P–V diagram, the efficiency is given by

$$\eta = 1 - \frac{\text{Heat rejected}}{\text{Heat received}} \qquad . \qquad . \qquad . \qquad \text{(IV,1)}$$

i.e.
$$\eta = 1 - \frac{C_v(T_4 - T_1)}{C_p(T_3 - T_2)} \qquad . \qquad . \qquad . \qquad . \qquad \text{(i)}$$

The best procedure now is to express all temperatures in terms of any one of them, say T_1. Let $r = \dfrac{V_1}{V_2} =$ compression ratio, and

$$a = \frac{V_3}{V_2} = \text{cut-off ratio,}$$

then,

by (I,17) $\qquad T_2 = T_1\left(\dfrac{V_1}{V_2}\right)^{\gamma-1} = T_1 r^{\gamma-1},$

by (I,7)
$$T_3 = T_2 \frac{V_3}{V_2} = T_1 a r^{\gamma-1},$$

by (I,17)
$$T_4 = T_3 \left(\frac{V_3}{V_4}\right)^{\gamma-1} = T_1 a r^{\gamma-1} \left(\frac{V_3 V_2}{V_2 V_4}\right)^{\gamma-1}$$

$$= T_1 a r^{\gamma-1} \left(\frac{a}{r}\right)^{\gamma-1} = T_1 a^\gamma,$$

∴ in (i)
$$\eta = 1 - \frac{T_1 a^\gamma - T_1}{\gamma(T_1 a r^{\gamma-1} - T_1 r^{\gamma-1})}$$

$$= 1 - \frac{1}{r^{\gamma-1}} \times \frac{1}{\gamma}\left[\frac{a^\gamma - 1}{a - 1}\right]. \qquad . \qquad . \qquad \text{(ii)}$$

This is the usual expression for the efficiency of the Diesel cycle, cf. (IV,3). We know that a constant volume cycle with the same compression ratio has an efficiency given by $1 - \dfrac{1}{r^{\gamma-1}}$, so that for (ii) to be smaller numerically, the factor $\dfrac{a^\gamma - 1}{\gamma(a - 1)}$ would have to be greater than 1.

Let $a = \dfrac{x}{y} > 1$, and $x - y = \delta$, where δ is small.

Then
$$\frac{y}{x} = 1 - \frac{\delta}{x}$$

and
$$a = \frac{x}{y} = \left(1 - \frac{\delta}{x}\right)^{-1} = 1 + \frac{\delta}{x} + \left(\frac{\delta}{x}\right)^2 + \left(\frac{\delta}{x}\right)^3 + \ldots$$

Also,
$$a^\gamma = \left(\frac{x}{y}\right)^\gamma = \left(1 - \frac{\delta}{x}\right)^{-\gamma}$$

$$= 1 + \gamma\left(\frac{\delta}{x}\right) + \frac{\gamma(\gamma + 1)}{2!}\left(\frac{\delta}{x}\right)^2 + \frac{\gamma(\gamma + 1)(\gamma + 2)}{3!}\left(\frac{\delta}{x}\right)^3 + \ldots$$

∴ Our factor $\dfrac{a^\gamma - 1}{\gamma(a - 1)}$ now becomes

$$= \frac{\left(\dfrac{\delta}{x}\right) + \dfrac{\gamma + 1}{2!}\left(\dfrac{\delta}{x}\right)^2 + \dfrac{(\gamma + 1)(\gamma + 2)}{3!}\left(\dfrac{\delta}{x}\right)^3 + \ldots}{\dfrac{\delta}{x} + \left(\dfrac{\delta}{x}\right)^2 + \left(\dfrac{\delta}{x}\right)^3 + \ldots}$$

$$= \frac{1 + \dfrac{\gamma + 1}{2!}\left(\dfrac{\delta}{x}\right) + \dfrac{(\gamma + 1)(\gamma + 2)}{3!}\left(\dfrac{\delta}{x}\right)^2 + \ldots}{1 + \left(\dfrac{\delta}{x}\right) + \left(\dfrac{\delta}{x}\right)^2 + \ldots}.$$

Now, $\dfrac{\delta}{x}$ is small, but always positive; $\dfrac{\gamma + 1}{2!} > 1$, also $\dfrac{(\gamma + 1)(\gamma + 2)}{3!} > 1$, and all further coefficients are greater than 1, so that the numerator is greater than the denominator, i.e. $\dfrac{a^\gamma - 1}{\gamma(a - 1)} > 1$, which proves the proposition.

As the amount of heat received is increased, the cycle will deviate more and more from the Carnot cycle, and therefore the efficiency must decrease. This statement is proved rather more carefully in another example in this chapter in relation to the constant volume cycle, to which the argument also applies.

Referring to the P–V diagram of this question, $r = \dfrac{V_1}{V_2} = 10$, $t_1 = 140°$ F., $t_3 = 2,200°$ F.

By (I,17) $T_2 = 600 \times 10^{0.4} = 600 \times 2.512 = 1,507°$ F. abs.

$$\therefore\ a = \frac{2,660}{1,507} = 1.765.$$

In (ii) $\eta = 1 - \dfrac{1}{10^{0.4}} \dfrac{1.765^{1.4} - 1}{1.4 \times 0.765}.$

$$\eta = 1 - \frac{1.215}{1.4 \times 2.512 \times 0.765} = \underline{54.9\%}.\quad \text{Ans.}$$

5. *An engine works on the ideal dual-combustion cycle, the compression ratio being 11·0. The pressure at the commencement of compression is 14·5 lb. per sq. in. and the temperature 90° C. If the maximum pressure in the cycle is 700 lb. per sq. in., and the constant pressure heat reception continues for $\frac{1}{20}$ of the stroke, find the work done per lb. of air and the ideal thermal efficiency.*

$$(C_v = 0.17.\quad C_p = 0.238.)$$

$$(U.L.C.I.)$$

$$t_1 = 90 \times \frac{9}{5} + 32 = 194° \text{ F.}$$

$$\therefore\ T_1 = 654° \text{ F. abs.}$$

Let $V_1 = 11$, $V_2 = 1$, then

$$V_4 = \frac{1}{20}(11 - 1) + 1 = 1.5$$

$$\gamma = \frac{0.238}{0.170} = 1.40.$$

By (I,17), $T_2 = 654 \times 11^{0.4}$
$$= 654 \times 2.61 = 1,710° \text{ F.}$$

$$P_1V_1{}^\gamma = P_2V_2{}^\gamma$$
$$\therefore P_2 = 14\cdot5 \times 11_j^{1\cdot4}$$
$$= 14\cdot5 \times 28\cdot6 = 415 \text{ lb. per sq. in.}$$

$$T_3 = T_2\frac{P_3}{P_2} = 1{,}710 \times \frac{700}{415} = 2{,}880° \text{ F.}$$

or, by (I,16) $$T_3 = \frac{P_3V_3}{P_1V_1} \times T_1 = \frac{700 \times 1 \times 654}{14\cdot5 \times 11} = 2{,}880° \text{ F.}$$

$$T_4 = T_3\frac{V_4}{V_3} = 2{,}880 \times 1\cdot5 = 4{,}320° \text{ F.}$$

By (I,17) $$T_5 = 4{,}320 \times \left(\frac{1\cdot5}{11}\right)^{0\cdot4} = \frac{4{,}320}{(7\cdot33)^{0\cdot4}}$$

$$T_5 = \frac{4{,}320}{2\cdot22} = 1{,}950° \text{ F.}$$

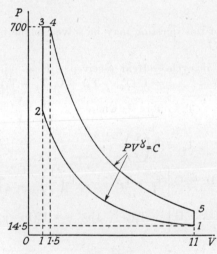

FIG. IV,6.

In an ideal cycle,

W.D. = Heat received − Heat rejected,

i.e. W.D. $= C_v(T_3 - T_2) + C_p(T_4 - T_3) - C_v(T_5 - T_1)$

$= 0\cdot17[(2{,}880 - 1{,}710) - (1{,}950 - 654)] + 0\cdot238(4{,}320 - 2{,}880)$

$= 0\cdot17 \times (1{,}170 - 1{,}296) + 0\cdot238 \times 1{,}440$

$= \underline{321 \text{ B.T.U. per lb. air.}}$ Ans.

Ideal Thermal $\eta = \dfrac{321}{(0\cdot17 \times 1{,}170) + (0\cdot238 \times 1{,}440)}$

$= \dfrac{321}{541} = \underline{59\cdot3\%.}$ Ans.

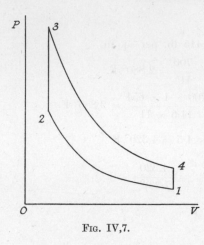

FIG. IV,7.

6. *Obtain an expression for the air-standard efficiency of an internal combustion engine working on the Otto cycle in terms of the ratio of compression r and the ratio of the specific heats γ.*

Show that, for the maximum work to be done per lb. of air in this cycle between given upper and lower limits of absolute temperature T_3 and T_1 respectively, the ratio of compression should have the value $\left(\dfrac{T_3}{T_1}\right)^{1 \cdot 25}$ when γ = 1·4.

(*U. Camb.*)

The first part of this question may be solved in the manner explained on pages 76 and 77.

$$\text{W.D. in cycle} = \text{Heat received} - \text{Heat rejected}$$
$$= C_v(T_3 - T_2) - C_v(T_4 - T_1).$$

Now, by (I,17) $T_2 = T_1 r^{\gamma-1}$, where $r = \dfrac{V_1}{V_2} = \dfrac{V_4}{V_3}$

and also $T_4 = T_3\left(\dfrac{1}{r}\right)^{\gamma-1}.$

$$\therefore \text{W.D.} = C_v\left[T_3 - T_1 r^{\gamma-1} - T_3\left(\frac{1}{r}\right)^{\gamma-1} - T_1\right]$$

$$\frac{d}{dr}(\text{W.D.}) = C_v\left[-T_1(\gamma-1)r^{\gamma-2} - T_3(1-\gamma)r^{-\gamma}\right].$$

By equating $\dfrac{d}{dr}$ (W.D.) to zero, we shall obtain the value of r which will make the W.D. a maximum, i.e.

$$T_1(\gamma-1)r^{\gamma-2} = T_3(\gamma-1)r^{-\gamma}$$

$$r^{2-2\gamma} = \frac{T_1}{T_3}$$

or $$r^{2 \cdot 8-2} = \frac{T_3}{T_1}, \quad \because \gamma = 1 \cdot 4.$$

$$r = \left(\frac{T_3}{T_1}\right)^{\frac{1}{0 \cdot 8}} = \underline{\left(\frac{T_3}{T_1}\right)^{1 \cdot 25}}. \quad \text{Q.E.D.}$$

7. *On the blue-print provided draw the T–ϕ diagrams for the following cycles :*

    (a) *The constant volume cycle, ratio of compression 6.*

    (b) *The dual-combustion cycle, ratio of compression 12.*

In each cycle the temperature and pressure at the beginning of compression are 360° C. (abs.) and 14 lb. per sq. in. (abs.), the heat supplied per cycle is 300 C.H.U. per lb. and the maximum pressures are to be the same.

Compare the maximum temperatures, the thermal efficiencies and the mean effective pressures of the two cycles.   (U. Manch.)

In order to provide a graphical illustration for this question, the diagrams have been drawn approximately to scale and will thus show the student what was expected as an answer to this question.

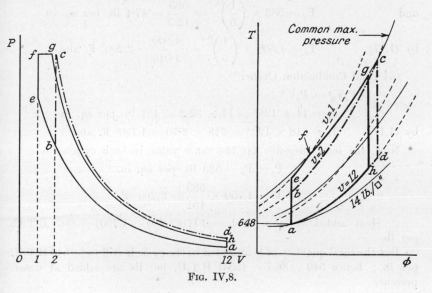

Fig. IV,8.

360° C. abs. ≡ 648° F. abs. = T_a.

All compression and expansion curves must be adiabatic for air-standard cycles. $\gamma = 1{\cdot}40$, $C_p = 0{\cdot}238$, $C_v = 0{\cdot}170$.

(i) Constant Volume Cycle :

By (I,17)

$$T_b = 648 \times 6^{0 \cdot 4} = 648 \times 2 \cdot 046 = 1,329° \text{ F. abs.}$$

Heat added $= 300 \times 1 \cdot 8 = 540$ B.T.U. per lb.

$$\therefore \; 540 = C_v(T_c - T_b)$$

$$T_c = \frac{540}{0 \cdot 170} + 1,329 = 4,500° \text{ F. abs.}$$

and

$$P_b = 14 \times \left(\frac{12}{2}\right)^{1 \cdot 4} = 14 \times 12 \cdot 3 = 172 \text{ lb. per sq. in.}$$

$$\therefore \; P_c = 172 \times \frac{4,500}{1,329} = 583 \text{ lb. per sq. in.}$$

and

$$P_d = 583 \times \left(\frac{1}{6}\right)^{1 \cdot 4} = \frac{583}{12 \cdot 3} = 47 \cdot 4 \text{ lb. per sq. in.}$$

by (I,17)

$$T_d = 4,500 \times \left(\frac{1}{6}\right)^{0 \cdot 4} = \frac{4,500}{2 \cdot 046} = 2,200° \text{ F. abs.}$$

(ii) Dual Combustion Cycle :

$$P_a V_a{}^\gamma = P_e V_e{}^\gamma$$

$$\therefore \; P_e = 14 \times 12^{1 \cdot 4} = 14 \times 32 \cdot 2 = 451 \text{ lb. per sq. in.}$$

by (I,17) $T_e = 648 \times 12^{0 \cdot 4} = 648 \times 2 \cdot 70 = 1,750° \text{ F. abs.}$

Now, the max. pressure has the same value in both cycles, i.e.

$$P_f = P_c = 583 \text{ lb. per sq. in.}$$

$$\therefore \; T_f = 1,750 \times \frac{583}{451} = 2,260° \text{ F.}$$

$\therefore$ Heat added at const. vol. $= 0 \cdot 170(2,260 - 1,750) = 86 \cdot 7$ B.T.U. per lb.

But the total quantity of heat added in the cycle is still to be 540 B.T.U. per lb. ; hence $540 - 86 \cdot 7 = 453 \cdot 3$ B.T.U. per lb. are added at const. pressure.

$$\therefore \; 453 \cdot 3 = 0 \cdot 238(T_g - 2,260)$$

$$T_g = \frac{453 \cdot 3}{0 \cdot 238} + 2,260 = 4,165° \text{ F. abs.}$$

Then $V_g = V_f \dfrac{T_g}{T_f} = 1 \times \dfrac{4,165}{2,260} = 1 \cdot 843.$

By (I,17)

$$T_h = 4,165 \times \left(\frac{1 \cdot 843}{12}\right)^{0 \cdot 4} = \frac{4,165}{6 \cdot 51^{0 \cdot 4}} = \frac{4,165}{2 \cdot 12} = 1,965° \text{ F. abs.}$$

and $$P_h = 583 \times \left(\frac{1}{6\cdot51}\right)^{1\cdot4} = \frac{583}{13\cdot8} = 42\cdot2 \text{ lb. per sq. in.}$$

Hence, we get these results :

(i) Constant Volume Cycle,

$$\text{Max. temperature} = t_c = 4{,}040° \text{ F.} \quad \text{Ans.}$$

$$\eta = 1 - \frac{\text{Heat rejected}}{\text{Heat supplied}}$$

$$= 1 - \frac{0\cdot170(2{,}200 - 648)}{540} = 1 - 0\cdot489$$

$$= 51\cdot1\%. \quad \text{Ans.}$$

$$\text{m.e.p.} = \frac{\text{Area of diagram}}{\text{Length of diagram}}.$$

But, area of diagram = W.D. = Heat supplied − Heat rejected
$$= \text{Heat supplied} \times \text{Thermal efficiency}$$
$$= 0\cdot511 \times 540 \text{ B.T.U. per lb.}$$

If the volumes of 12 and 2 (fig. IV,8) represent cu. ft., we have by (I,7)

$$w = \frac{14 \times 144 \times 12}{53\cdot3 \times 648} = 0\cdot70 \text{ lb.}$$

$$\therefore \text{ m.e.p.} = \frac{0\cdot511 \times 540 \times 0\cdot7 \times 778}{(12 - 2) \times 144} = 104 \text{ lb. per sq. in.} \quad \text{Ans.}$$

(ii) Dual Combustion Cycle,

$$\text{Max. temperature} = t_g = 3{,}705° \text{ F.} \quad \text{Ans.}$$

Proceeding as before,

$$\eta = 1 - \frac{0\cdot17(1{,}965 - 648)}{540} = 1 - 0\cdot415.$$

$$= 58\cdot5\%. \quad \text{Ans.}$$

$$\text{m.e.p.} = \frac{0\cdot585 \times 540 \times 0\cdot7 \times 778}{(12 - 1) \times 144} = 109 \text{ lb. per sq. in.} \quad \text{Ans.}$$

Note, the constant volume cycle has the greater maximum temperature ; for the same amount of heat supplied, this will be clear from the construction of the entropy diagram. Also, for the *same amount of heat* supplied, the dual-combustion cycle must be more efficient as $T_h < T_d$, i.e. the heat rejected is less in the mixed cycle. The m.e.p. is nearly the same with a slightly higher value in the mixed cycle.

8. *Show that the ideal air-standard efficiency of an engine working on the constant volume cycle depends only on the ratio of compression. Sketch the phases of the cycle on an entropy–temperature diagram, and demonstrate that the divergence of the efficiency of this cycle from the Carnot efficiency increases as the heat supplied per lb. increases.*

A two-cylinder two-stroke cycle engine working on the constant volume cycle has cylinder diameters of 13·5 in., and stroke 20 in. The clearance volume is $\frac{1}{15}$ of the swept volume, and the exhaust ports are closed by the piston when it has travelled 3·25 in. from dead centre on the compression stroke. The indicated mean effective pressure is 67·2 lb. per sq. in., and the specific consumption is 0·42 lb. per h.p.hr.; the calorific value of the fuel is 18,750 B.T.U. per lb.

Find :

> (a) *the indicated horse-power at 180 r.p.m. ;*
> (b) *the relative efficiency based on the effective compression ratio of the engine.*

(U. Lond.)

The first part of the question consists of the derivation of the air-standard efficiency, dealt with earlier.

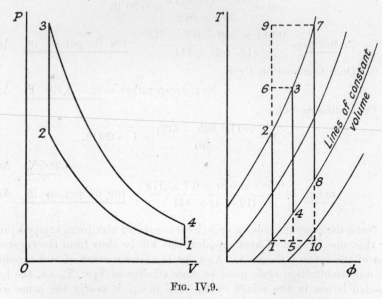

FIG. IV,9.

The well-known result, equation (IV,2),

$$\eta = 1 - \left(\frac{1}{r}\right)^{\gamma-1}, \text{ where } r = \frac{V_1}{V_2}$$

shows that the efficiency depends on the compression ratio only.

The cycle 1 2 3 4 1, fig. IV,9, on the T–ϕ diagram is equivalent to the P–V diagram. The heat added in the cycle is given by the area under the curve 2–3 in the T–ϕ diagram, measured down to absolute zero of temperature. The Carnot cycle, working between the same two temperatures would be given by the rectangle 1 6 3 5 1. In the constant volume cycle 1 2 7 8 1 the heat added is clearly increased; the corresponding Carnot cycle is given by 1 9 7 10 1, and it is clear that this cycle diverges more from the constant volume cycle 1 2 7 8 1, than did the Carnot cycle 1 6 3 5 1 from the constant volume cycle 1 2 3 4.

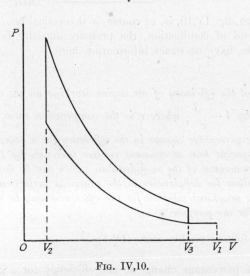

FIG. IV,10.

Cylinder Area $= \dfrac{\pi}{4} \times 13 \cdot 5^2 = 143$ sq. in.

$V_1 - V_2$ (fig. IV,10) = Stroke Vol. $= 143 \times 20 = 2,860$ cu. in.

$V_2 =$ Clearance Vol. $= \dfrac{1}{15} \times 2,860 = 190 \cdot 7$ cu. in.

$V_1 - V_3 = 143 \times 3 \cdot 25 = 465$ cu. in.
$V_1 = 2,860 + 190 \cdot 7 = 3,050 \cdot 7$ cu. in.
$V_3 = 3,050 \cdot 7 - 465 = 2,585 \cdot 7$ cu. in.

$\therefore$ effective compression ratio $= \dfrac{2,585 \cdot 7}{190 \cdot 7} = 13 \cdot 5.$

(a) $\underline{\text{i.h.p.}} = \dfrac{67 \cdot 2 \times 143 \times \dfrac{20}{12} \times 180}{33,000} \times 2$

$= \underline{175}$ Ans.

(b)   Thermal Efficiency $= \dfrac{2{,}546}{0\cdot42 \times 18{,}750} = 32\cdot3\%.$

$\left(\text{Note, 1 h.p.-hr. of work} = \dfrac{33{,}000 \times 60}{778} = 2{,}546 \text{ B.T.U.}\right)$

Air-standard Efficiency $= 1 - \left(\dfrac{1}{13\cdot5}\right)^{0\cdot4} = 1 - \dfrac{1}{2\cdot837} = 64\cdot7\%.$

$\underline{\text{Relative Efficiency}} = \dfrac{32\cdot3}{64\cdot7} = \underline{49\cdot9\%.}$ Ans.

The diagram, fig. IV,10, is, of course, a theoretical one. It is unlikely that, at the end of combustion, the pressure actually falls at constant volume, but we have no exact information here.

9. *Show that the efficiency of an engine working on the constant volume cycle is given by $1 - \dfrac{1}{r^{\gamma-1}}$ where r is the compression ratio.*

What is the percentage change in the efficiency for a compression ratio of 7 to 1 if the specific heat at constant volume increases by 1% ?

Give a short account of the modifications which can be made in the above expression to allow for deficiencies in the practical performance of the cycle. Explain how a graphical solution for the efficiency may be obtained from a chart devised for the purpose. (U. Lond.)

The proof follows readily from (IV,1).

To find the percentage change in the efficiency for a given fractional change in C_v, we shall have to obtain an expression for the fractional change in efficiency, $\dfrac{de}{e}$, in terms of the fractional change in C_v, i.e. $\dfrac{dC_v}{C_v}$. This suggests a differentiation. Thus

$$e = 1 - \left(\frac{1}{r}\right)^{\gamma-1}, \text{ cf. IV,2.}$$

But from (I,6) and (I,14)

$$C_v = \frac{R}{J(\gamma - 1)}, \quad \text{i.e. } \gamma - 1 = \frac{R}{JC_v}$$

$$\therefore \ e = 1 - r^{-\frac{R}{JC_v}}$$

or, $$\log (1 - e) = -\frac{R}{JC_v} \log r.$$

Differentiating this as an implicit function,

$$-\frac{1}{1 - e} de = + \frac{R}{JC_v{}^2} \log r \, dC_v, \text{ for constant R and } r$$

$$de = -\frac{(1 - e)R \log r}{JC_v{}^2} dC_v, \text{ and again } \frac{R}{J} = C_v(\gamma - 1)$$

$$\frac{de}{e} = -\frac{(1 - e)(\gamma - 1) \log r}{e} \times \frac{dC_v}{C_v}.$$

Now, $$e = 1 - \frac{1}{7^{0.4}} = 1 - \frac{1}{2.178} = 54.1\%, \text{ for } r = 7$$

$$\therefore \ \frac{de}{e} = -\frac{0.459}{0.541} \times 0.4 \times \log_e 7 \times \frac{1}{100}.$$

$$\frac{de}{e} = -0.66 \times \frac{1}{100} = \underline{\text{a decrease of } 0.66\%}. \quad \text{Ans.}$$

The deficiencies referred to, cause—on the whole—a decrease in the effective values of the specific heats. Various investigators have suggested methods of allowing for these variations. Such investigations are usually based on the total energy content of unit volume of a specified mixture of air and fuel. Thus, for the expression $1 - \left(\dfrac{1}{r}\right)^{\gamma - 1}$, values ranging from 0.250 to 0.295 have been suggested for $\gamma - 1$, under different conditions.

With a view to allowing for dissociation of the products of combustion and the resulting variation in C_v, C_p and γ, charts of total internal energy have been prepared for different mixture strengths. These afford graphical means of solving what otherwise becomes a highly complicated, if not impossible, analytical task. The reader is referred to works by H. R. Ricardo, D. R. Pye, or C. B. Dicksee for further information.

It is worth noting that the above result depends on the fact that R is an absolute constant, even when the specific heats are considered as variable (cf. page 9).

10. *A power plant, using air as the working substance, consists of a heater, turbine, compressor and regenerator, and is shown in fig. IV,11. The excess power from the turbine is transformed into electrical energy in the electrical generator. The ideal cycle of operations is shown on the T–φ diagram and it may be assumed that there is no fall of pressure between the points D and A or between B and C and that the regenerator is perfect. If the upper and lower limits of temperature are T_1 and T_3 respectively, show that the ideal thermodynamic efficiency of the plant is*

$$1 - \frac{T_3\beta \log \beta}{T_1(\beta - 1)},$$

where P_1 and P_2 are the upper and lower pressures respectively, and

$$\beta = \left(\frac{P_1}{P_2}\right)^{\frac{\gamma-1}{\gamma}}.$$

(*U. Camb.*)

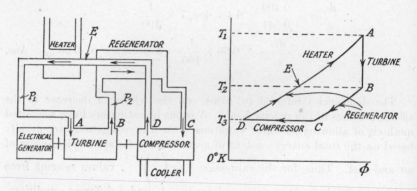

FIG. IV,11.

This example shows well how non-standard cycles can be dealt with from first principles.

It may be helpful to construct a P–V diagram from the given T–φ diagram and the data.

The point E must lie on an isothermal through B, parallel to CD. AB is an adiabatic.

It must be realized that, from the point of view of the efficiency of the whole *cycle*, the only heat quantities which matter are those received from or rejected to *external* sources; so that the heat interchanged in the "perfect" regenerator within the phases of the cycle, does not arise in an expression for the efficiency. Thus,

Heat rejected to external sources $= Q_{C-D}$

And by (I,2), as $\Delta E = 0$ for an isothermal operation,

$$Q_{C-D} = \text{W.D.}_{C-D} = RT_3 \log_e \frac{P_1}{P_2} \text{ ft.lb. per lb. numerically by (I,5)}$$

and (I,7).

Heat received from external sources $= Q_{E-A}$

and at constant pressure $Q_{E-A} = C_p(T_1 - T_2)$ B.T.U. per lb.

$$\therefore \eta = 1 - \frac{RT_3 \log_e \dfrac{P_1}{P_2}}{JC_p(T_1 - T_2)}, \qquad \text{by (IV, 1).}$$

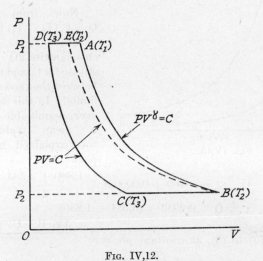

FIG. IV,12.

By (I,6) and (I,18)

$$\eta = 1 - \frac{(C_p - C_v)T_3 \log_e \left(\dfrac{P_1}{P_2}\right)}{C_p\left(T_1 - \dfrac{T_1}{\beta}\right)}, \text{ where } \beta = \left(\frac{P_1}{P_2}\right)^{\frac{\gamma-1}{\gamma}}$$

$$= 1 - \frac{\gamma - 1}{\gamma} \frac{T_3 \log_e \left(\dfrac{P_1}{P_2}\right)}{\dfrac{T_1}{\beta}(\beta - 1)}$$

$$= 1 - \frac{T_3 \beta \log_e \beta}{T_1(\beta - 1)}. \quad \text{Q.E.D.}$$

11. *Each pound of charge working the ideal cycle shown in fig. IV,13 liberates 820 B.T.U. Assuming that combustion commences at the point (1) where the temperature is 1,420° F., determine :*

    (a) *the amount of heat used between (1) and (2) ;*

    (b) *the temperature at the end of combustion (3) given that*

$$C_p = 0{\cdot}227 + 0{\cdot}000024T \text{ where } T \text{ is } ° \text{ F. absolute}$$
$$C_v = 0{\cdot}160 + 0{\cdot}000024T. \hspace{2cm} \textit{(U. Lond.)}$$

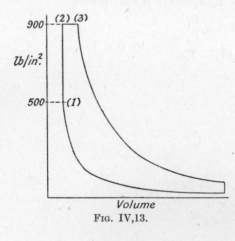

FIG. IV,13.

    (a) $T_1 = 1{,}880°$ F. abs.

$$\therefore \ T_2 = 1{,}880 \times \frac{900}{500}$$
$$= 3{,}384° \text{ F. abs.}$$

Now from (1) to (2) $Q = C_v(T_2 - T_1)$ B.T.U. per lb. Since C_v is variable, we should write $dQ = C_v \, dT$, substitute for C_v and then integrate between the known temperature limits. In this case, it is, however, permissible to work with a "mean" value of C_v, as was explained in chapter I, page 14.

Thus, $C_{v \text{ mean}} = 0{\cdot}160 + 0{\cdot}000024 \times \dfrac{1{,}880 + 3{,}384}{2} = 0{\cdot}2232$

$$\therefore \ \ Q = 0{\cdot}2232 \times (3{,}384 - 1{,}880)$$
$$= \underline{336 \text{ B.T.U. per lb.}} \ \ \text{Ans.}$$

(b) From (2) to (3), at constant pressure

$$Q = \int_{T_2}^{T_3} C_p \, dT,$$

i.e. $820 - 336 = \displaystyle\int_{3{,}384}^{T_3} (0{\cdot}227 + 0{\cdot}000024T)dT.$

Integrating,

$$484 = 0{\cdot}227(T_3 - 3{,}384) + 0{\cdot}000024\frac{{T_3}^2 - (3{,}384)^2}{2},$$

i.e. $0{\cdot}000012{T_3}^2 + 0{\cdot}227T_3 - 1{,}390 = 0,$

$$T_3 = \frac{-0{\cdot}227 \pm \sqrt{0{\cdot}0515 + 0{\cdot}000048 \times 1{,}390}}{0{\cdot}000024}$$
$$= \frac{-0{\cdot}227 \pm 0{\cdot}347}{0{\cdot}000024} = \underline{4{,}874° \text{ F. abs.}} \ \ \text{Ans.}$$

It would be possible to use a mean value of C_p in part (b), but as one of the temperatures is now unknown, no saving of arithmetic would result.

EXAMPLES

1. Sketch pressure–volume diagrams for the Otto, Carnot and Diesel cycles. In a Diesel cycle the temperature at the beginning of compression is 87° C. If the compression ratio is 14, find the temperature at the end of compression.

If the temperatures at the beginning and end of expansion are 1,795° C. and 677° C. respectively, what is the efficiency of this cycle ? Assume $\gamma = 1\cdot4$ and $C_p = 0\cdot24$.   (*U.L.C.I.*)

$$\left[t_2 = 1,405° \text{ F.} ; \quad \eta = 1 - \frac{\text{Heat rejected}}{\text{Heat supplied}} = \underline{59\cdot1\%.} \right]$$

2. An engine working on the Otto cycle has a swept volume of 0·44 cu. ft. and the heat supplied by combustion at constant volume = 16 B.T.U. If the ratio of compression is 5 : 1, calculate the ideal efficiency of the cycle and the mean effective pressure. Assume that the ratio of specific heats = 1·4 and prove any formulæ which are used in the solution.   (*U. Manch.*)

$[\eta = \underline{47\cdot4\%} ; \quad \text{m.e.p.} = \underline{93\cdot1} \text{ lb. per sq. in.}]$

3. In an ideal cycle the charge is compressed adiabatically, explosion occurs at the end of the stroke and is followed by adiabatic expansion to such a condition that subsequent isothermal compression restores the charge to its original pressure and volume.

Show that the air-standard efficiency of the cycle is

$$1 - \left[\frac{\log_e x^{\gamma-1} - \log_e r^{\gamma-1}}{x^{\gamma-1} - r^{\gamma-1}} \right].$$

(r = ratio of compression ; x = ratio of expansion.)   (*U. Dur.*)

[Heat is supp. during const. vol. burning ; heat is rejected during isothermal operation and $= \text{RT} \log_e \dfrac{x}{r}$ per lb. ; $\eta = 1 - \dfrac{\text{Heat rejected}}{\text{Heat supplied}}.$]

4. On the given pressure–volume diagram, fig. IV,14, three ideal cycles are shown :

(*a*) a constant volume cycle 1235 ; (*b*) an Atkinson cycle 1236 ; and (*c*) a Diesel cycle 1245.

In each case the volume compression ratio is 10 and the temperature at the beginning of compression is 100° F. Assuming that the temperature at point 3 is 4,000° F., calculate the thermal efficiency of each cycle. Take $\gamma = 1\cdot4$.   (*U. Glas.*)

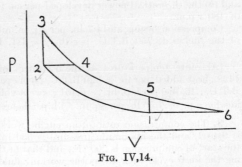

FIG. IV,14.

[By I,17, $T_2 = 1,407$; since $\dfrac{T_3}{T_2} = \dfrac{T_5}{T_1}$, $T_5 = 1,775$; $P_3 = 79\cdot64P_1$; by (I,18), $T_6 = 1,276$; $T_4 = 3,210$; (*a*) $\underline{60\cdot2\%}$; (*b*) $\underline{67\cdot2\%}$; (*c*) $\underline{51\cdot9\%.}$]

5. The cycle of an imaginary engine, using a perfect gas as the working agent, consists of three stages :

    (i) an isothermal compression ;
    (ii) an increase of pressure at constant volume ;
    (iii) an adiabatic expansion.

If r is the volume ratio for expansion and compression, show that the efficiency is equal to

$$1 - \frac{R \log_e r}{JC_v\{r^{\gamma-1} - 1\}}.$$

In such a cycle a gas is supplied at 15 p.s.i. at the beginning of the isothermal compression at 80° F., and is compressed isothermally to 75 p.s.i., $C_p = 0.238$ and $C_p = 0.170$.

Find, per lb. of gas, the heat supplied in B.T.U.; also the work done in ft.lb. per cycle.

(*U. Melb.*)

[Heat rej. = W.D. during (i); Heat supp. = $C_v(T_3 - T_1)$; $T_3 = 1,028°$ F. abs. Heat supp. = __83 B.T.U. per lb.__; $r = \dfrac{75}{15}$; $\eta = 0.287$; W.D. = __18,550 ft.lb. per lb.__]

6. Five cubic feet of gas at 25° C. and 14 lb. per sq. in. are compressed adiabatically to one cubic foot. The volume is then increased to 1·5 cu. ft. at constant pressure, followed by isothermal expansion to the initial volume. The cycle is closed at constant volume.

Determine the mean effective pressure of this cycle.

($C_p = 0.238$; $C_v = 0.169$.)   (*U. Sheff.*)

[Max. pres. = 135 lb. per sq. in.; m.e.p. = $\dfrac{\text{area of cycle}}{\text{stroke vol.}}$ = 38 lb. per sq. in.]

7. In the theoretical diagram of a four-stroke cycle semi-Diesel engine the pressure at the end of adiabatic compression is 240 lb. per sq. in., and the combustion is such that the temperature rises first at constant volume and then at a constant pressure of 420 lb. per sq. in. The heat of combustion is shared equally between the two phases, and the expansion is adiabatic. If the relative efficiency is 55 per cent., estimate (*a*) the actual specific consumption in lb. per h.p.-hr., and (*b*) the theoretical power developed per cu. ft. displacement at an engine speed of 180 r.p.m.

Compression begins at 14·7 lb. per sq. in. and 100° F. and the calorific value of the fuel is 18,750 B.T.U. per lb. $\gamma = 1.4$, R = 53·3 ft.lb.° F. units.

(*U. Lond.*)

[Absolute temperatures at the 5 corners of the cycle 560, 1243, 2178, 2845, 1428; heat added per lb. = 320 B.T.U.; η of cycle = 53·5%; W.D. per lb. = 171·3 B.T.U.; lb. fuel per h.p.-hr. = 0·461; swept volume per lb. of air = 12·175 cu. ft.; ideal m.e.p. = 76·0 lb. per sq. in.; i.h.p. (theoretical) = 29·9 per cu. ft. swept vol.]

8. The compression ratio of an engine working on the dual combustion cycle is 9 to 1, and the maximum pressure is 550 lb. per sq. in. The temperature at the start of compression is 200° F., and that of the exhaust is 1,010° F. Considering the ideal cycle with air as the working fluid, and assuming that the pressure at the start of compression is 14·5 lb. per sq. in., find:

(*a*) the thermal efficiency;
(*b*) the mean effective pressure of the indicator diagram.

(R = 53·3 ft.lb. per lb. ° F.; $\gamma = 1.4$.)   (*U. Lond.*)

[$C_v = 0.171$; $C_p = 0.240$; $T_2 = 1,588$; $P_2 = 313$; $T_3 = 2,790$; $P_5 = 32.3$; $T_4 = 3,300$; heat supp. = 330·8 B.T.U. per lb.; $\eta = 58.2\%$; W.D. = 192·3 B.T.U. per lb. = 79,900 ft.lb. for 8 cu. ft. of swept vol.; __m.e.p. = 69·4 lb. per sq. in.__]

CHAPTER V

GENERAL I.C. ENGINE PROBLEMS AND TESTS

1. *A four-cylinder petrol engine, bore $3\frac{1}{2}$ in., stroke $5\frac{1}{8}$ in., running at 1,500 r.p.m., develops 37 b.h.p. when using a 20% rich mixture. If the volume of air drawn into the cylinders when measured at 15° C. and 30 in. Hg, is 0·7 of the swept volume, the theoretically correct quantity of air for the combustion of 1 lb. of petrol = 14·8 lb. ; the C.V. of the petrol is 19,800 B.T.U. per lb. and the mechanical efficiency of the engine is 0·9, calculate the indicated thermal efficiency and b.m.e.p.*

$$(R = 53\cdot3.) \qquad\qquad (U.\ Manch.)$$

$$\text{i.h.p.} = \frac{37}{0\cdot9} = 41\cdot1$$

$$15°\ \text{C.} = 15 \times \frac{9}{5} + 32 = 59°\ \text{F.}$$

Swept Vol. $= \dfrac{\pi}{4} \times 3\cdot5^2 \times 5\cdot125 = 49\cdot3$ cu. in. per cylinder.

Vol. of air drawn in at S.T.P. $= 0\cdot7 \times 49\cdot3 = 34\cdot5$ cu. in. per cyl.

$$\therefore\ \text{Weight of air per cylinder} = \frac{PV}{RT} = \frac{30 \times 0\cdot49 \times 34\cdot5 \times \frac{1}{12}}{53\cdot3 \times 519}$$

$$= 0\cdot00153\ \text{lb.}$$

Quantity of petrol associated with this air, for 20% rich

$$= \frac{0\cdot00153}{14\cdot8} \times 1\cdot2 = 0\cdot000124\ \text{lb. per cyl.}$$

It is, of course, impossible for the air to burn *more* fuel than that at chemically correct mixture strength,

i.e. Heat liberated $= \dfrac{0\cdot00153}{14\cdot8} \times 19{,}800 = 2\cdot045$ B.T.U. per cyl. per charge

But

Heat Value in fuel $= 2\cdot045 \times 1\cdot2 = 2\cdot46 \qquad ,, \qquad ,, \quad ,, \quad ,, \qquad ,,$

$$\underline{\text{Indicated Thermal } \eta} = \frac{41\cdot1 \times 42\cdot4}{2\cdot46 \times 4 \times 750} = \underline{23\cdot6\%.} \quad \text{Ans.}$$

If P = b.m.e.p. in lb. per sq. in.

$$\therefore\ \frac{37}{4} = \frac{P \times 49\cdot3 \times \frac{1}{12} \times 750}{33{,}000}$$

i.e. $\underline{\text{P} = 99\cdot0\ \text{lb. per sq. in.}}$ Ans.

2. *A four-stroke cycle four-cylinder petrol engine has cylinders 2·5 in. diameter × 3·75 in. stroke. On test it develops a torque of 46·2 lb. ft. when running at 3,000 r.p.m. If the clearance volume in each cylinder is 3·85 cu. in., the brake efficiency ratio based on the air-standard cycle 0·5 and the C.V. of petrol 19,200 B.T.U. per lb., determine the fuel consumption in lb. per hr. and the b.m.e.p. The efficiency of the air-standard cycle is* $1 - \dfrac{1}{(r_c)^{0·4}},$ *where* r_c *is the ratio of compression.*

(U. Glas.)

Stroke Vol. $= \dfrac{\pi}{4} \times 2·5^2 \times 3·75 = 18·40$ cu. in. per cylinder.

$$\therefore \text{Compression Ratio} = \frac{18·40 + 3·85}{3·85} = \frac{22·25}{3·85} = 5·78.$$

$$\text{Air-standard } \eta = 1 - \frac{1}{5·78^{0·4}} = 1 - \frac{1}{2·018}$$

$$= 0·504,$$

i.e. $$0·5 = \frac{\text{Brake Thermal } \eta}{0·504}$$

$$\text{Brake Thermal } \eta = 25·2\%$$

$$\text{b.h.p.} = \frac{46·2 \times 2\pi \times 3,000}{33,000} = 26·4,$$

$$\therefore \text{Heat supplied} = \frac{26·4 \times 42·4}{0·252} = 4,440 \text{ B.T.U. per min.}$$

$$\text{Fuel Consumption} = \frac{4,440 \times 60}{19,200}$$

$$= \underline{13·9 \text{ lb. per hr.}} \quad \text{Ans.}$$

For each cylinder, $\quad \dfrac{26·4}{4} = \dfrac{\text{P} \times 18·42 \times \frac{1}{12} \times 1,500}{33,000},$

where $\qquad$ P = b.m.e.p. in lb. per sq. in.

$\qquad$ 1,500 = No. of power cycles per min. (four-stroke)

$18·42 \times \frac{1}{12}$ = Piston Area (sq. in.) × Stroke (ft.).

$$\therefore \text{P} = \frac{6·6 \times 33,000}{18·40 \times 125} = \underline{94·7 \text{ lb. per sq. in.}} \quad \text{Ans.}$$

3. *A four-stroke cycle gas engine has a bore of 8 in. and a stroke of 15 in. The compression ratio is 6 to 1. In a test on the engine the indicated m.e.p. was 75 lb. per sq. in., the air-to-gas ratio was 6 to 1, and the calorific value of the gas 450 B.T.U. per cu. ft. at 32° F. and 14·7 lb. per sq. in. At the beginning of the compression stroke the temperature was 190° F. and the pressure 14 lb. per sq. in.*

Neglecting residual gases, determine the thermal efficiency of the engine, the relative efficiency and the indicated horse-power at 240 r.p.m.

Show, by means of sketches of indicator diagrams, the effects of running with over-strong, correct and weak mixtures. (*U. Lond.*)

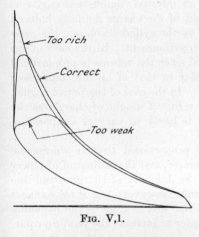

FIG. V,1.

Stroke Vol. $= \dfrac{\pi}{4} \times 64 \times 15 = 754$ cu. in.

∴ For an air-to-gas ratio of 6 to 1,

volume of gas in cylinder $= \frac{1}{7} \times 754 = 107\cdot7$ cu. in. per cycle.

This assumes a volumetric efficiency of 100% which is implied in the instruction to neglect residual gases.

Now 107·7 cu. in. at 14 lb. per sq. in. and 190° F. are equivalent to

$$107\cdot7 \times \frac{14}{14\cdot7} \times \frac{492}{650} = 77\cdot6 \text{ cu. in. at S.T.P.}$$

$$\therefore \text{ Heat added} = 450 \times \frac{77\cdot6}{1,728} = 20\cdot2 \text{ B.T.U. per cycle}$$

$$\underline{\text{i.h.p.}} = \frac{75 \times 754 \times \frac{1}{12} \times 120}{33,000} = \underline{17\cdot1}. \quad \text{Ans.}$$

$$\text{Thermal } \eta = \frac{17\cdot1 \times 42\cdot4}{120 \times 20\cdot2} = \underline{29\cdot9\%}. \quad \text{Ans.}$$

$$\text{Air-standard } \eta = 1 - \frac{1}{6^{0\cdot4}} = 1 - \frac{1}{2\cdot046} = 0\cdot512.$$

$$\underline{\text{Relative } \eta} = \frac{0\cdot299}{0\cdot512} = \underline{58\cdot4\%}. \quad \text{Ans.}$$

The last part of the question is answered by fig. V,1, the interpretation of which is left to the student as an exercise.

4. *Define, carefully, the term " volumetric efficiency " as used in internal combustion engine work, and explain its importance with reference to the power output of an engine.*

A four-stroke cycle gas engine has a bore of 8 in. and a stroke of 12 in. and runs at 300 r.p.m., firing every cycle. If the air-to-fuel ratio is 4 to 1 by volume and the volumetric efficiency on an N.T.P. basis is 78%, determine the volume of gas used per min.

If the calorific value of the gas is 180 C.H.U. per cu. ft., at N.T.P., and the brake thermal efficiency 23%, determine the b.h.p. of the engine.

(*U.L.C.I.*)

The overall volumetric efficiency of an internal combustion engine is generally taken as the ratio of the weight of the charge actually induced to the weight of the charge represented by the cylinder volume, the pressure and temperature being those of the environment. In the case of gas and Diesel engines the matter is simplified since the volume is proportional to the weight, the case being then similar to that of an air compressor (cf. introduction to chapter III, page 44). In the case of the petrol engine, it is usually best to use the definition in terms of weight of charge, as the temperature, and therefore the volume, is likely to vary as evaporation of the liquid petrol proceeds.

The power output of an engine is proportional to the volumetric efficiency provided the combustion is complete, and the falling off of power at high speeds is due almost entirely to the difficulty of charging and discharging the cylinder. Other factors intrude, however ; e.g. if the exhaust is not fully completed, there is more dilution and heating of the incoming charge resulting in slower burning. In order to increase the power output, the volumetric efficiency should be increased as far as possible by inducing a cool charge, but in the case of carburettor engines, this may lead to carburation difficulties. Supercharging is the usual means of increasing the volumetric efficiency.

$$\text{Swept Vol.} = \frac{\pi}{4} \times 64 \times 12 \times \frac{1}{1,728} = 0 \cdot 350 \text{ cu. ft.}$$

$$\therefore \text{ Total charge per stroke} = 0 \cdot 78 \times 0 \cdot 350 = 0 \cdot 273 \text{ cu. ft. at N.T.P.}$$

$$\text{Vol. of Gas used per min.} = \frac{0 \cdot 273}{5} \times 300$$

$$= \underline{16 \cdot 4 \text{ cu. ft. at N.T.P.}} \quad \text{Ans.}$$

$$\text{Heat supplied} = (180 \times 1 \cdot 8) \times 16 \cdot 4 = 5,320 \text{ B.T.U. per min.}$$

$$\text{b.h.p.} = 0 \cdot 23 \times \frac{5,320}{42 \cdot 4} = \underline{28 \cdot 9.} \quad \text{Ans.}$$

It is evident that the numerical part of this question refers to the " absolute " volumetric efficiency, instead of the overall value. See also equations (III,5) and (III,6).

5. *In a test on a small petrol engine, the air intake to the cylinder was measured by drawing it through a $1\frac{1}{4}$-in. diameter sharp-edged orifice, the coefficient of discharge for which was 0·6.*

The pressure difference across the orifice was found to be 0·240 in. water, whilst 0·25 lb. petrol was consumed in 302 sec.

If the air conditions at the orifice were 67° F. and 29·5 in. of mercury, calculate the ratio by weight of air to petrol in the mixture drawn into the engine. The density of air at 32° F. and 30 in. mercury = 0·0807 lb. per cu. ft., and water weighs 62·4 lb. per cu. ft. (U. Manch.)

The question of air-flow measurement by means of sharp-edged orifices is discussed more fully in example No. 6 in this chapter, and it is shown there that for small pressure differences (about 5–6 in. water) the compressibility effect may be neglected, so that approx.

$$W = C_D A \sqrt{\frac{2gH}{V}} \text{ lb. per sec.}$$

where H = pressure difference across orifice in lb. per sq. ft.

V = specific volume of air at orifice conditions in cu. ft. per lb. (assumed constant across orifice).

A = area of orifice in sq. ft.

C_D = coefficient of discharge.

Using the figures given in the question, the specific volume of air at orifice conditions

$$V = \frac{1}{0·0807} \times \frac{30}{29·5} \times \frac{527}{492} = 13·50 \text{ cu. ft. per lb.}$$

$$H = \frac{0·240}{12} \times 62·4 = 1·25 \text{ lb. per sq. ft.}$$

$$A = \frac{\pi}{4} \times \left(\frac{5}{4}\right)^2 \times \frac{1}{144} = 0·00853 \text{ sq. ft.}$$

$$W = 0·6 \times 0·00853 \sqrt{\frac{64·4 \times 1·25}{13·50}} = 0·0125 \text{ lb. air per sec.}$$

Petrol Consumption $= \dfrac{0·25}{302} = 0·000828$ lb. per sec.

$$\frac{\text{lb. air}}{\underline{\text{lb. petrol}}} = \frac{125}{8·28} = \underline{15·1}. \quad \text{Ans.}$$

6. *Describe an arrangement for measuring the air consumption of a multi-cylinder internal combustion engine, explaining what observations must be taken. Show that under certain conditions the weight of air per sec. flowing through an orifice is proportional to the square root of the head across the orifice.*

In a test made under a barometric pressure of 28·7 in. of mercury and a temperature of 80° F., the pressure difference across an orifice of 1½ in. diameter was 6·6 in. of water. Find the weight of air passing per sec. if the coefficient of discharge of the orifice was 0·96.

$$(R \text{ for } air = 53\text{·}3 \text{ ft.lb. F. units.})$$

(U. Lond.)

The usual method is to ensure that all the air supplied to the engine is derived exclusively from an air-box, or tank, which is connected to the induction system of the engine by an air-tight pipe of a diameter well in excess of that required theoretically for the predicted air-flow. The box itself must be air-tight. But at a point well removed from the engine connection, a sharp-edged orifice is fitted, and the pressure difference across it is measured by means of a water manometer. As it is usually desirable to keep the calculations simple, it is necessary to keep the manometer reading down to 5 or 6 in. of pressure difference, in which case the variation in density of the air across the orifice is negligible. The box or tank should have internal baffles so as to avoid any air surges or pulsations, and the volume should be large enough in relation to the total capacity of the engine to be tested, say 500–600 times the total capacity to prevent undue pressure pulsations. The observations would be :

h—in. water, pressure difference across orifice by simple, inclined, or differential manometer.

P_A—in. mercury, atmospheric pressure.

t_A—° F., atmospheric temperature.

d—in., diameter of orifice.

C_D—coefficient of discharge of orifice, which is a constant for this purpose, and will normally have been obtained during a special calibration experiment against a standard orifice or flow-meter.

Now, cu. secs. flowing

$= W$ lb. per sec. $\times V$ cu. ft. per lb. $= v$ ft. per sec. $\times A$ sq. ft.

i.e.
$$W = \frac{vA}{V} = \frac{v_2 A_2}{V_2} \text{ say.}$$

But an orifice is only a small nozzle and we can say (cf. chapter XV)

K.E. gained = W.D. in expanding

$$\frac{v_2{}^2}{2g} = \frac{n}{n-1} P_2 V_2 \left\{ \left(\frac{P_1}{P_2}\right)^{\frac{n-1}{n}} - 1 \right\}$$

where $P_1 - P_2 = H$, the pressure drop across orifice in lb. per sq. ft.

i.e.
$$P_1 - P_2 = H = \frac{h}{12} \times 62 \cdot 4$$

$$\therefore \left(\frac{P_1}{P_2}\right)^{\frac{n-1}{n}} = \left(\frac{P_2+H}{P_2}\right)^{\frac{n-1}{n}} = \left(1 + \frac{H}{P_2}\right)^{\frac{n-1}{n}}$$

$$= 1 + \frac{n-1}{n}\frac{H}{P_2} + \dots \quad \text{other terms which}$$

will involve higher powers of $\dfrac{H}{P_2}$ and may be neglected if h is limited to 5 or 6 in. of water.

Then,
$$v_2 = \sqrt{\frac{2gn}{n-1}P_2 V_2 \left\{\frac{n-1}{n} \cdot \frac{H}{P_2}\right\}} \quad \text{approx.}$$

$$= \sqrt{2gH V_2}$$

$$\therefore \text{ Theoretical } W = \frac{A_2}{V_2}\sqrt{2gH V_2}$$

$$= A\sqrt{\frac{2gH}{V}}, \quad \text{where } V = V_1 = V_2 \text{ approx.,}$$

and $A = $ area of orifice

$$\text{Actual } W = C_D A \sqrt{\frac{2gH}{V}} \qquad C_D = \text{coeff. of discharge.}$$

i.e.
$$\underline{W \propto \sqrt{H}.} \quad \text{Q.E.D.}$$

Now
$$A = \frac{\pi}{4} \times 1 \cdot 5^2 \times \frac{1}{144} = 0 \cdot 01229 \text{ sq. ft.}$$

$$V = \frac{RT}{P} = \frac{53 \cdot 3 \times 540}{144 \times 28 \cdot 7 \times 0 \cdot 49} = 14 \cdot 20 \text{ cu. ft. per lb.}$$

$$H = \frac{6 \cdot 6}{12} \times 62 \cdot 4 = 34 \cdot 3 \text{ lb. per sq. ft.}$$

$\therefore$ In consistent units,

$$W = 0 \cdot 96 \times 0 \cdot 01229 \sqrt{\frac{64 \cdot 4 \times 34 \cdot 3}{14 \cdot 20}}$$

$$= 0 \cdot 96 \times 0 \cdot 01229 \times 12 \cdot 48$$

$$\underline{W = 0 \cdot 147 \text{ lb. per sec.}} \quad \text{Ans.}$$

7. *A two-stroke oil engine gave the following results at full load : speed, 350 r.p.m. ; net brake load, 135 lb. ; mean effective pressure, 39 lb. per sq. in. ; oil consumption, 9·31 lb. per hr. ; jacket water, 1,092 lb. per hr. ; temperature of jacket water at inlet and outlet, 55° F. and 100° F. respectively ; air used per lb. of oil, 32 lb. ; temperature of air in test room, 66° F. ; temperature of exhaust gases, 695° F.*

The following data also apply to the test : cylinder, 8¼ in. diameter ; stroke, 11 in. ; brake, 3 ft. 3 in. diameter ; calorific value of fuel oil, 19,200 B.T.U. per lb. ; proportion of hydrogen in oil, 15% ; mean specific heat of dry exhaust gases, 0·24 ; specific heat of steam, 0·5.

Draw up a heat balance for the test in B.T.U. per hour and in percentages. Criticize the accuracy, etc., of the apportionment of the heat supplied to the various items in the heat balance. (*U. Lond.*)

$$\text{i.h.p.} = \frac{39 \times \frac{\pi}{4} \times 8\cdot25^2 \times \frac{11}{12} \times 350}{33,000} = 20\cdot3 \equiv 51,700 \text{ B.T.U. per hr.}$$

$$\text{b.h.p.} = \frac{135 \times 3\cdot25 \times \pi \times 350}{33,000} = 14\cdot6 \equiv 37,200 \text{ B.T.U. per hr.}$$

$$\therefore \text{ f.h.p.} = \text{i.h.p.} - \text{b.h.p.} = 5\cdot7 \equiv 14,500 \text{ B.T.U. per hr.}$$

Heat supplied $= 9\cdot31 \times 19,200 = 178,800$ B.T.U. per hr.
Jacket Water $= 1,092 \times 45 = 49,150$ B.T.U. per hr.

H_2O of combustion per lb. fuel $= 0\cdot15 \times 9 = 1\cdot35$ (cf. intro. to ch. VI)
and   Air used per lb. fuel $= 32$ lb.

$$\therefore \text{ Dry Gases per lb. fuel} = (32 + 1) - 1\cdot35 = 31\cdot65 \text{ lb.}$$

Heat to Dry Gases $= 9\cdot31 \times 31\cdot65 \times 0\cdot24 \times 629 = 44,500$ B.T.U. per hr.
Heat to $H_2O = 9\cdot31 \times 1\cdot35 \times [(212 - 66) + 970 + 0\cdot5(695 - 212)]$
$= 12\cdot58(146 + 970 + 242) = 17,100$ B.T.U. per hr.

.	B.T.U. per hr.		B.T.U. per hr.	%
By Fuel . . .	178,800	To b.h.p.	37,200	20·80
		,, f.h.p.	14,500	8·12
		,, jacket water . . .	49,150	27·50
		,, dry gases	44,500	24·90
		,, steam	17,100	9·57
		,, radiation, etc. (by diff.)	16,350	9·15
	178,800		178,800	100·04

No allowance is made for the pumping losses, the m.e.p. being probably
the mean height of the positive loop of the diagram. A more serious
objection is the inclusion of the f.h.p. in the heat balance of an engine of
this type. Most of the f.h.p. will re-appear as heat in the jacket water;
some of it may also re-appear in the dry and wet exhaust gases, and in
the radiation item. It is customary to omit the f.h.p. item altogether
from such a heat balance, for the reasons stated, but the data of the question rather suggest that it should be included here.

A more correct method of presenting the heat balance is as follows:

A

	B.T.U. per hr.		B.T.U. per hr.	%
By Fuel . . .	178,000	To b.h.p.	37,200	20·80
		„ jackets	49,150	27·50
		„ dry gases	44,500	24·90
		„ steam	17,100	9·57
		„ difference as losses to		
		environment . . .	30,850	17·25
	178,800		178,800	100·02

B

	B.T.U. per hr.		B.T.U. per hr.
By i.h.p.	51,700	To b.h.p.	37,200
		„ f.h.p.	14,500
	51,700		51,700

Sometimes the balance A is referred to as the gross or overall balance
and the balance B as the internal balance. Apart from the difficulty of
estimating how the f.h.p. is accounted for, the ratio of the amount of heat
reappearing in the jacket water and in the exhaust depends a good deal
on the actual engine design as far as the cooling of the exhaust valve and
seat and the jacket are concerned.

8. *A petrol engine has a stroke volume 0·042 cu. ft. and volume compression ratio 5·5. At the end of the compression stroke the pressure is 120 lb. per sq. in., and the temperature 650° F. Ignition is set so that the pressure rises along a straight line during explosion and attains its highest value of 400 lb. per sq. in. after the piston has travelled $\frac{1}{30}$ of the working stroke. The charge consists of a petrol-air mixture in proportion by weight 1 to 16. Take R for the mixture as 51·2 ft.lb. per lb. per ° F. ; calorific value of fuel, 19,000 B.T.U. per lb. and $C_v = 0·23$. Calculate the heat lost per lb. of charge during explosion.*
(I.Mech.E.)

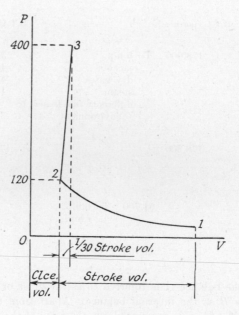

FIG. V,2.

$$V_1 - V_2 = 0·042 \times 1,728 = 72·6 \text{ cu. in.}$$

$$V_2 = \frac{72·6}{4·5} = 16·1 \text{ cu. in.}$$

and

$$V_3 = \frac{72·6}{30} + 16·1 = 18·52 \text{ cu. in.}$$

$$T_2 = 1,110° \text{ F. abs.}$$

By (I,16) $T_3 = T_2 \dfrac{P_3 V_3}{P_2 V_2} = 1,110 \times \dfrac{400}{120} \times \dfrac{18·52}{16·1} = 4,260° \text{ F. abs.}$

In order to calculate the heat actually added to the mixture from 2 to 3, we shall have to use equation (I,2) and shall therefore require the work done and the increase of internal energy between 2 and 3, fig. V,2.

$$\text{W.D.}_{2-3} = \text{area under graph}$$

$$= \frac{400 + 120}{2}(18 \cdot 52 - 16 \cdot 1) = 630 \text{ in.lb.}$$

By (I,7) Mass of mixture present $= \dfrac{120 \times 16 \cdot 1}{51 \cdot 2 \times 1,110 \times 12}$

$$= 0 \cdot 00283 \text{ lb.}$$

By (I,19) $\Delta E = E_3 - E_2 = 0 \cdot 00283 \times 0 \cdot 23 \times (4,260 - 1,110)$
$$= 2 \cdot 050 \text{ B.T.U.}$$

By (I,2) $\qquad\qquad Q = 2 \cdot 050 + \dfrac{630}{12 \times 778}$

$$= 2 \cdot 050 + 0 \cdot 0675 = 2 \cdot 118 \text{ B.T.U.}$$

This is the quantity of heat actually given to the mixture in one cycle. But, the heat liberated in one cycle must have been

$$\frac{1}{17} \times 0 \cdot 00283 \times 19,000 = 3 \cdot 162 \text{ B.T.U.}$$

(Note, as the engine admits a *mixture* of air and petrol of ratio 16 : 1, $\therefore$ lb. of petrol $= \frac{1}{17}$ lb. of total charge.)

$\therefore$ Heat lost during explosion $= 3 \cdot 162 - 2 \cdot 118 = 1 \cdot 044$ B.T.U.

$$= \frac{1 \cdot 044}{0 \cdot 00283} = 369 \text{ B.T.U. per lb. of charge.} \quad \text{Ans.}$$

9. *Discuss briefly the effect of the variation of the specific heats on the thermal efficiency of an internal combustion engine.*

The products of combustion in an oil engine have a mean molecular weight of 31·1 and the values of the specific heat at constant volume, which varies linearly with the temperature, are given below in ft.lb. per standard cubic foot :

Temp., ° F.	900	3,600
Specific heat	16·2	19·5

Express these values of the specific heat in B.T.U. per lb.mol and find the work done in expanding 1 lb. of the gases adiabatically from a temperature of 2,500° F. to 1,000° F. What is the mean value of γ over this range ?

The standard cubic foot is measured at a pressure of 14·7 lb. per sq. in. and temperature of 32° F. (U. Lond.)

The specific heat increases with rising temperatures, so that for a *fixed* amount of heat supplied the maximum temperature will be less than it would be with constant specific heats. The effect of this is to reduce the area of the indicator diagram, i.e. the work done, and hence the thermal efficiency.

By (I,7a) the volume of 1 lb.mol at S.T.P. $= \dfrac{mR_{mol}T}{P}$

$$= \frac{1 \times 1\cdot985 \times 778 \times 492}{14\cdot7 \times 144}$$

$$= 358\cdot7 \text{ S.C.F.}$$

This figure is so well known, that it is often quoted.

$\therefore$ Molar Heats (B.T.U. per lb.mol $^\circ$ F.) $= C_v$ (ft.lb. per S.C.F.) $\times \dfrac{358\cdot7}{778}$.

i.e. at 900° F., $\qquad$ $\underline{C_{v\,mol} = 7\cdot46 \text{ B.T.U. per lb.mol } ^\circ \text{ F.}}$ $\quad$ Ans.

$\quad$ at 3,600° F., $\qquad$ $\underline{C_{v\,mol} = 8\cdot97 \text{ B.T.U. per lb.mol } ^\circ \text{ F.}}$ $\quad$ Ans.

$\therefore$ By (I,10) and bearing in mind that C_v varies linearly with T,

$$\frac{7\cdot46}{31\cdot1} = b + s \times 1,360 \text{ B.T.U. per lb. } ^\circ \text{ F.}$$

and $\qquad$ $\dfrac{8\cdot97}{31\cdot1} = b + s \times 4,060 \text{ B.T.U. per lb. } ^\circ \text{ F.,}$

whence $\qquad$ $s = \dfrac{0\cdot289 - 0\cdot240}{2,700} = 0\cdot0000181$

$$b = 0\cdot289 - 0\cdot0735 = 0\cdot2155.$$

But, by (I,2) in an adiabatic operation,

$$\text{W.D.} = -\varDelta E = E_1 - E_2,$$

$$\therefore \text{ W.D. per lb.} = \int_{1,460}^{2,960} dE = \int_{1,460}^{2,960} (b + sT)dT$$

$$= b(2,960 - 1,460) + \frac{s}{2}(2,960^2 - 1,460^2)$$

$$= 0\cdot2155 \times 1,500 + 0\cdot00000905 \times 4,420 \times 1,500$$

$$= 323\cdot2 + 59\cdot7 = \underline{382\cdot9 \text{ B.T.U. per lb.}} \quad \text{Ans.}$$

The mean value of γ over this range could be found by evaluating the mean value of $C_{v\,mol}$, whence by adding R_{mol} the mean value of $C_{p\,mol}$ can be found, and γ follows as the ratio $\dfrac{C_{p\,mol}}{C_{v\,mol}}$.

Alternatively, by (I,4) with (I,7)

$$\text{W.D. per lb.} = \frac{R(T_1 - T_2)}{\gamma - 1}.$$

But $\qquad$ $R = \dfrac{JR_{mol}}{\text{mol. wt.}}$ (cf. I,9) $= \dfrac{1\cdot985 \times 778}{31\cdot1}$ ft.lb. per lb. $^\circ$F.

$$\therefore 778 \times 382\cdot9 = \frac{1\cdot985 \times 778 \times 1,500}{31\cdot1 \times (\gamma - 1)}$$

$$\gamma - 1 = \frac{95\cdot9}{382\cdot9}. \qquad\qquad \underline{\gamma = 1\cdot251.} \quad \text{Ans.}$$

10. *A single-cylinder gas engine, having a bore and stroke of 10 and 20 in. respectively and running at 240 r.p.m., fires 100 times per min. The quantity of coal gas used is 7·6 cu. ft. per min. at 4 in. of water head (barometric pressure 14·5 lb. per sq. in.) and 56° F., while the air used is 6·2 lb. per min. Assuming that an extra volume of air is taken in during a missed cycle equal to that of the coal gas normally taken in, if both are measured at N.T.P., find (a) the charge of air per working cycle as measured at N.T.P.; (b) the volumetric efficiency.*

$$(R = 53\text{·}3.)$$

(U. Lond.)

$$\text{Gas Pressure} = 14\text{·}5 + \frac{4}{13\text{·}6} \times 0\text{·}49$$

$$= 14\text{·}644 \text{ lb. per sq. in. abs.}$$

$$\therefore \text{ Vol. of coal gas at N.T.P.} = 7\text{·}6 \times \frac{14\text{·}644}{14\text{·}70} \times \frac{492}{516}$$

$$= 7\text{·}22 \text{ cu. ft. per min.}$$

$$\therefore \text{ Vol. of coal gas per explosion} = 0\text{·}0722 \text{ cu. ft. at N.T.P.}$$

$$\therefore \text{ Extra air per missed cycle} = 0\text{·}0722 \text{ cu. ft. at N.T.P.}$$

$$\text{Now, vol. of air taken in at N.T.P.} = \frac{w\text{RT}}{\text{P}} = \frac{6\text{·}2 \times 53\text{·}3 \times 492}{14\text{·}7 \times 144}$$

$$= 76\text{·}7 \text{ cu. ft. per min.}$$

But the engine is running at 240 r.p.m. and fires 100 times per min.; therefore there are 20 missed cycles, and the 76·7 cu. ft. of air per min. at N.T.P. must be made up of 120 normal air charges, V, together with 20 extra weights of air each equivalent to 0·0722 cu. ft. at N.T.P.

i.e.

$$20 \times 0\text{·}0722 + 120\text{V} = 76\text{·}7$$

$$\text{V} = \frac{76\text{·}7 - 1\text{·}444}{120} = \frac{75\text{·}256}{120} = 0\text{·}626$$

$$\therefore \text{ Total vol. of charge} = 0\text{·}626 + 0\text{·}0722 = 0\text{·}698 \text{ cu. ft. at N.T.P.}$$

But

$$\text{Swept vol.} = \frac{\pi}{4} \times \frac{10^2 \times 20}{1,728} = 0\text{·}909 \text{ cu. ft.}$$

$$\underline{\text{Vol. } \eta = \frac{0\text{·}698}{0\text{·}909} = 76\text{·}9\%.} \quad \text{Ans.}$$

11. *Describe briefly the method of finding the i.h.p. of a multi-cylinder petrol engine by cutting out one cylinder at a time.*

Discuss fully the assumptions made and explain why the outer cylinders, i.e. Nos. 1 and 4 of a four-cylinder machine, often gives less i.h.p. than do Nos. 2 and 3.

A four-cylinder engine at 1,200 r.p.m. gave 25·3 b.h.p. The average torque when one cylinder was cut out was 77 lb. ft. Find the thermal efficiency on the i.h.p. basis, if the calorific value of the fuel is 18,000 B.T.U. per lb. and the engine uses 0·595 lb. of petrol per b.h.p.-hr. (U. Lond.)

This method is known as the " Morse Test ". It is necessary to run the engine and dynamometer at constant speed and to short out one plug at the time, taking readings of the resulting reduced b.h.p., as well as the value of the b.h.p. with all cylinders firing, at the given angle of advance, throttle setting, and jet size.

The fundamental assumptions are that the friction and pumping h.p. of the shorted cylinder remain the same after shorting as they were when the cylinder was fully operative. This would not be a valid assumption if it were not for the fact that it is possible to carry this test out in a very short space of time. It need—and should—only take a few seconds to cut out one cylinder and adjust the load to keep the speed constant ; over this short period the assumptions may be considered reasonable. After cutting out one cylinder, the engine should be allowed to run on all cylinders for a short while, before cutting out the next cylinder.

Take the case of a four-cylinder engine :

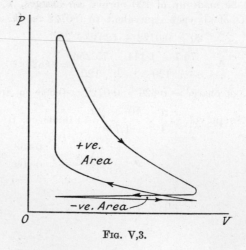

FIG. V,3.

Net i.h.p. = [+ ve area] − [− ve area]

$$I = W - P$$

where W = gross work done
      P = pumping horse-power
and if F = friction horse-power
      B = brake horse-power

and if suffices denote the number of cylinders in operation, then

$$B_4 = W_4 - P_4 - F_4$$
and
$$B_3 = W_3 - P_4 - F_4,$$

making the assumptions already discussed.

$$\therefore B_4 - B_3 = W_4 - P_4 - F_4 - W_3 + P_4 + F_4$$
$$= W_4 - W_3,$$

i.e. the reduction in b.h.p. is equal to the reduction in gross work done, and hence approx.

$$B_4 - B_3 = (W_4 - P_4) - (W_3 - P_3) = I_4 - I_3$$

provided the p.h.p. is but a small fraction of the i.h.p. It is thus seen that the reduction in b.h.p. is equal to the i.h.p. of the shorted cylinder.

If the outer cylinders give less i.h.p. than the inner cylinders we may have a bad mixture distribution in the inlet manifold, and/or the inner cylinders may be better scavenged during the exhaust stroke. Both these effects depend upon the engine speed and the resonant properties of the inlet and exhaust manifolds which control ramming and scavenging effects.

Now

$$\text{Average b.h.p. on 3 cylinders} = \frac{77 \times 2\pi \times 1,200}{33,000} = 17\cdot6$$

$$\therefore \text{Average i.h.p. of each cylinder} = 25\cdot3 - 17\cdot6 = 7\cdot7$$
$$\text{Total i.h.p.} = 7\cdot7 \times 4 = 30\cdot8$$

$$\text{Petrol used, lb. per i.h.p.-hr.} = \frac{0\cdot595 \times 25\cdot3}{30\cdot8}$$

$$= 0\cdot489$$

$$\underline{\text{Indicated Thermal } \eta} = \frac{2,546}{0\cdot489 \times 18,000} = \underline{29\cdot0\%.} \quad \text{Ans.}$$

12. *In a test on a four-stroke cycle petrol engine of 330 cu. in. capacity the following figures were obtained at a constant speed of 2,400 r.p.m. :*

b.h.p.	97·8	102	106	110	112	112	110	107
lb. fuel per hour .	56·3	57·6	59·3	63·5	71·1	82·6	87·8	90·0

Plot the values of the brake mean effective pressure against the specific consumption in lb. per b.h.p.-hr., and discuss the important features of the curve.

Give a description of the method you would adopt to obtain the above data.

Describe the symptoms which you would expect to develop in the engine after running for a protracted period (a) on the weakest mixture, and (b) on the richest mixture. (*U. Lond.*)

The brake horse-power of an I.C. engine is frequently expressed as

$$\text{b.h.p.} = \frac{P_b \text{LAN}}{33,000}$$

where P_b = brake mean effective pressure, in lb. per sq. in.
  L = stroke, in ft.
  A = cylinder area, in sq. in.
  N = number of power cycles per min.,

i.e. $$\text{b.h.p.} = \frac{P_b \times 330 \times \frac{1}{12} \times 1,200}{33,000} = P_b,$$

i.e. the b.h.p. is numerically equal to the brake mean effective pressure in lb. per sq. in. We therefore have the following values :

B.m.e.p. (lb. per sq. in.)	97·8	102	106	110	112	112	110	107
Spec. cons. (lb. per b.h.p.-hr.)	0·577	0·565	0·559	0·577	0·635	0·736	0·798	0·840

The resulting curve is shown in fig. V,4, and this type of graph is usually known as the hook curve or consumption loop for the engine. The two important features are the points marked A and B on the graph. Point A is the point of minimum consumption, i.e. greatest economy, giving a specific consumption of 0·56 lb. per b.h.p.-hr. at 106 lb. per sq. in. b.m.e.p. The point B is the point of maximum power, giving 112·2 lb. per sq. in. b.m.e.p. at 0·69 lb. per b.h.p.-hr.

The experimental method will be familiar to most students from their laboratory work. A dynamometer will be required to measure the brake torque, a tachometer for the speed and a calibrated orifice tank to measure the consumption in lb. or pints per min. The latter is often replaced by providing the fuel supply from an auxiliary tank for a short time and finding, with a stop-watch, the time taken for a known volume of petrol to pass between two engraved marks on the stems of a glass bulb. It is

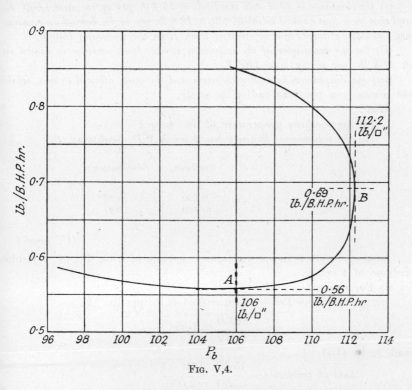

FIG. V,4.

better, however, to use a revolution counter instead of a stop-watch to measure the rate of consumption, as this method eliminates time errors in both speed and rate of consumption.

(a) Weakest mixture	(b) Richest mixture
Jackets, valves and manifolds will be excessively hot to keep the engine running on the weakest mixtures.	Excessive heat at piston crown unless very well cooled.
May lead to cracks in head and burned exhaust valves.	Heavy carbon deposits on valves, cylinder and piston due to unburnt fuel.
Plugs become " white " and " powdery " and insulators may fail.	Plugs may be fouled
	Exhaust becomes smoky and may be objectionable.

13. *In an attempt to estimate the temperature at the end of the suction stroke of a petrol engine having a compression ratio of 5, the following assumptions are made :*

(i) the clearance is filled with residuals at 15·4 lb. per sq. in., and 1,600° F. and that these first expand adiabatically to 12·8 lb. per sq. in. behind an imaginary insulating diaphragm separating them from the incoming charge ;

(ii) for the remainder of the induction stroke, fresh mixture is drawn in at 12·8 lb. per sq. in. and 140° F. ;

(iii) the diaphragm is now withdrawn and the gases allowed to mix, while the piston is at the outer end of the stroke.

Find :

    (a) the resulting temperature of the charge ;

    (b) the volumetric efficiency based on N.T.P. conditions.

	Residuals	Incoming gas
C_p	0·250	0·24
C_v	0·179	0·17

(U. Lond.)

Assume for convenience a clearance volume of 1 cu. ft., i.e. a stroke volume of 4 cu. ft.

(i) For residuals,
$$R = 778(0·250 - 0·179) = 55·4 \text{ ft.lb. per lb. ° F.}$$
$$\gamma = \frac{0·250}{0·179} = 1·396$$

and $\therefore$ by (I,7)
$$\text{Mass of residuals} = \frac{15·4 \times 144 \times 1}{55·4 \times 2,060}$$
$$= 0·0194 \text{ lb. per cu. ft. of clearance.}$$

This mass expands adiabatically behind the imaginary diaphragm, so that
$$15·4 \times 1^\gamma = 12·8 \times V_2{}^\gamma$$
$$V_2 = \left(\frac{15·4}{12·8}\right)^{\frac{1}{1·396}} = 1·144 \text{ cu. ft.}$$

In expanding adiabatically, the temperature will have fallen, and by (I,18)
$$T_2 = 2,060 \times \left(\frac{12·8}{15·4}\right)^{\frac{0·396}{1·396}}$$
$$= 2,060 \times \left(\frac{2·08}{2·50}\right)^{\frac{1}{3·52}} = 2,060 \times \frac{1·2315}{1·2975}$$
$$= 1,960° \text{ F. abs.}$$

(ii) The residuals have expanded to 1·144 cu. ft., so that the fresh charge admitted is now $5 - 1·144 = 3·856$ cu. ft.

But $R = 778(0·24 - 0·17) = 54·5$ ft.lb. ° F. units.

$$\therefore \text{ Mass of fresh charge} = \frac{PV}{RT} = \frac{12·8 \times 144 \times 3·856}{54·5 \times 600}$$

$$= 0·2175 \text{ lb.}$$

(iii) The residuals and the fresh charge mix at constant volume (piston at O.D.C.), no net external work being done. Neglecting any loss during the mixing process,

Internal energy lost by residuals = Internal energy gained by fresh charge.

i.e. $0·0194 \times 0·179 \times (1,960 - T) = 0·2175 \times 0·17 \times (T - 600)$

$$6·80 - 0·00347T = 0·0370T - 22·20.$$

$$T = \frac{29·0}{0·04047} = 717° \text{ F. abs. } \underline{\text{Ans.}}$$

If 4 cu. ft. of fresh charge (i.e. the entire swept vol.) had been admitted at N.T.P., the mass so admitted would have been

$$\frac{PV}{RT} = \frac{14·7 \times 144 \times 4}{54·5 \times 492} = 0·3136 \text{ lb.}$$

$$\therefore \underline{\text{Volumetric }} \eta = \frac{0·2175}{0·3163} = \underline{68·7\%.} \quad \text{Ans.}$$

Examples

1. A four-stroke gas engine, of bore 11 in. and stroke 19 in., runs at 270 r.p.m. with gas of calorific value 450 B.T.U. per cu. ft. at 60° F. and 30 in. Hg. The ratio by volume of air to gas for theoretically complete combustion is 3·5 : 1. If the clearance volume of the cylinder is 450 cu. in. and the air and gas mixture is supplied at 60° F., calculate the theoretical maximum engine output.

What are the various factors which would prevent the attainment of the theoretical maximum output ? (*U. Manch.*)

[Compression ratio $= 5$; air std. $\eta = 0·476$; heat supplied $= 104·5$ B.T.U. per cycle assuming 100% volumetric η ; W.D. $= 49·7$ B.T.U. per cycle ; h.p. $= 158·3$.]

2. The compression ratio of an oil engine is 10 to 1, and half the fuel is burned at constant volume and the remainder at constant pressure. The pressure and temperature at the commencement of compression are 14 lb. per sq. in. and 170° F. respectively, and the maximum pressure during combustion is 450 lb. per sq. in. Assuming an index of 1·3 for both compression and expansion, and that the heat is rejected at constant volume at the end of the stroke, estimate the mean effective pressure of the indicator diagram.

(R $= 53·3$ ft.lb. ° F. units ; $\gamma = 1·4$.) (*U. Lond.*)

[Since the expansion and compression phases are not adiabatic, the heat received during combustion—Heat rejected at const. vol. $\neq$ W.D. ; $P_2 = 280$;

$T_3 = 2,021$; $T_4 = 2,566$; $V_4 = 1·27$; $P_5 = 30·9$; for 9 cu. ft. of stroke vol., area of diagram = 76,500 ft.lb. ; m.e.p. = 59 lb. per sq. in.]

3. A single-acting gas engine working on the four-stroke cycle has an overall volumetric efficiency of 71 per cent. when the brake horse-power is 30. The barometer pressure is 14·76 lb. per sq. in. and the temperature is 68° F. The piston diameter is 12·5 in. and the stroke 15 in. The speed is 280 r.p.m., and the gas used has a calorific value of 500 B.T.U. per cu. ft. measured at 60° F. and 14·7 lb. per sq. in. The air/fuel ratio by volume is 7·5.

If the brake thermal efficiency is 28·5 per cent., estimate :
  (*a*) the number of missed cycles per min.,
  (*b*) the air consumption in lb. per minute, assuming that during each missed cycle a volume of air equal to the usual volume of gas is admitted,
  (*c*) the gas consumption as metered, if the gas pressure is 5 in. of water.
(*U. Lond.*)

[Vol. aspirated at 60° F. and 14·7 lb. per sq. in. = 0·749 cu. ft. ; vol. of gas $= \dfrac{0·749}{8·5}$ cu. ft. ; $\therefore$ 101 power cycles per min. ; 39 missed cycles ; vol. of air = 95·9 cu. ft. at 60° F. and 14·7 lb. per sq. in. = 7·32 lb. per min. ; gas press. = 14·94 lb. per sq. in. ; 8·90 cu. ft. gas per min. as metered.]

4. A petrol engine working on the four-stroke cycle has four single-acting cylinders, each 2·54 in. diameter × 3·74 in. stroke and volume compression ratio 5·7. At a speed of 2,500 r.p.m. it is found to develop 22 b.h.p. with a fuel consumption of 13·5 lb. of petrol per hour, of calorific value 19,000 B.T.U. per lb. If the mechanical efficiency is 0·78, find the indicated m.e.p. developed, the indicated thermal efficiency and the efficiency ratio relative to the air standard cycle. Compare the output of this engine with the R.A.C. rating which assumes m.e.p. 90 lb. per sq. in., mechanical efficiency 0·75, and piston speed 1,000 ft. per min. (*I.Mech.E.*)

[i.m.e.p. = 118 lb. per sq. in. ; i. th. $\eta = 28·0\%$; η ratio = 55·8% ; R.A.C. rating (brake) = 10·35.]

5. The following results were obtained during a test on a single-cylinder four-stroke-cycle oil engine, cylinder diameter 10 in. ; stroke 15 in. Duration of test 60 min. ; total revolutions, 19,710 ; fuel oil used, 13·79 lb. ; average area of indicator diagrams, 0·881 sq. in. ; length, 3 in. ; spring number 300 ; net brake load, 140 lb. at 4 ft. radius ; cooling water, 12·5 lb. per min. with temperature at inlet 50° F., at outlet 128° F. ; atmospheric temperature, 60° F. ; exhaust gas temperature, 743° F. ; air supplied per lb. of fuel, 30 lb. ; C.V. of fuel, 19,200 B.T.U. per lb. ; assume the mean specific heat of the exhaust gases to be 0·25.

Calculate the i.h.p. and b.h.p. developed. Draw up a heat balance on a basis of one minute and express each item as a percentage of the heat supplied.
(*U. Glas.*)

[i.h.p. = 43·0 ; b.h.p. = 35·0 ; in gross heat balance we have b.h.p., cooling water, exhaust, radiation and errors, viz. taken in order : 1485, 975, 1217, 733 B.T.U. per min., or 33·7, 22·1, 27·6, 16·6%.]

6. A four-stroke-cycle single-cylinder gas engine, bore 10¼ in. and stroke 15 in., runs at 300 r.p.m. The air consumption is measured by means of an air-box, the orifice of which is 1½ in. diameter. The coefficient of discharge for the orifice is 0·97 and the U-tube shows a difference of pressure across the orifice of 2·24 in. water. The atmospheric temperature is 15° C., and the barometer 29·2 in. Hg.

The gas consumption metered at a pressure of 4·5 in. water and a temperature of 21° C., is 0·18 cu. ft. per sec.   Find the mean volumetric efficiency of the engine referred to free air conditions.

$$(\text{R} = 53·3 \text{ ft.lb. } °\text{ F. units.}) \qquad (U. \text{ Lond.})$$

[Air consumption = 0·0890 lb. per sec. ≡ 1·196 cu. ft. per sec. at 29·2 in. Hg. and 59° F. ; gas consumption = 0·179 cu. ft. per sec. under the same conditions ; vol. effy. = 76·8%.]

7. A petrol engine has six cylinders, diameter 3 in., stroke 4 in.   It is single-acting, works on the four-stroke cycle and uses a volatile fuel containing 84% carbon and 16% hydrogen.   The diameter at the throat of the choke tube is 1·55 in.   At 3,000 r.p.m. the volumetric efficiency is 0·75 (referred to 32° F. and 14·7 lb. per sq. in. abs.), the pressure at the throat of the choke tube is 13 lb. per sq. in. abs., and the temperature there is 60° F.   If the fuel-air mixture is chemically " correct " for combustion estimate (a) the fuel consumption in lb. per hour, and (b) the speed of the air through the choke.   Take R for air as 53·3 and for fuel 18 ft.lb. per lb. per ° F.   Composition of air by weight is oxygen 23 to nitrogen 77. Atomic weights are :   carbon 12, hydrogen 1, oxygen 16.

$$(I.Mech.E.)$$

[Fuel analysis is gravimetric ; " correct " air-fuel ratio = 15·3 by weight = 45·3 by vol. ; vol. of mixture taken in = 110·5 S.C.F. per min., i.e. 2·385 S.C.F. of fuel per min. ≡ 34·2 lb. of fuel per hour ; 0·145 lb. of air per sec. of spec. vol. 14·8 cu. ft. per lb. ; $v = \dfrac{WV}{A} = 164·3$ ft. per sec.   N.B.—R for mixture = 51·15 may be used instead of vol. air-fuel ratio.]

8. During the trial of a single-acting oil-engine, cylinder diameter 12 in., stroke 18 in., working on the four-stroke cycle and firing every cycle, the following observations were made :

   Duration of trial, 1 hour.
   Total fuel used, 17·0 lb. ;   H.C.V. 19,250 B.T.U. per lb.
   Total number of revolutions 12,624.
   m.e.p. 98 lb. per sq. in.
   Net brake load applied to a drum 6 ft. diameter 342 lb.
   Total weight of cooling water 1,200 lb.
   Inlet temperature 61° F., Outlet temperature 141° F.
Estimate the thermal efficiency on the i.h.p. and b.h.p. basis and draw up the heat balance as far as the data allow. (U. Birm.)

[ind. th. η = 41·1% ;   b. th. η = 31·9% ;   in heat balance :   b.h.p., cooling water, exhaust and radiation in order 31·9%, 29·3%, 38·8%.]

CHAPTER VI

COMBUSTION APPLIED TO ENGINES

Introduction : Combustion of Fuels

The general topic of combustion as understood in Engineering Thermodynamics is a wide one and includes the analytical and qualitative treatment of furnace problems, I.C. engines, Gas Producers, I.C. turbines, and many specialized problems relating to specific fuels when used under special conditions. The subject is wide, yet the underlying principles are few and are similar in all cases. It is rather difficult to sub-divide the questions on combustion, and although an attempt at a logical division has been made, many similarities will be found as well as liberal reference to the various gas laws, notably about molar heats, gas constants, and partial pressures.

It is assumed that the student knows the following molecular weights, as adopted by engineers :

$$C—12, \quad O_2—32, \quad N_2—28, \quad H_2—2, \quad S—32$$

The fundamental chemical equations of combustion are :

(a)	$C + O_2 \quad \rightarrow CO_2$
i.e.	12 lb. + 32 lb. = 44 lb.
and	1 mol + 1 mol = 1 mol
(b)	$2C + O_2 \quad \rightarrow 2CO$
i.e.	24 lb. + 32 lb. = 56 lb.
and	2 mols + 1 mol = 2 mols
(c)	$2H_2 + O_2 \quad \rightarrow 2H_2O$
i.e.	4 lb. + 32 lb. = 36 lb.
and	2 mols + 1 mol = 2 mols
(d)	$S + O_2 \quad \rightarrow SO_2$
i.e.	32 lb. + 32 lb. = 64 lb.
and	1 mol + 1 mol = 1 mol

Special attention is drawn to the combustion equations (a)–(d) above in relation to the contraction in volume which occurs in many combustion processes. The lb.mol is used in these equations, but any other unit of volume could be employed. This reduction in volume, or molecular contraction, closely affects the thermal efficiency of I.C. engines, although it is usually only a few per cent of the original volume when dealing with an air-fuel mixture.

114

The term "theoretically complete combustion" as used throughout this book is meant to convey that all the hydrogen is burnt to H_2O, and *all* the carbon to CO_2. This is in accordance with the convention usually followed in Great Britain, though another interpretation is sometimes used in other countries.

A working knowledge of the method of operation of the Orsat apparatus, and of the appropriate calculations, is assumed in this chapter.

1. *Show by means of a diagram how the percentages of CO_2 and O_2 in the dry exhaust gas analysis vary with the air-fuel ratio in a petrol engine. Give approximate values when the engine is running under maximum output conditions, and also when under maximum economy conditions.*

In a petrol engine the dry exhaust analysis gave 1·5% CO, and the O_2 was negligible. If the fuel used had an ultimate analysis by weight C, 0·84 and H_2, 0·16, what weight of air was supplied per lb. of fuel? Air is 23·1% O_2 by weight, and all the carbon in the fuel may be assumed to have been burned either completely or incompletely. (*U. Lond.*)

Approximate values are :
(*a*) for max. output, $CO_2 = 12·5\%$, $O_2 = $ nil.
(*b*) for max. economy, $CO_2 = 10·1\%$, $O_2 = 5\%$.

A discussion of these graphs can be found in most standard textbooks on petrol engines.

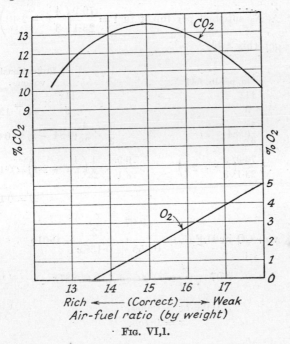

FIG. VI,1.

The numerical part of the question serves as a very good example of the weight and volume methods of tackling combustion problems and both methods will therefore be set out in full. In some cases, one method may be a little shorter than the other, depending on the data and the unknown quantities; ultimately most students decide on the method which they themselves understand best.

A. Working by weight:

Let x lb. C burn to CO_2, then, using the fundamental combustion equations for CO_2, H_2O and CO (cf. introduction to chapter VI),

$$x(C) + \frac{8}{3}x(O_2) = \frac{11}{3}x(CO_2)$$

and

$$(0\cdot84 - x)(C) + \frac{4}{3}(0\cdot84 - x)(O_2) = \frac{7}{3}(0\cdot84 - x)(CO)$$

and

$$0\cdot16(H_2) + (8 \times 0\cdot16)O_2 = (9 \times 0\cdot16)(H_2O).$$

$$\therefore O_2 \text{ needed per lb. of fuel} = \frac{8}{3}x + \frac{4}{3}(0\cdot84 - x) + 1\cdot28$$

$$= \frac{4}{3}x + 2\cdot40,$$

since the O_2 in the exhaust is negligible.

$$\therefore N_2 \text{ supplied per lb. of fuel} = \frac{76\cdot9}{23\cdot1}\left(\frac{4}{3}x + 2\cdot40\right),$$

whence we get this table,

Stuff	lb. per lb. fuel	Proportional volumes $\left(\dfrac{\text{weight}}{\text{mol. wt.}}\right)$
CO_2	$\dfrac{11x}{3}$	$\dfrac{11x}{3} \times \dfrac{1}{44} = \dfrac{x}{12}$
CO	$\dfrac{7}{3}(0\cdot84 - x)$	$\dfrac{7}{3} \times \dfrac{1}{28}(0\cdot84 - x) = 0\cdot07 - \dfrac{x}{12}$
N_2	$\dfrac{76\cdot9}{23\cdot1}\left(\dfrac{4}{3}x + 2\cdot4\right)$	$\dfrac{76\cdot9}{23\cdot1} \times \dfrac{1}{28}\left(\dfrac{4}{3}x + 2\cdot4\right) = 0\cdot158x + 0\cdot285$

$$\Sigma = 0\cdot158x + 0\cdot355$$

$$\therefore \% \text{ vol. CO in D.F.G.} = \frac{0\cdot07 - \dfrac{x}{12}}{0\cdot355 + 0\cdot158x} = 0\cdot015$$

i.e.

$$0\cdot07 - \frac{x}{12} = 0\cdot00533 + 0\cdot00237x$$

$$0\cdot0857x = 0\cdot0647$$
$$x = 0\cdot755.$$

$$\therefore\ O_2 \text{ needed} = \left(\frac{4}{3} \times 0.755\right) + 2.4 = 3.407 \text{ lb. per lb. of fuel.}$$

lb. of air supplied per lb. of fuel $= 3.407 \times \dfrac{100}{23.1} = \underline{14.75 \text{ lb.}}$ Ans.

B. Working with volumes (say lb.mols) :

We write down the combustion equation for this case, for 100 lb. of fuel,

$$\frac{84}{12}[C] + \frac{16}{2}[H_2] + x[O_2] + \frac{79.2}{20.8}x[N_2] \rightarrow$$
$$a[CO_2] + b[CO] + 8[H_2O] + 3.88x[N_2].$$

(Note, $8[H_2O]$ can be written down straight away for balance of H_2 ; 20.8% O_2 by volume is equivalent to 23.1% O_2 by weight (see below) ; x is defined as the number of lb.mols of O_2 supplied per 100 lb. of fuel.)

For balance of C, $a + b = 7$.   .   .   .   .   (i)

For balance of O_2, $x - a - \dfrac{b}{2} - 4 = 0$.   .   .   .   (ii)

For CO in D.F.G., $0.015 = \dfrac{b}{a + b + 3.88x}$.   .   .   (iii)

(i) in (ii) $x - 7 + b - \dfrac{b}{2} - 4 = 0$,   i.e. $b = 22 - 2x$.

Substituting this value of b in (iii), and also using (i),

$$0.015 = \frac{b}{7 + 3.88x} = \frac{22 - 2x}{7 + 3.88x}$$

i.e. $0.105 + 0.0582x = 22 - 2x$
$$2.058x = 21.895$$
$$x = \underline{10.64 \text{ lb.mols per 100 lb. of fuel.}}$$

Since the mean molecular weight of air is 28.9 (see below) and air contains 20.8% O_2 by vol.,

$$\therefore\ 10.64 \times \frac{100}{20.8} = 51.15 \text{ lb.mols of air per 100 lb. of fuel,}$$

i.e. $51.15 \times 28.9 = 1,477$ lb. of air per 100 lb. of fuel,

i.e.   lb. of air supplied per lb. of fuel $= \underline{14.77.}$ Ans.

It will be seen that good agreement exists between the two methods outlined. The student should always be in a position to convert a weight analysis, of air e.g., to the corresponding volumetric analysis. In this example we were given 23.1% O_2 by weight in air,

$$\therefore \% \ O_2 \text{ by vol.} = \frac{\dfrac{23 \cdot 1}{32}}{\dfrac{23 \cdot 1}{32} + \dfrac{76 \cdot 9}{28}} \times 100$$

$$= \frac{0 \cdot 722}{0 \cdot 722 + 2 \cdot 743} \times 100 = 20 \cdot 8\%.$$

Since the gas constant for air is 53·3 ft.lb. per lb. ° F., then the mean molecular weight of air can always be deduced by equation (I,9), viz.

$$\frac{1 \cdot 985 \times 778}{53 \cdot 3} = 28 \cdot 9 \text{ very nearly.}$$

This also gives a convenient method for arriving at a value of the density of air at 14·7 lb. per sq. in. and 32° F., viz.

$$\frac{28 \cdot 9}{358 \cdot 7} = 0 \cdot 0806 \text{ lb. per S.C.F.}$$

Another way of finding the mean molecular weight knowing the volumetric analysis is thus :

$$\text{Mean mol. wt.} = \frac{0 \cdot 208 \times 32 + 0 \cdot 792 \times 28}{0 \cdot 208 + 0 \cdot 792}$$

$$= \frac{6 \cdot 663 + 22 \cdot 19}{1 \cdot 0} = 28 \cdot 853$$

or if the weight analysis is known :

$$\text{Mean mol. wt.} = \frac{0 \cdot 231 + 0 \cdot 769}{\dfrac{0 \cdot 231}{32} + \dfrac{0 \cdot 769}{28}}$$

$$= \frac{1 \cdot 0}{0 \cdot 00722 + 0 \cdot 02743} = \frac{1 \cdot 0}{0 \cdot 03465}$$

$$= 28 \cdot 9.$$

Note. When the chemical element is enclosed in square brackets, e.g. [O_2], this is intended to refer to lb.mols or volumes of the stuff ; ordinary brackets, e.g. (O_2), are used when referring to lb. or mass of the stuff.

2. *A petrol engine is supplied with fuel having the formula* C_7H_{16}. *Calculate the weight of air per lb. of fuel which would just suffice for theoretically complete combustion.*

In an actual experiment, an analysis of the exhaust gases showed equal volumes of unused oxygen and carbon dioxide ; there was no carbon monoxide. Find the ratio of air to fuel by weight as actually supplied.

(Atomic weights : hydrogen, 1 ; carbon, 12 ; nitrogen, 14 ; oxygen, 16. Air contains 23·2% *oxygen by weight.)*

(*U. Camb.*)

The combustion equation for theoretically complete combustion is given by

$$1[C_7H_{16}] + 11[O_2] + \dots [N_2] = 7[CO_2] + 8[H_2O] + \dots [N_2]$$

i.e. $(7 \times 12 + 8 \times 2) + (11 \times 32) + \dots = \dots$

$$100 \text{ lb. fuel} + 352 \text{ lb. } O_2 + 352 \times \frac{76 \cdot 8}{23 \cdot 2} \text{ lb. } N_2 = \dots$$

$$\therefore \frac{352}{100} \times \frac{100}{23 \cdot 2} = 15 \cdot 2 \text{ lb. of air per lb. of fuel.} \quad \text{Ans.}$$

Now, in the actual experiment we have,

$$1[C_7H_{16}] + x[O_2] + \dots [N_2] = a[CO_2] + 8[H_2O] + a[O_2] + \dots [N_2].$$

This is the new combustion equation written in " volumes " or " lb.mols " the volumes of CO_2 and O_2 being equal, with no CO present, and the usual assumption that *all* the hydrogen is burnt to H_2O. x are the number of lb.mols of O_2 supplied perlb. mol of fuel.

Now, by comparing the mols of carbon, we must have 7 mols of CO_2, of all the carbon is burnt.

$\therefore x = 7 + 4 + 7$, from the CO_2, H_2O, and O_2 terms respectively.

i.e. $x = 18$.

$$\therefore \frac{18 \times 32}{100} \times \frac{1}{0 \cdot 232} = 24 \cdot 8 \text{ lb. air per lb. fuel.} \quad \text{Ans.}$$

3. *A fuel gas has composition by volume :* H_2, 50% ; CO, 40% ; CO_2, 6% ; N_2, 4%.

Determine the volume of air required for complete combustion of 1 cu. ft. of the gas. If the dry exhaust gas from an engine using this fuel contains 9·2% by volume carbon dioxide and no carbon monoxide, what air-to-gas ratio (by volume) has been used ? What would be the percentage by volume of oxygen in the dry exhaust ? (Air contains 21% *by volume of oxygen.)* (U. Camb.)

(*a*) For complete combustion,

$$50[H_2] + 40[CO] + 6[CO_2] + x[O_2] + \left(\frac{79}{21}x + 4\right)[N_2] \longrightarrow$$
$$a[CO_2] + b[H_2O] + \left(\frac{79}{21}x + 4\right)[N_2],$$

where $\dfrac{x}{100}$ is the oxygen-fuel ratio, by volume.

Now, for balance of H_2, $b = 50$
and for C, $a = 40 + 6 = 46$
and for O_2, $\dfrac{40}{2} + 6 + x = a + \dfrac{b}{2}$

i.e. $x = 46 + 25 - 26 = 45$ cu. ft. (say) of O_2 per 100 cu. ft. of gas.

i.e. $\dfrac{45}{100} \times \dfrac{100}{21} = 2\text{·}14$ cu. ft. of air per cu. ft. of gas.   Ans.

(*b*) In the actual case we shall have

$$50[H_2] + 40[CO] + 6[CO_2] + y[O_2] + \left(\frac{79}{21}y + 4\right)[N_2] \longrightarrow$$
$$d[CO_2] + 50[H_2O] + e[O_2] + \left(\frac{79}{21}y + 4\right)[N_2].$$

where $\dfrac{y}{100}$ is the new oxygen-fuel ratio, by volume.

Note that the 9·2% CO_2 is given relative to the *dry* exhaust gases i.e. excluding the H_2O.

Now, $d = 40 + 6 = 46$ (by C balance)

and $0\text{·}092 = \dfrac{46}{46 + e + \dfrac{79}{21}y + 4}$ (by CO_2 in D.F.G.).   (i)

and $\dfrac{40}{2} + 6 + y = 46 + 25 + e$ (by O_2 balance)   .   (ii)

(i) gives $50 + e + 3\text{·}76y = 500$
(ii) gives $-45 - e + y = 0$
          $\therefore\ 5 + 4\text{·}76y = 500,\quad y = 104$
and $e = 104 - 45 = 59$

$\therefore$ Air-to-Gas Ratio (by vol.) $= \dfrac{104}{100} \times \dfrac{100}{21} = 4\text{·}95$.   Ans.

% vol. of O_2 in dry gas $= \dfrac{59}{46 + 59 + \dfrac{79}{21} \times 104 + 4} = \dfrac{59}{500} = 11\text{·}8\%$.   Ans.

4. *A gas producer supplies gas to an internal combustion engine, and its volumetric composition (per cent.) is : CO_2, 6·7 ; O_2, 1·3 ; CO, 22·5 ; H_2, 2·2 ; CH_4, 0·4 ; N_2, 66·9. The dry exhaust gas analysis gave (by volume) 0·8% of oxygen, and no CO. Find the ratio of air to gas by volume in the mixture supplied to the engine, and estimate the volumetric percentages of CO_2 and N_2 in the dry exhaust gases.*

(Composition of air by volume N_2, 79 ; O_2, 21.) (I.C.E.)

As all the data are given in terms of volumes and the answers are required in the same units, the problem is most readily solved by working in lb.mols throughout.

Thus, if x lb.mols of O_2 are supplied with each 100 lb.mols of fuels,

$$6 \cdot 7[CO_2] + 1 \cdot 3[O_2] + 22 \cdot 5[CO] + 2 \cdot 2[H_2] + 0 \cdot 4[CH_4] + 66 \cdot 9[N_2]$$

$$+ x[O_2] + \frac{79}{21}x[N_2] \rightarrow a[CO_2] + b[O_2] + c[H_2O] + \left(66 \cdot 9 + \frac{79}{21}x\right)[N_2],$$

where $\dfrac{x}{100}$ is the oxygen-fuel ratio, by volume.

In accordance with the data, the right-hand side of this equation contains no CO term.

For C balance, $6 \cdot 7 + 22 \cdot 5 + 0 \cdot 4 = a$,   i.e. $a = 29 \cdot 6$.

For H_2 balance, $2 \cdot 2 + (2 \times 0 \cdot 4) = c$,   i.e. $c = 3 \cdot 0$.

For O_2 balance, $6 \cdot 7 + 1 \cdot 3 + \dfrac{22 \cdot 5}{2} + x = a + b + \dfrac{c}{2}$,

i.e. $19 \cdot 25 + x = 29 \cdot 6 + b + \dfrac{3 \cdot 0}{2}$

$$b = x - 11 \cdot 85 \quad . \quad . \quad . \quad . \quad . \quad \text{(i)}$$

But we are told that the *dry* exhaust gas contained 0·8% of O_2 by volume,

$$\therefore \; 0 \cdot 008 = \frac{b}{a + b + 66 \cdot 9 + \dfrac{79}{21}x} = \frac{b}{96 \cdot 5 + b + 3 \cdot 76x}$$

$$0 \cdot 7720 + 0 \cdot 008b + 0 \cdot 0301x = b \quad . \quad . \quad . \quad \text{(ii)}$$

From (i) $0 \cdot 7720 + 0 \cdot 0301x = 0 \cdot 992(x - 11 \cdot 85)$

whence $x = 13 \cdot 02$ and $b = 1 \cdot 17$.

$$\therefore \; \underline{\text{Air-to-Gas Ratio (by vol.)}} = \frac{13 \cdot 02}{100} \times \frac{1}{0 \cdot 21} = \underline{0 \cdot 620}. \quad \text{Ans.}$$

$$\% \text{ vol. of } CO_2 \text{ in dry gases} = \frac{29 \cdot 6}{29 \cdot 6 + 1 \cdot 17 + 66 \cdot 9 + 49} \times 100$$

$$= \underline{20 \cdot 2\%}. \quad \text{Ans.}$$

$$\% \text{ vol. of } N_2 \text{ in dry gases} = \frac{66 \cdot 9 + 49}{29 \cdot 6 + 1 \cdot 17 + 66 \cdot 9 + 49} \times 100$$

$$= \underline{79 \cdot 0\%}. \quad \text{Ans.}$$

5. *The analysis of the fuel used in an engine is : C, 85% ; H_2, 15% ; and the air-fuel ratio by weight is 14 to 1. The bore of the engine is $4\frac{3}{4}$ in., and the stroke is $5\frac{1}{2}$ in., the compression ratio being 6·5 to 1. Find the composition of the exhaust gases by weight, assuming that the carbon is all burned either to CO_2 or CO. Assume air to contain 23% O_2 by weight.*

If, at the end of the exhaust stroke, the clearance volume is filled with exhaust gases at a temperature of 800° F. and a pressure of 15 lb. per sq. in., find the weight of exhaust gases left in the cylinder.   *(U. Lond.)*

Recalling the fundamental equations of combustion (*a*) and (*b*) quoted in the introduction to this chapter, we have

$$C + O_2 \rightarrow CO_2$$

i.e.
$$y + \frac{32}{12}y = \frac{44}{12}y, \qquad \text{all in lb.}$$

and also

$$2C + O_2 \rightarrow 2CO$$

$$x + \frac{32}{12}x = \frac{56}{12}x, \qquad \text{all in lb.}$$

We use the symbols x and y because we do not yet know how much C is burnt to CO_2 and how much to CO. Working per lb. of fuel throughout, we have

Total air supplied = 14 lb. per lb. of fuel

i.e.   ,, O_2 ,,   = 14 × 0·23 = 3·22 lb. per lb. of fuel

0·15 lb. H_2 per lb. of fuel require (0·15 × 8) = 1·20 lb. O_2

∴ O_2 available for C combustion = 3·22 − 1·20 = 2·02 lb. per lb. of fuel, assuming that the exhaust will not contain any free oxygen.

We may therefore say,

$$2·02 = \frac{32}{12}y + \frac{32}{12}x, \text{ from the combustion equations,}$$

i.e. $0·758 = x + y$
and in any case, $0·85 = 2x + y$
whence $y = 0·666$ and $x = 0·092$.

Per lb. of fuel we therefore have

$$\frac{44}{12} \times 0·666 = 2·440 \text{ lb. } CO_2,$$

$$\frac{56}{12} \times 0·092 = 0·430 \text{ lb. CO,}$$

$$9 \times 0·15 = 1·35 \text{ lb. } H_2O,$$

and $14 \times 0·77 = 10·78$ lb. N_2,

i.e. a total of 15·00 lb. of flue gases (this agrees with an air-fuel ratio of 14 : 1 by weight).

∴ Weight Analysis (including the H_2O) is

$$16·25\% \ CO_2, \ 2·88\% \ CO, \ 9·0\% \ H_2O, \ 71·9\% \ N_2. \quad \text{Ans.}$$

Several possible approaches are now possible ; a method which is generally useful is to find the density of the gases (i.e. their mean molecular weight) and then the mass filling a known volume at a certain pressure and temperature can easily be deduced. Thus,

	lb. per lb. fuel	Prop. volumes $\left(m = \dfrac{w}{\text{mol. wt.}}\right)$
CO_2	2·440	$\dfrac{2·440}{44} = 0·05540$
CO	0·430	$\dfrac{0·430}{28} = 0·01535$
H_2O	1·350	$\dfrac{1·350}{18} = 0·07500$
N_2	10·780	$\dfrac{10·78}{28} = 0·38500$
	15·000	0·53075

Now, mean molecular wt. $= \dfrac{\Sigma(m \times \text{molecular wt.})}{\Sigma m}$

i.e. $\qquad\qquad = \dfrac{15}{0·53075} = 28·25$

∴ Density at S.T.P. $\quad = \dfrac{28·25}{358·7} = 0·0788$ lb. per cu. ft.,

because 1 lb.mol of any gas occupies 358·7 cu. ft. at S.T.P.

∴ Density at 15 lb. per sq. in. and 800° F.

$$= 0·0788 \times \frac{492}{1,260} \times \frac{15}{14·7} = 0·0314 \text{ lb. per cu. ft.}$$

Clearance Volume $= \dfrac{\pi}{4} \times \dfrac{(4\frac{3}{4})^2 \times 5\frac{1}{2}}{1,728} \times \dfrac{1}{5·5} = 0·01025$ cu. ft.

∴ Weight of exhaust gases left in cylinder

$$= 0·0314 \times 0·01025 = \underline{0·000322 \text{ lb.}} \quad \text{Ans.}$$

6. *From a test carried out on a four-cylinder petrol engine running on a rich mixture the following figures were obtained :*

$$Volume\ CO_2 = \quad 9\cdot8\%$$
$$O_2 = \quad 0\cdot2\%$$
$$CO = \quad 7\cdot6\%$$
$$N = 82\cdot4\ (remainder).$$

Determine the air-fuel ratio by weight and the probable composition of the fuel on the assumption that this consists solely of hydrogen and carbon.

(*U. Manch.*)

In this example, the tabular method of setting out exhaust gas calculations will be demonstrated ; this is recommended whenever the *complete* D.F.G. analysis is known.

Stuff	% by vol.	Mol. wt.	Proportional weights		lb. stuff per 100 lb. D.F.G. (or weight analysis %)
CO_2 . . .	9·8	44	$44 \times 9\cdot8 =$	431·1	$\dfrac{431\cdot1}{2,959\cdot4} = 14\cdot56$
O_2 . . .	0·2	32	$32 \times 0\cdot2 =$	6·4	etc. = 0·22
CO . . .	7·6	28	$28 \times 7\cdot6 =$	212·9	= 7·20
N_2 . . .	82·4	28	$28 \times 82\cdot4 =$	2,309·0	78·00
Totals . .	100·0		$\Sigma = 2,959\cdot4$		$\Sigma = 99\cdot98$

The last column should add up to 100, the difference being due to small slide-rule inaccuracy. It is better to acknowledge such errors, rather than to make an arbitrary adjustment to the figures.

$$\text{lb. C per 100 lb. of dry flue gas} = \left(\frac{12}{44} \times 14\cdot56\right) + \left(\frac{12}{28} \times 7\cdot20\right)$$
$$= 3\cdot97 + 3\cdot08 = 7\cdot05.$$

Also, lb. O_2 supplied per 100 lb. of dry flue gas

$$= \left(\frac{32}{44} \times 14\cdot56\right) + 0\cdot22 + \left(\frac{16}{28} \times 7\cdot20\right)$$
$$= 10\cdot58 + 0\cdot22 + 4\cdot11 = 14\cdot91.$$

Since the fuel contains no O_2, the whole of this oxygen is derived from the air supplied. But, the total air supplied per 100 lb. D.F.G. (by N_2)

$$= 78 \times \frac{100}{76\cdot9} = 101\cdot4 \text{ lb., of which } 101\cdot4 \times \frac{23\cdot1}{100} = 23\cdot41 \text{ lb. per 100 lb.}$$

D.F.G. is O_2 (assuming air contains 23·1% O_2 by weight).

∴ $23\cdot41 - 14\cdot91 = 8\cdot50$ lb. O_2 per 100 lb. D.F.G. is used to produce H_2O. This required $\frac{1}{8} \times 8\cdot50 = 1\cdot06$ lb. H_2 in fuel per 100 lb. D.F.G.

[Note, 1 lb. $(H_2) + 8$ lb. $(O_2) \rightarrow 9$ lb. (H_2O).]

Hence, for a pure hydro-carbon fuel we have 7·05 lb. C and 1·06 lb. H_2 per 100 lb. D.F.G., i.e. 8·11 lb. of fuel per 100 lb. D.F.G.,

i.e. $\dfrac{7\cdot05}{8\cdot11} = 86\cdot9\%$ C   and $\dfrac{1\cdot06}{8\cdot11} = 13\cdot1\%$ H_2. Ans.

Again, per 100 lb. D.F.G. we have 101·4 lb. of air supplied for D.F.G. and for H_2O production ; at the same time we have used a total of 8·11 lb. of fuel.

∴ Air-to-Fuel Ratio (by weight) $= \dfrac{101\cdot4}{8\cdot11} = 12\cdot5.$ Ans.

7. *Describe briefly, with a diagram, an apparatus for analysing the exhaust gases of an internal combustion engine.*

A fuel oil has the following analysis by weight : C, 85 ; H_2, 12·5 ; O_2, 2·0 ; and residue 0·5%. The dry exhaust gas has the following volumetric analysis : CO_2, 9 ; CO, 1·0 ; O_2, 7·77 ; and N_2, 82·23%.

Find what percentage of the air is used and state what usually limits the load which can be put on an oil engine used for road transport.

(Air contains 23·1% of O_2 by weight.)

(U. Lond.)

It is assumed that the student knows and understands the Orsat apparatus for exhaust gas analysis.

Stuff	% by vol.	Mol. wt.	Proportional weight	lb. stuff per lb. D.F.G.		lb. C per lb. D.F.G.	
CO_2	9·0	44	396	$\dfrac{396}{2977\cdot9} = 0\cdot1330$	$\dfrac{12}{44} \times 0\cdot133$	$= 0\cdot03630$	
CO	1·0	28	28	$\dfrac{28}{2977\cdot9} = 0\cdot00941$	$\dfrac{12}{28} \times 0\cdot00941$	$= 0\cdot00403$	
O_2	7·77	32	248·6	$\dfrac{248\cdot6}{2977\cdot9} = 0\cdot0835$			
N_2	82·23	28	2305·3				
			$\Sigma = 2977\cdot9$			$\Sigma = 0\cdot04033$	

Since the fuel contains 0·85 lb. C per lb.

$$\therefore \frac{0\cdot85}{0\cdot04033} = 21\cdot08 \text{ lb. D.F.G. per lb. of fuel.}$$

Also, $9 \times 0\cdot125 = 1\cdot125$ lb. H_2O per lb. of fuel.

$\therefore 21\cdot08 + 1\cdot125 - (1 - 0\cdot005) = 21\cdot21$ lb. of air actually supplied per lb. of fuel.

(Note, 0·005 lb. of residual ash per lb. of fuel.)

Again $0\cdot0835 \times 21\cdot08 = 1\cdot76$ lb. O_2 in D.F.G. per lb. of fuel,

i.e. $1\cdot76 \times \dfrac{100}{23\cdot1} = 7\cdot62$ lb. of air remain unused due to the free O_2 in flue

$$\therefore \underline{\% \text{ air used}} = \frac{21\cdot21 - 7\cdot62}{21\cdot21} = \frac{13\cdot59}{21\cdot21} = \underline{64\%}. \quad \text{Ans.}$$

It will be seen that the figure of 2·0% O_2 in the fuel has apparently not been used. This depends on the method of calculation ; one could proceed thus during the latter part of the question :
lb. O_2 used per lb. of fuel

$$= \left(\frac{32}{12} \times 0\cdot9 \times 0\cdot85\right) + \left(\frac{32}{24} \times 0\cdot1 \times 0\cdot85\right) + \left(\frac{32}{4} \times 0\cdot125\right) - 0\cdot02$$

$$= 2\cdot04 + 0\cdot1134 + 1\cdot0 - 0\cdot02 = 3\cdot1334$$

$\therefore$ lb. of air required per lb. of fuel $= 3\cdot1334 \times \dfrac{100}{23\cdot1} = 13\cdot57,$

i.e. as before. Note, $0.9 \times 0.85 =$ lb. C burnt to CO_2, since Avagadro's Hypothesis gives

$$\frac{\text{lb. C burnt to } CO_2}{\text{lb. C to CO} + \text{lb. C to } CO_2} = \frac{CO_2\% \text{ by vol.}}{CO_2\% + CO\%}$$

As it is never possible to reach 100% utilization of the air charge in an oil engine, after a certain point the fuel is only partly burned as more fuel is injected to meet the increased load. This results in heavy carbon deposits in the engine, clogging of injectors and objectionable exhaust.

EXAMPLES

1. The following particulars refer to a test on a suction producer and gas engine plant :

Coal burned per hr. = 62·5 lb. (calorific value 7,800 C.H.U. per lb.) ; producer gas consumed per hr. = 3,930 cu. ft. at N.T.P. ; ratio of air to gas in mixture = 1·5 ; b.h.p. = 57·4.

The percentage composition of the producer gas was $CO = 30$, $CO_2 = 6$, $H_2 = 12$, $N_2 = 52$.

If the calorific values of hydrogen and CO are 193 and 190 C.H.U. per cu. ft. at N.T.P. respectively, find (a) the efficiency of the producer ; (b) the overall efficiency of the plant ; and (c) the percentage composition by volume of the exhaust gases.   (*U.L.C.I.*)

[C.V. of producer gas = 144·4 B.T.U. ; (a) <u>64·6%</u> ; (b) <u>16·7%</u> ; (c) assume 21% O_2 by vol. in air ; <u>CO_2 15·7%, H_2O 5·2%, O_2 4·6%, N_2 74·5%</u>.]

2. The charge in a petrol engine is at 660° F. abs. at the beginning of adiabatic compression and at 1,070° F. abs. at the end. The temperature at the end of constant volume firing is 4,070° F. abs.

Calculate (a) the work done on the charge per lb.mol during compression ; (b) the heat liberated per lb.mol of original charge, if during combustion there is a 2% molecular decrease.

$C_p = 8·085 + 4·45 \times 10^{-4}$ T° F. abs. B.Th.U. per lb.mol per ° F.
$C_v = 6·1 \quad + 4·45 \times 10^{-4}$ T° F. abs.   „   „   „   „   „
            (*U. Lond.*)

[(a) <u>2,660 B.T.U.</u> by (I,2) and (I,19) ; (b) <u>21,300 B.T.U.</u>, cf. ch. II, ex. No. 12.]

3. In a test on an oil engine the air consumption was 210·0 lb. per hr. and the fuel consumption 7·0 lb. per hr. The fuel, which may be assumed to be a pure hydrocarbon, contained 13% by weight of hydrogen.

An exhaust calorimeter took 21,000 C.H.U. per hr. from the exhaust gases, after which their temperature was 126° C.

Calculate the heat leaving the engine in the exhaust gases.

Assume the dew-point of the gases to be at 50° C., the total heat of dry saturated steam at 50° C. as 617 C.H.U. per lb., the mean specific heat of superheated steam as 0·48, and the mean specific heat of the dry gases as 0·24.

Take 15° C., the temperature of the air and fuel supplies, as datum.
            (*I.Mech.E.*)

[lb. H_2O per lb. fuel = 1·17 ; lb. D.F.G. per lb. fuel = 29·83 ; above 59° F. and after exhaust calorimeter, heat in H_2O = 1,345 B.T.U. per lb. fuel ; ditto, heat in dry gases = 1,433 B.T.U. per lb. fuel ; Heat leaving engine (above 50° F.) = 57,200 B.T.U. per hr.]

4. Octane (C_8H_{18}) is burnt with an air supply 40% in excess of that theoretically required for complete combustion. Find the complete analysis by weight of the products of combustion, and the ratio by volume of oxygen to nitrogen in them.

For air, composition by weight, $O_2 = 23\cdot2\%$, $N_2 = 76\cdot8\%$.

(*U. Camb.*)

[Correct air-fuel ratio $= 15\cdot12$; per lb. fuel: CO_2 $3\cdot09$ lb., H_2O $1\cdot42$ lb., O_2 $1\cdot41$ lb., N_2 $16\cdot3$ lb.; percentages, <u>$13\cdot9$</u>, $6\cdot4$, $6\cdot3$, $73\cdot4$; $\dfrac{O_2}{N_2}$ (by vol.) $=$ <u>$7\cdot6\%$</u>.]

5. The fuel used in an oil engine has a composition by weight: Carbon, $84\cdot83$; Hydrogen, $12\cdot24$; Oxygen, $2\cdot84$; and Nitrogen, $0\cdot09$; while the dry exhaust gas shows a volumetric composition: CO_2, $7\cdot26$; CO, $0\cdot08$; O_2, $11\cdot16$; and N_2, $81\cdot5$. Calculate, per lb. of fuel, the excess air in the exhaust gases and the heat lost due to incomplete combustion of the carbon in the fuel. Any formula used must be proved. One lb. carbon burning to CO_2 gives 14,500 B.T.U. and to CO 4,400 B.T.U. Composition of air by weight is Oxygen 23 to Nitrogen 77. Atomic weights: Carbon, 12; Hydrogen, 1; Oxygen, 16; Nitrogen, 14.

(*I.Mech.E.*)

[Use tabular method; lb. C per lb. D.F.G. $= 0\cdot02972$; lb. D.F.G. per lb. fuel $= 28\cdot50$; lb. air per lb. fuel $= 27\cdot61$; min. O_2 from air per lb. fuel $= 3\cdot213$ lb.; <u>Excess air $= 13\cdot65$ lb.</u>; heat loss due to CO $=$ <u>$93\cdot3$ B.T.U.</u>]

6. A gas of the following percentage volumetric composition: CH_4, 36; H_2, 46; CO, 8; N_2, 10—is contained in a mixture in which the air-gas ratio is 6 : 1 by volume. Find the percentage volumetric contraction on combustion. If this mixture has a volume of $0\cdot52$ cu. ft., temperature $223°$ F., and pressure 14 lb. per sq. in. before compression, estimate the temperature on the expansion stroke at the point where the volume is $0\cdot47$ cu. ft. and pressure 65 lb. per sq. in. Air contains 21% O_2 by volume.

(*U. Lond.*)

[Work in lb.mol; per 100 lb.mols of fuel there are $44[CO_2]$, $118[H_2O]$, $484[N_2]$, $27[O_2]$; <u>Contraction $= 3\cdot86\%$</u>; by (I,7a) allowing for $\dfrac{m_1}{m_2} = \dfrac{1}{0\cdot961}$, <u>$t_2 = 2{,}520°$ F.</u>]

7. The percentage analysis by volume of the gas supplied to a gas engine was: CH_4, $19\cdot5$; C_3H_6, $1\cdot6$; CO, $18\cdot0$; H_2, $44\cdot4$; O_2, $0\cdot4$; N_2, $13\cdot1$; CO_2, $3\cdot0$; and the dry exhaust analysis was: CO_2, $9\cdot4$; O_2, $6\cdot0$; N_2, $84\cdot5$. Estimate the air-gas ratio by volume on the basis of (a) the N_2 balance and (b) the O_2 balance, and find the percentage of excess air supplied.

(*U. Lond.*)

[Take O_2 : N_2 in air as 21 : 79; per 100 lb.mols of fuel: $45\cdot3$ lb.mols of CO_2 and $88\cdot2$ lb.mols of H_2O; also, by balancing N_2 in combustion equation 407 lb.mols N_2 after combustion; air : gas $= 4\cdot99$; by balancing O_2, $105\cdot9$ lb.mols O_2 from air; <u>air : gas $= 5\cdot04$</u>; " correct " air : gas $= 3\cdot67$; <u>$\%$ excess $= 36\cdot8$</u> based on mean of (a) and (b).]

8. In a petrol engine the combustible mixture is compressed adiabatically through a compression ratio of $7\cdot5$ to 1. The mean value of γ is $1\cdot32$. The combustion, which is under constant volume conditions, releases 31,800 B.T.U. per mol of mixture and produces a molecular increase of $7\frac{1}{2}\%$. The pressure and temperature at the start of compression are 14 lb. per sq. in. and $180°$ F. respectively.

Estimate the pressure and the temperature at the end of combustion, assuming there is no heat lost to the jackets.

The mean volumetric heats per lb.mol of the products of combustion reckoned from $180°$ F. are given below:

C_v	.	.	.	6·89	7·0	7·1	7·15
$t°$ F.	.	.	.	4,000	4,500	5,000	5,500

(*U. Lond.*)

[Cf. ch. II, No. 13, for similar method; $E_2 = -$ W.D.$_{1-2} = 3{,}590$ B.T.U. per lb.mol; $E_3 = 35{,}390$ B.T.U. per original lb.mol; plot C_v against t, hence by trial <u>$t_3 = 4{,}840°$ F.</u>; <u>$P_3 = 935$ lb. per sq. in.</u> by (I,7a).]

CHAPTER VII

COMBUSTION APPLIED TO BOILERS

1. *During a boiler test it was found that the flue gas was leaving the boiler at a temperature of 520° F. The volumetric composition of the flue gas was 11·6% CO_2, 6·8% O_2 and 0·5% CO, and the inlet air temperature 62° F.*

If the coal supplied to the furnace had 79·5% by weight of carbon, estimate the heat carried away by the exit gas per lb. of coal burnt. Assume the average specific heat of the flue gas to be 0·24. (U. Manch.)

The data of the question will restrict us to a consideration of the *dry* flue gases (D.F.G.), as no H_2 percentage is given for the ultimate analysis of the coal.

We draw up the following table:

Stuff	% by vol.	Mol. wt.	Proportional weights	lb. stuff per lb. D.F.G.	lb. C per lb. D.F.G.
CO_2	11·6	× 44 =	510·4	0·1693	$\times \dfrac{12}{44} = 0\cdot04620$
O_2	6·8	× 32 =	217·6	0·0722	
CO	0·5	× 28 =	14·0	0·00465	$\times \dfrac{12}{28} = 0\cdot00199$
N_2	81·1 (by diff.)	× 28 =	2,272	0·7540	
	$\Sigma = 100\cdot0$		$\Sigma = 3,014\cdot0$	1·00015	$\Sigma = 0\cdot04819$

i.e. 0·04819 lb. C is burnt to produce 1 lb. D.F.G.

$$\therefore \frac{0\cdot795}{0\cdot04819} = 16\cdot50 \text{ lb. D.F.G. are produced per lb. of coal fired}$$

∴ Heat carried away by dry gases per lb. of coal burnt

$$= 0\cdot24 \times 16\cdot50 \times (520 - 62)$$

$$= \underline{1,815 \text{ B.T.U.}} \quad \text{Ans.}$$

2. *The analysis of the coal used in a boiler trial is as follows : C, 82% ;*
H_2, 6% ; O_2, 4% ; ash, 8% ; moisture, 2%.
Determine the theoretical minimum air required for complete combustion
of 1 lb. of the coal.
If the actual air supply is 18 lb. per lb. of coal, the hydrogen is completely
burned, and 80% of the carbon is burned to CO_2, the remainder to CO, determine
the volumetric analysis of the dry products of combustion.

(*Air contains 23% O_2 by weight.*)

(*U.L.C.I.*)

For complete combustion we must have all the C burnt to CO_2 ; thus

$$\text{Minimum } O_2 \text{ required} = 0.82 \times \frac{32}{12} + 8 \times 0.06 - 0.04$$

$$= 2.187 + 0.48 - 0.04$$
$$= 2.625 \text{ lb. } O_2 \text{ per lb. of coal.}$$

$$\text{Minimum Air} = 2.627 \times \frac{100}{23} = \underline{11.41 \text{ lb. per lb. of coal.}} \quad \text{Ans.}$$

Now $0.8 \times 0.82 \times \dfrac{44}{12} = 2.403$ lb. CO_2 are actually produced, requiring

$0.8 \times 0.82 \times \dfrac{32}{12} = 1.749$ lb. O_2.

Also, $0.2 \times 0.82 \times \dfrac{28}{12} = 0.383$ lb. CO are actually produced, requiring

$0.2 \times 0.82 \times \dfrac{16}{12} = 0.219$ lb. O_2.

Also,

$0.06 \times 9 = 0.54$ lb. H_2O are produced, requiring $0.06 \times 8 = 0.48$ lb. O_2.

And 18 lb. air contain $18 \times \dfrac{23}{100} = 4.14$ lb. O_2.

$$\therefore \text{ Free } O_2 \text{ in flue} = 4.14 + 0.04 - 1.749 - 0.219 - 0.48$$
$$= 1.732 \text{ lb. per lb. of coal}$$
$$N_2 \text{ in flue} = 18 \times 0.77 = 13.87 \text{ lb. per lb. of coal.}$$

Stuff	lb. per lb. coal	÷	Mol. wt.	Prop. vol.	%.vol.
CO_2	2.403	÷	44	0.0546	8.84 ⎫
CO	0.383	÷	28	0.0137	2.22 ⎬ Ans.
O_2	1.732	÷	32	0.0541	8.76 ⎭
N_2	13.87	÷	28	0.4953	80.20

$$\Sigma = 0.6177 \quad \Sigma = 100.02$$

3. *The analysis of the coal in a boiler trial was as follows :* $C, 81\%$; $H_2, 4\cdot5\%$; $O_2, 8\%$, *remainder incombustible.*

The analysis of the dry flue gas was : $CO_2, 8\cdot3\%$; $CO, 1\cdot4\%$; $N_2, 80\cdot3\%$; $O_2, 10\%$.

Determine :

    (a) *the weight of air supplied per lb. of coal ;*

    (b) *the percentage excess air.*

(U.L.C.I.)

This is best attempted by the "tabular" method, since the *complete* dry exhaust gas analysis is given :

Stuff	% vol.	Mol. wt.	Prop. weight	lb. stuff per lb. D.F.G.		lb. C per lb. D.F.G.
CO_2 . .	$8\cdot3 \times$	$44 =$	$365\cdot2$	$0\cdot1228$	$\times \dfrac{12}{44} =$	$0\cdot0335$
CO . .	$1\cdot4 \times$	$28 =$	$39\cdot2$	$0\cdot0132$	$\times \dfrac{12}{28} =$	$0\cdot00566$
N_2 . .	$80\cdot3 \times$	$28 =$	$2,249$	$0\cdot756$		—
O_2 . .	$10\cdot0 \times$	$32 =$	$320\cdot0$	$0\cdot1076$		—
			$\Sigma = 2,973\cdot4$	$0\cdot9996$		$0\cdot03916$

$$\therefore \frac{0\cdot81}{0\cdot03916} = 20\cdot68 \text{ lb. D.F.G. per lb. of coal}$$

$$9 \times 0\cdot045 = 0\cdot405 \text{ lb. water vapour per lb. of coal}$$

$$1 - (0\cdot81 - 0\cdot045 - 0\cdot08) = 0\cdot065 \text{ lb. of incombustibles per lb. of coal}$$

$$\therefore \text{ lb. air supplied per lb. of coal} = 20\cdot68 + 0\cdot405 - (1 - 0\cdot065)$$
$$= 21\cdot085 - 0\cdot935 = \underline{20\cdot15}. \quad \text{Ans.}$$

lb. air required for theoretically complete combustion

$$= \left(0\cdot81 \times \frac{32}{12} + 0\cdot045 \times 8 - 0\cdot08\right)\frac{100}{23}$$

$$= (2\cdot16 + 0\cdot36 - 0\cdot08)\frac{100}{23} = 10\cdot61$$

$$\therefore \text{ Percentage Excess Air} = \frac{20\cdot15 - 10\cdot61}{10\cdot61} \times 100 = \underline{89\cdot9\%}. \quad \text{Ans.}$$

4. *Coal with a C.V. of 12,800 B.T.U. per lb. has a composition by weight C, 0·78; H, 0·05; O, 0·08; S, 0·02; N, 0·02: remainder ash. It is burned in a furnace with 50% excess air. The flue gases enter the chimney at 620° F. and the atmospheric temperature is 60° F. Calculate the proportion of the heat of the fuel carried away by the flue gases. Assume perfect combustion; C_p for air, 0·24, C_p for dry products of combustion, 0·25; heat carried off per lb. of moisture in the flue gases, 1,300 B.T.U.; composition of air by weight, O_2, 0·23, N_2, 0·77.* (U. Glas.)

Since we are asked to assume perfect combustion, we must take it that all C is burnt to CO_2, all H_2 to H_2O, and all S to SO_2. Thus, *per lb. of coal*, we produce

$$0.78 \times \frac{44}{12} = 2.860 \text{ lb. } CO_2$$

$$0.05 \times \ \ 9 = 0.450 \text{ lb. } H_2O$$
$$0.02 \times \ \ 2 = 0.040 \text{ lb. } SO_2$$

and we require $\quad\quad 0.78 \times \dfrac{32}{12} = 2.078 \text{ lb. } O_2$

$$0.05 \times \ \ 8 = 0.400 \text{ lb. } O_2$$
$$0.02 \times \ \ 1 = 0.020 \text{ lb. } O_2$$

i.e. 2·498 lb. O_2 per lb. of coal are required for theoretically complete combustion; but 1 lb. of coal contains 0·080 lb. O_2.

$\therefore$ O_2 to be supplied = 2·418 lb. per lb. of coal.

and with 50% excess air,

O_2 actually supplied = 3·627 lb. per lb. of coal

i.e. N_2 actually supplied = $3.627 \times \dfrac{77}{23} = 12.14$ lb. per lb. of coal.

Total free O_2 in flue = $3.627 - 2.418 = 1.209$ lb. per lb. of coal
Total N_2 in flue = $12.14 + 0.02 = 12.16$ lb. per lb. of coal.

Heat carried away by dry products = $(2.860 + 0.040) \times 0.25 \times (620 - 60)$
$$= 406 \text{ B.T.U.}$$
,, ,, ,, ,, steam $\quad = 0.450 \times 1,300$
$$= 585 \text{ B.T.U.}$$
,, ,, ,, ,, O_2 and N_2 $\ = (12.16 + 1.209) \times 0.24 \times (620 - 60)$
$$= 1,797 \text{ B.T.U.}$$

$\therefore$ Total quantity of heat carried away per lb. of coal
$$= 406 + 585 + 1,797 = 2,788 \text{ B.T.U.}$$

$$\text{Proportion of C.V.} = \frac{2,788}{12,800} = 21.8\%. \quad \text{Ans.}$$

5. *Waste gas from a furnace fired, without preheating of the air or gas, by coal gas of the composition stated below is leaving the furnace setting at 700° C. The waste gas is found to contain 10·5% of CO_2 and no combustible matter. Calculate the waste gas heat loss per cu. ft. of coal gas burned.*

Coal gas							% by vol.
CO_2	.	.	.	.	.	.	2·0
O_2 .	.	.	.	.	.	.	0·3
C_nH_m	.	.	.	.	.	.	2·2 (assume C_4H_8)
CO	.	.	.	.	.	.	10·0
CH_4	.	.	.	.	.	.	25·5
H_2 .	.	.	.	.	.	.	48·5
N_2 .	.	.	.	.	.	.	11·5

Mean Sp. Hts. in C.H.U.
per cu. ft. at 0° per ° C.
between 15° and 700° C.

CO_2	.	.	.	.	.	0·0314
H_2O	.	.	.	.	.	0·0243
O_2	.	.	.	.	.	0·0214
N_2	.	.	.	.	.	0·0202

(*I.Chem.E.*)

$$700° \text{ C.} \equiv 1,292° \text{ F.}$$

We know that all diatomics are generally considered as having equal volumetric heats, but the values quoted here are mean values over a large range of temperature and although the values would be equal for practical purposes at S.T.P., they vary at other conditions.

Combustion equation per 100 lb.mols or per 100 cu. ft.

$$2\cdot0[CO_2] + 2\cdot2[C_4H_8] + 10\cdot0[CO] + 25\cdot5[CH_4] + 48\cdot5[H_2] + (0\cdot3 + x)[O_2]$$
$$+ \left(11\cdot5 + \frac{79}{21}x\right)[N_2] \rightarrow a[CO_2] + b[H_2O] + c[O_2] + (11\cdot5 + 3\cdot76x)[N_2]$$

where x volumes of O_2 are supplied per 100 volumes of coal gas, air contains 21% O_2 by volume, and the waste gas contains no CO or other combustible matter.

For C balance,

$$a = 2\cdot0 + 4 \times 2\cdot2 + 10\cdot0 + 25\cdot5, \text{ i.e. } a = 46\cdot3.$$

For H_2 balance,

$$b = 4 \times 2\cdot2 + 2 \times 25\cdot5 + 48\cdot5, \quad \text{i.e. } b = 108\cdot3.$$

For O_2 balance,

$$2\cdot0 + \frac{10\cdot0}{2} + 0\cdot3 + x = 46\cdot3 + \frac{108\cdot3}{2} + c$$

i.e. $$x - c = 93\cdot15 \quad . \quad . \quad . \quad . \quad . \quad \text{(i)}$$

We also know that the waste gas contains 10·5% CO_2 (by volume), but it is not explicitly stated whether this figure refers to the total or wet flue gases, or to the dry flue gases only. However, the student should know that the usual method of analysing the flue gases is carried out at a temperature considerably lower than the dew-point and the sample should first be passed through a drying tube.

$$\therefore \text{ For } CO_2\% \text{ in D.F.G., } 0.105 = \frac{46.3}{46.3 + c + 11.5 + 3.76x}$$

i.e. $\qquad\qquad 6.07 + 0.105c + 0.395x = 46.3.$. (ii)

Substituting for x from (i), $\quad 0.105c + 0.395(93.15 + c) = 40.23$

$$0.500c + 36.8 = 40.23$$
$$c = 6.86$$

and from (i) $\qquad\qquad x = 93.15 + 6.86 = 100.$

Thus, we have per 100 cu. ft. of coal gas, 46·3 cu. ft. CO_2, 108·3 cu. ft. H_2O, 6·86 cu. ft. O_2, and 11·5 + 376 = 387·5 cu. ft. N_2.

Taking an initial temperature of 60° F. for the coal gas,

Heat Loss = $(1,292 - 60)[(46.3 \times 0.0314) + (108.3 \times 0.0243)$
$$+ (6.86 \times 0.0214) + (387.5 \times 0.0202)]$$
$$= 1,232[1.46 + 2.63 + 0.15 + 7.83]$$
$$= 1,232 \times 12.07 \text{ B.T.U. per 100 cu. ft. of coal gas at } 32° \text{ F.}$$
$$= 1,232 \times 12.07 \times \frac{492}{520} = \underline{141 \text{ B.T.U. per cu. ft. of gas at } 60° \text{ F.}} \quad \text{Ans.}$$

(Note, the numerical value of a volumetric heat in C.H.U. per cu. ft. ° C. is equal to the value in B.T.U. per cu. ft. ° F.)

If the student had overlooked the fact that the 10·5% CO_2 must be taken as referring to the D.F.G., the following equation would have resulted for the CO_2 content of the wet gases :

$$0.105 = \frac{46.3}{46.3 + 108.3 + c + 11.5 + 3.76x}$$

i.e. $\qquad\qquad 17.45 + 0.105c + 0.395x = 46.3.$

Substituting for x, $\quad 0.105c + 0.395(93.15 + c) = 28.85$

$$0.500c + 36.8 = 28.85,$$

i.e. c is negative, which is impossible ; or in other words the data are inconsistent when used in this way. $\therefore$ the $CO_2\%$ must be given relative to the *dry* gases as already evaluated. As a useful check on the arithmetic, we have

$$\frac{46.3}{46.3 + 6.86 + 387.5} \times 100 = \% \ CO_2 \text{ in D.F.G.}$$

i.e. $\qquad\qquad \frac{46.3}{4,401} \times 100 = 10.52\% \ CO_2.$

6. *During a boiler trial it was observed that for every ton of coal supplied to the furnace, $2\frac{1}{2}$ cwt. of ashes were collected from the ash pit. The analysis of the dry flue gas gave 14·6% CO_2 and 2·3% CO by volume. The ultimate analysis of the coal fired was: C, 86%; H_2, 4%; incombustibles, 10%; and its higher calorific value was 14,000 B.T.U. per lb. The ashes were found to contain 20% carbon.*

Calculate:

    (a) the weight of air supplied to the furnace per lb. of coal fired;
    (b) the furnace efficiency.

1 lb. of carbon, burnt to CO_2, yields 14,500 B.T.U., and if burnt to CO yields 4,430 B.T.U. Air contains 23% oxygen by weight or 21% by volume.

(*U. Lond.*)

Per 20 cwt. of coal we have $2\frac{1}{2}$ cwt of ashes, of which $\frac{1}{5}$ is C,

i.e. $\frac{1}{8} \times \frac{1}{5} = 0.025$ lb. C are in the ashes per lb. of fuel fired,

    $\therefore$ $0.860 - 0.025 = 0.835$ lb. useful C per lb. of fuel fired.

Let $x =$ lb.mols of air per lb. of fuel; then the combustion equation becomes in lb.mols

$$\frac{0.835}{12}[C] + \frac{0.04}{2}[H_2] + 0.21x[O_2] + 0.79x[N_2] \rightarrow$$
$$a[CO_2] + b[CO] + 0.02[H_2O] + d[O_2] + 0.79x[N_2].$$

It may be asked on what grounds it is assumed that the dry gases will contain free O_2 when it is known that CO has been produced. In practical cases it is quite common to have small quantities of CO in addition to free O_2; this is due to imperfect air distribution and may be especially marked in the case of large surface area grates with natural draught. In I.C. engines it shows lack of turbulence. So far as the solution of problems is concerned, it is not usually safe to assume from the outset that O_2 or CO will be absent unless information to this end is supplied in the question. The safe way is to write down a general equation as above and then deduce as many relations between the unknown as the question will permit. In this example we have 4 unknowns and if we can only deduce 3 statements connecting them, then we should *have* to assume $d = 0$ as the last condition. Sometimes, this is necessary in a solution.

Here we have:

C balance, $0.0696 = a + b$.   .   .   .   (i)

CO and CO_2 in flue, $\dfrac{a}{b} = \dfrac{14\cdot6}{2\cdot3} = 6.34$.   .   .   (ii)

O_2 balance, $0.21x - a - \dfrac{b}{2} - \dfrac{0.02}{2} = d$.   .   (iii)

CO_2 in D.F.G., $0.146 = \dfrac{a}{a + b + d + 0.79x}$.   .   (iv)

It should be noted that a fifth equation for CO in D.F.G. similar to (iv) is not a new equation, as it is already given by (ii) and (iv). Thus we have 4 independent equations to find our 4 unknowns, and we deduce at once that the flue will contain free O_2.

From (i) and (ii),

$$b = \frac{0 \cdot 0696}{7 \cdot 34} = 0 \cdot 00948, \quad \text{and} \quad a = 0 \cdot 06012.$$

Substituting in (iii), $\quad 0 \cdot 21x - 0 \cdot 07486 = d \quad . \quad . \quad . \quad . \quad$ (v)

Substituting in (iv), $\quad 0 \cdot 146 = \dfrac{0 \cdot 06012}{0 \cdot 0696 + d + 0 \cdot 79x}$

i.e. $\quad\quad\quad\quad\quad 0 \cdot 79x = 0 \cdot 4115 - 0 \cdot 0696 - d \quad . \quad . \quad .$ (vi)

Adding (v) and (vi), $\quad x = 0 \cdot 41676$, and hence $d = 0 \cdot 01284.$

Since molecular weight of air is $28 \cdot 9 \left[\text{i.e. } \dfrac{1 \cdot 985 \times 778}{53 \cdot 3}, \text{ by (I,9)} \right]$,

$\therefore$ lb. air per lb. of coal fired $= 28 \cdot 9 \times 0 \cdot 41676 = \underline{12 \cdot 07}.$ Ans.

Now, Avogadro's Hypothesis may be used in this manner,

$$\frac{\text{lb. C burnt to CO}}{\text{lb. C burnt to CO} + \text{lb. C burnt to CO}_2} = \frac{\text{CO\% by vol.}}{\text{CO\% by vol.} + \text{CO}_2\% \text{ by vol.}}$$

i.e. lb. C burnt to CO $= \dfrac{2 \cdot 3}{16 \cdot 9} \times 0 \cdot 835 = 0 \cdot 1138$ per lb. of coal fired.

$\therefore$ C.V. lost per lb. of coal fired $= 0 \cdot 1138(14{,}500 - 4{,}430) + 0 \cdot 0250 \times 14{,}500$

$$= 1{,}145 + 363$$
$$= 1{,}508 \text{ B.T.U.}$$

$$\underline{\text{Furnace Efficiency}} = \frac{14{,}000 - 1{,}508}{14{,}000} \times 100 = \underline{89 \cdot 2\%}. \text{ Ans.}$$

We can check our arithmetic and at the same time see how much free O_2 will be in the D.F.G., thus

		No. of lb.mols	% vol.
CO_2	. . . . . .	$a = 0 \cdot 06012$	$14 \cdot 60$
CO	. . . . . .	$b = 0 \cdot 00948$	$2 \cdot 30$
O_2	. . . . . .	$d = 0 \cdot 01284$	$3 \cdot 12$
N_2	. . . . . .	$0 \cdot 79x = 0 \cdot 3295$	$80 \cdot 00$
		$\Sigma = 0 \cdot 41194$	$100 \cdot 02$

7. *The ultimate analysis of a fuel (proportions by weight) is given by :
C, carbon ; H, hydrogen ; O, oxygen ; S, sulphur ; the remainder being made
up of nitrogen, moisture and ash.   For such a fuel, the (higher) calorific value
is sometimes calculated from a formula of the type*

$$8{,}100C + 34{,}450\left(H - \frac{O}{8}\right) + 2{,}250S$$

*in C.H.U. per lb. of fuel.   Explain the origin of the various terms in the formula
and calculate the higher calorific value of a coal whose composition by weight
is (per cent.) : carbon, 83·95 ; hydrogen, 4·23 ; oxygen, 2·96 ; sulphur, 0·91 ;
moisture, 0·56 ; nitrogen plus ash, 7·39.*

*Explain what is meant by the " lower " calorific value of a fuel, and give
what you consider a reasonable lower calorific value for the above-mentioned
fuel.* (I.C.E.)

It should be noted that the question is set in C.H.U.'s.   Multiplying
through by $\dfrac{9}{5}$, we get the now more usual figures in B.T.U.   Thus,

$$\text{H.C.V.} = 14{,}580C + 62{,}000\left(H - \frac{O}{8}\right) + 4{,}050S \text{ B.T.U. per lb.}$$

The figure of 14,580 represents the calorific value of 1 lb. of carbon, and
that of 4,050 the calorific value of 1 lb. of sulphur.   62,000 B.T.U. per lb.
is the higher calorific value of 1 lb. of hydrogen, i.e. the heat evolved when
1 lb. of hydrogen burns to H_2O, the resulting H_2O being cooled back to
the original temperature of the fuel.   If the fuel itself contains oxygen
according to its ultimate analysis, then it is generally assumed that the
whole of this oxygen will be combined with a corresponding amount of
hydrogen at the start of combustion.   The result is to reduce the useful
percentage of hydrogen by subtracting $\dfrac{O}{8}$ from the hydrogen figure.   This
is an approximate method, due to Dulong, and the only accurate method
for finding the H.C.V. is by direct experiment, such as is done in a bomb
calorimeter.

$$\text{H.C.V.} = 0{\cdot}8395 \times 14{,}580 + 62{,}000\left(0{\cdot}0423 - \frac{0{\cdot}0296}{8}\right) + 4{,}050 \times 0{\cdot}0091$$

$$= 12{,}240 + 2{,}392 + 37$$

$$= \underline{14{,}670 \text{ B.T.U. per lb.}} \quad \text{Ans.}$$

The L.C.V. is the difference between the H.C.V. and the heat absorbed
by the H_2O (due to combustion and surface moisture) in having its state
changed to vapour, the constituents having been supplied at approximately
air temperature.   The amount of latent heat thus required will depend on
the pressure at which evaporation may be said to take place.   It is difficult

to arrive at a reliable figure for this, but the common practice [1] is now to assume that evaporation takes place at the saturation pressure corresponding to normal temperature, i.e. 60° F. The latent heat is then 1,055 B.T.U. per lb. (extended steam tables are required to look this up).

$$\therefore \text{ L.C.V.} = 14,669 - (9 \times 0.0423 + 0.0056)1,055$$
$$= 14,669 - 408$$
$$= \underline{14,260 \text{ B.T.U. per lb.}} \quad \text{Ans.}$$

8. *A boiler is fired with a fuel having a composition by weight : C, 86% ; H, 3.9% ; O, 1.4% ; ash, 8.7%.*

The volumetric analysis of the dry flue gas was : CO_2, 12.7% ; CO, 1.4% ; O, 4.1% ; N, 81.8%.

The temperature of the air supply to the furnace was 64° F. and the temperature of the flue gases leaving the boiler 410° F. Taking the dew-point of the wet flue gases as 122° F., the specific heat of steam (superheated) as 0.36 per unit mass, the specific heat of the dry flue gas as 0.24 per unit mass, and the calorific value of CO as 4,370 B.T.U. per lb., calculate per lb. of fuel burned :

    (a) *the heat carried away by the dry flue gas ;*
    (b) *the heat carried away by the moisture from combustion ;*
    (c) *the heat lost due to incomplete combustion of the carbon.*

To what points would you pay particular attention in order to increase overall efficiency of the installation, and what is the advantage of a low dew-point ?   *(I.Chem.E.)*

Stuff	% vol.	×	Mol. wt.	=	Prop. weight	lb. stuff per lb. D.F.G.
CO_2	12.7	×	44	=	558.5	0.185
CO	1.4	×	28	=	39.2	0.0130
O_2	4.1	×	32	=	131.3	0.0435
N_2	81.8	×	28	=	2,290.0	0.759

$$\Sigma = 3,019 \qquad \Sigma = 1.0005$$

$$\text{lb. C per lb. D.F.G.} = \frac{12}{44} \times 0.185 + \frac{12}{28} \times 0.0130 = 0.0560$$

$$\text{lb. D.F.G. per lb. of fuel} = \frac{0.86}{0.056} = 15.35.$$

Heat carried away by D.F.G. $= 15.35 \times 0.24 \times (410 - 64)$
$$= \underline{1,275 \text{ B.T.U. per lb. of fuel}} \quad \text{Ans. } (a).$$

lb. H_2O produced per lb. of coal $= 9 \times 0.039 = 0.351.$

---

[1] This definition of L.C.V. is in accordance with the recommendations of the Heat Engines Trials Committee of the Institution of Civil Engineers and has been incorporated in B.S.S. 526–1933 as the recognized method for finding the L.C.V. of a fuel.

If the dew-point is 122° F., i.e. the superheated H_2O commences to condense at that temperature, then the partial pressure of the H_2O is the saturation pressure corresponding to 122° F. and this is found from the steam tables (by interpolation), viz. 1·79 lb. per sq. in. absolute. At that pressure $H_s = 1114·5$ B.T.U. per lb. from the tables, so that using the data of the question

Heat carried away by $H_2O = 0·351[1,114·5 + 0·36(410 - 122) - (64 - 32)]$
$$= 0·351[1,114·5 + 103·7 - 32]$$
$$= 416 \text{ B.T.U. per lb. of fuel.} \quad \text{Ans. } (b).$$

Note, (64 - 32) is the sensible heat in the H_2O reckoned from the datum of 32° F., i.e. the same datum as that for H_s. Since the fuel is supplied at approximately the air temperature of 64° F., this amount of sensible heat may be taken to be supplied to the grate.

The heat lost due to CO formation depends on the lb. CO formed per lb. of fuel. We already know that 0·0130 lb. CO are produced per lb. D.F.G. and that 15·35 lb. D.F.G. are produced per lb. of fuel ;

$$\therefore \text{ lb. CO per lb. of fuel} = 0·0130 \times 15·35 = 0·1995.$$
Heat lost due to CO formation $= 0·1995 \times 4,370$
$$= 872 \text{ B.T.U. per lb. of fuel.} \quad \text{Ans. } (c).$$

The overall efficiency would be increased by using an air pre-heater, economizer, and feed water heating ; also by the use of the hot exhaust gases for space heating or some other process, in addition to the economizer. The question of air distribution over the grate should be studied as an appreciable amount of CO is being produced. This may be due to a lack of secondary air and a blower may help. If a chain grate is used, the depth and speed of grate should be adjusted, the former increased and the latter decreased.

The advantage of a low dew-point is principally that at low partial pressures of the superheated steam the decrease in specific heat is much more rapid than the corresponding increase in the latent heat. This reduces the heat loss. Also, if the exhaust gases are used in an economizer or other form of heat interchanger, one of the principal difficulties in practice is the condensation of the H_2O in the heat interchanger, since this promotes rapid corrosion. This usually limits the quantity of heat which can be usefully abstracted from the exhaust gases and a low dew-point thus increases the potential availability of the hot gases,

9. *A boiler is supplied with coal which contains 15% of moisture. The dried coal analysed is found to have 87% by weight carbon, 4% hydrogen, 7% incombustible matter and 2% presumably oxygen by difference. The boiler is rated at 75% thermal efficiency and has to supply 12,000 lb. of steam per hr. at a temperature of 200° C. and pressure of 200 lb. per sq. in.*

Find :

(a) *the weight of coal used per hr., and*

(b) *the temperature and condition of the products of combustion if 18% of the heat value of the coal passes into the chimney.*

For convenience of calculation assume that—

1 lb. of carbon has a calorific value of 8,000 C.H.U.

1 lb. of hydrogen has a lower calorific value of 29,000 C.H.U.

1 lb. of air has a volume of 12·5 cu. ft. at N.T.P.

Temperature of hot-well 60° C. temperature of boiler-house 25° C.

Carbon dioxide content in flue gases 10% by volume.

Mean specific heat of dry flue gases 0·2.

(W.S.S.)

$$200° C. \equiv 392° F. ; \quad 60° C. \equiv 140° F. ; \quad 25° C. \equiv 77° F.$$

The saturation temperature at 200 lb. per sq. in. is 381·8° F. (from the steam tables), so that we must supply steam having approx. 10° F. of superheat ; $\therefore H_1 = 1,206$ B.T.U., very nearly.

Hot-well sensible heat, $h = 140 - 32 = 108$ B.T.U.

Heat to be supplied by combustion $= \dfrac{1}{0·75}(1,206 - 108)$

$$= 1,464 \text{ B.T.U. per lb. of steam}$$
$$= 1,464 \times 12,000 \text{ B.T.U. per hr.}$$

L.C.V. of dry coal $= \left[0·87 \times 8,000 + \left(0·04 - \dfrac{0·02}{8} \right) \times 29,000 \right] \times \dfrac{9}{5}$

$$= [6,960 + 1,088] \times \dfrac{9}{5}$$

$$= 14,490 \text{ B.T.U.}$$

L.C.V. of coal as fired $= 0·85 \times 14,490 = 12,310$ B.T.U. per lb.

$$\therefore \text{ Coal used} = \dfrac{1,464 \times 12,000}{12,310} = \underline{1,427 \text{ lb. per hr.}} \quad \text{Ans.}$$

By " condition " of the products of combustion is meant the analysis of the gases, including the wet gases. Now, the combustion equation in lb.mols becomes per 100 lb. of fuel as fired,

$$0.85 \times \frac{87}{12}[C] + 0.85 \times \frac{4}{2}[H_2] + \left(0.85 \times \frac{2}{32} + x\right)[O_2] + \frac{79}{21}x[N_2] + \frac{15}{18}[H_2O] \rightarrow$$

$$a[CO_2] + \left(0.85 \times \frac{87}{12} - a\right)[CO] + b[O_2] + \left(0.85 \times \frac{4}{2} + \frac{15}{18}\right)[H_2O] + \frac{79}{21}x[N_2]$$

where x lb.mols of O_2 are supplied in the form of air per 100 lb. of fuel as fired. We can write down two equations, one for O_2 balance and one for the CO_2 content in the dry flue gases. Since no data is available for a third equation, we shall have to assume that the CO content is negligible and $a = 0.85 \times \dfrac{87}{12} = 6.16$.

$$O_2 \text{ balance, } 0.85 \times \frac{2}{32} + x - 6.16 - \frac{0.85 \times \frac{4}{2}}{2} = b, \text{ i.e. } x - 6.957 = b \quad \text{(i)}$$

$$CO_2 \% \text{ in } dry \text{ gases,}^1 \quad \frac{6.16}{6.16 + b + 3.76x} = 0.10$$

i.e. $$5.544 = 0.1b + 0.376x \quad . \quad . \quad . \quad . \quad \text{(ii)}$$

From (i) and (ii) $x = 13.10$, $b = 6.143$. Hence we have this table,

Stuff	Prop. vols.	Prop. weights	lb. stuff per lb. flue gas
CO_2	6.16	271.0	0.1422 ⎫
O_2	6.143	196.8	0.1033 ⎬ Ans.
H_2O	2.533	45.6	0.0239 ⎬
N_2	49.30	1,392	0.7305 ⎭
		$\Sigma = 1,905.4$	$\Sigma = 0.9999$

$$\therefore \text{ lb. C per lb. of wet flue gas} = \frac{12}{44} \times 0.1422 = 0.0388$$

$$\therefore \text{ lb. of wet flue gas per lb. of coal fired} = \frac{0.85 \times 0.87}{0.0388} = 19.07$$

lb. H_2O per lb. of coal fired $= 0.15 + 9 \times 0.85 \times 0.04 = 0.456$

lb. of dry gases per lb. of coal fired $= 19.07 - 0.456 = 18.614$

Since 18% of the L.C.V. per lb. of coal as fired passes into flue gases,

$$0.18 \times 12,310 = 0.2 \times 18.614 \times (t - 77) + 0.456(H_{sup} - 45)$$

where H_{sup} is the total heat of the H_2O in flue, and 45 is the sensible heat corresponding to a boiler-house temperature of 77° F. On reference to the total heat–entropy chart it will be seen that, at 15 lb. per sq. in. and lower pressures, the total heat is practically proportional to the temperature, the increase in H from $t = 300°$ F. to $t = 800°$ F. being approx. 48 B.T.U. per 100° F., i.e. $C_p \simeq 0.48$.

---

¹ It is more realistic to assume that the CO_2 percentage given refers to the *dry* gases (not the total or wet gases) in view of the usual method of analysis.

$\therefore$ $0.18 \times 12{,}310 = 0.2 \times 18.614(t-77) + 0.456[1{,}151 + 0.48(t-213) - 45]$

$\qquad 2{,}215 = 3.72t - 287 + 458 - 0.219t$

$\qquad\quad = 3.50t + 171$

$$t = \frac{2{,}044}{3.50} = 584° \text{ F.} \quad \text{Ans.}$$

EXAMPLES

1. A coal had the following analysis by weight: C, 84; H, 5; O, 4; and ash, 7%.

When burned in a boiler, the resulting dry flue gas had the following percentage analysis, by volume: CO_2, 13.76; CO, 1.53; O_2, 4.25; N_2, 80.46.

It was found that, per lb. of coal fired, 0.012 lb. of carbon had fallen through the fire-bars.

Calculate:

(a) the weight of air used per lb. of coal;

(b) the total loss by incomplete combustion.

(Calorific value of C to CO_2 14,540 B.T.U. per lb. Calorific value of C to CO 4,370 B.T.U. per lb. Air contains 23.1% by weight of O_2.)   (*U. Lond.*)

[Use tabular method, i.e. C balance, since complete flue analysis is available; lb. C per lb. D.F.G. = 0.0604; lb. D.F.G. per lb. of fuel fired = 13.70; lb. of air per lb. of coal = 13.22; lb. C to CO per lb. of coal = 0.0828; loss = 174 + 842 = 1,016 B.T.U. per lb. of coal.]

2. The analysis by weight of the dry coal fed to a boiler is C, 84; H, 5; O, 5; and non-combustible matter 6%. Contained in the coal is 2% of hygroscopic moisture. The ash falling through the fire-bars is 6% of the weight of dry coal fired and contains 20% of unburnt carbon, but no hydrogen.

An analysis of the dry flue gas shows 11% by volume of CO_2 and 1% of CO.

Calculate the weights of each of the gases, including the moisture, entering the flues per lb. of dry coal fired, given that air contains 23.1% by weight of oxygen.   (*U. Lond.*)

[All per lb. of *dry* coal: useful C = 0.828 lb.; lb. C to CO_2 = 0.759 lb.; lb. CO_2 = 2.783 lb.; lb. CO = 0.161; lb. H_2O = 0.47; O_2 used from air = 2.466 lb.; by balancing both sides of combustion equation, free O_2 in flue = 1.42 lb.; lb. N_2 = 12.9.]

3. A fuel oil containing 84% of carbon and 12% of hydrogen by weight is burnt by means of a high-pressure air burner. The products of combustion, on analysis, are found to contain 12% of carbon dioxide.

(i) Calculate the proportion of air in excess of that required for theoretical combustion.

(ii) Estimate approximately the percentage of the potential heat of combustion which would be lost if the waste gases were at a temperature of 400° F.   (*U. Sheff.*)

[Assume: air contains 23% O_2 by wt.; 12% CO_2 by vol. in *dry* gases, no CO in products, fuel fired at 60° F., C.V. of C to CO_2 = 14,500 B.T.U. per lb., H.C.V. of H_2 = 62,000 B.T.U. per lb. *Per lb. of fuel:* 13.90 lb. of air for complete combustion; products are 3.08 lb. CO_2, 1.08 lb. H_2O needing 3.20 lb. O_2 together; for 12% CO_2 by vol. in D.F.G., lb. free O_2 in flue = 0.872; actual air supplied = 17.70 lb., i.e. 27.3% excess. lb. D.F.G. = 17.58; heat lost in flue = 1,435 + 1,310 = 2,745 B.T.U.; H.C.V. = 19,620 B.T.U.; % lost = 14.0.]

4. The following data were obtained from a trial on a water-tube boiler.

lb. of steam per hr. . . . 4,600
Boiler pressure (gauge) lb. per
  sq. in. 120
Coal fired per hr. . . . 580 lb.
Temperature of feed water . 140° F.
Temperature of Flue Gases . 500° F.
Weight of Ash per hr. . . 50 lb.
Carbon in Ash . . . . 7·2%
Ultimate analysis of coal :

	%
Moisture	5·0
Carbon	72·0
Hydrogen	4·8
Oxygen	8·0

Calorific value of dry coal per lb.
  (higher) . . . 12,700 B.T.U.

Flue Gas Analysis (average) : %
  Carbon Dioxide . . . . 9·6
  Oxygen . . . . 8·1
  Carbon Monoxide . . . . 0·1
  Nitrogen . . . . . . 82·2
Temperature of Air (assumed dry) 73°F.
Sensible heat of gases above 32° F.
  (B.T.U. per lb.mol) :

Temp.	CO_2	CO	O	N	H_2O
73° F.	372	289	289	292	329
500° F.	4,650	3,295	3,383	3,290	3,835

Latent heat of vaporization of
water . 18,700 B.T.U. per lb.mol.

Calculate the boiler efficiency, and heat losses and prepare a heat balance.

(*I.Chem.E.*)

[*Everything per lb. as fired :* H.C.V. = 12,060 B.T.U. ; useful lb. C = 0· 714 ; lb. D.F.G. = 18·30 ; lb. H_2O = 0·482 ; overall $\eta = 71·2\%$; lb. CO_2 = 2·59, lb. free O_2 = 1·59, lb. CO = 0·0172, lb. N_2 = 14·10. Heat Balance (showing losses) in B.T.U. per lb. of coal as fired, reckoned *above 73° F.*, CREDIT : Fuel = 12,060, Feed Water = 532. DEBIT : Steam gener. = 9,120, C in ash = 90, CO loss = 173, D.F.G. = 1,918, H_2O in gases = 594, Rad. etc. = 697 (by difference).

Assumptions : steam generated in dry sat. ; C.V. of C to CO_2 = 14,500 B.T.U. ; C.V. of C to CO = 4,430 B.T.U.]

5. A boiler burns coal, the percentage analysis of which, for dry coal, is C, 84 ; H_2, 4·5 ; remainder, ash. The coal as fired contains 6% moisture. The percentage volumetric analysis of the dry flue gases is CO_2, 13·9 ; CO, 0·3 ; O_2, 4·9. The water evaporated is 9·2 lb. per lb. of coal as fired. The flue gases pass to an economizer at a temperature of 750° F. and leave at 450° F. and then to an air preheater where the temperature of the flue gases is further reduced to 250° F.

Estimate the rise of temperature of the feed water in the economizer and the temperature of the air on leaving the preheater.

Specific heat of air = 0·24 ; specific heat of dry products of combustion = 0·26 ; specific heat of superheated steam = 0·48. Efficiency of heat transmission in economizer = 70% and in preheater = 80%. Air contains 23·1% by weight of O_2.

(*U. Lond.*)

[Per lb. as fired : 0·790 lb. C ; 14·07 lb. D.F.G. ; 0·441 lb. H_2O ; 13·62 lb. air. Temp. rise of feed = 88·5° F. Air temp. = 250° F., assuming 60° F. ambient temp.]

CHAPTER VIII

COMBUSTION UNDER SPECIAL CONDITIONS; MOLAR HEATS

1. Find the value of the adiabatic index γ and also that of R in $PV = wRT$, where w is the mass in lb., for a 10% weak mixture of hexane vapour, C_6H_{14}, and air, given that air contains 21% of O_2 by volume.

	Molar	
	C_v	C_p
C_6H_{14}	40·3	42·285
Diatomics	5·18	7·165

(*U. Lond.*)

For chemically correct combustion,

$$2[C_6H_{14}] + 19[O_2] + 19 \times \frac{79}{21}[N_2] \rightarrow 12[CO_2] + 14[H_2O] + 71\cdot5[N_2].$$

For a 10% weak mixture, we have only 90% of the fuel with the *same* amount of air as for chemically correct combustion. Thus,

$$1\cdot8[C_6H_{14}] + 19[O_2] + 71\cdot5[N_2] \rightarrow \cdots$$

Now,   mean $C_{v\,mol} \times \Sigma m = \Sigma(C_{v\,mol} \times m)$

i.e. mean $C_{v\,mol} = \dfrac{(40\cdot3 \times 1\cdot8) + (5\cdot18 \times 90\cdot5)}{1\cdot8 + 90\cdot5} = \dfrac{72\cdot55 + 468\cdot6}{92\cdot3}$

$$= 5\cdot81.$$

$C_{p\,mol}$ may be found from the data in a similar way; on the other hand R_{mol} may always be assumed, so that by (I,6a)

$$\text{mean } C_{p\,mol} = 1\cdot985 + 5\cdot81 = 7\cdot795$$

$$\gamma = \frac{7\cdot795}{5\cdot81} = 1\cdot341. \quad \text{Ans.}$$

Mean molecular weight $= \dfrac{1\cdot8 \times 86 + 19 \times 32 + 71\cdot5 \times 28}{1\cdot8 + 19 + 71\cdot5}$

$$= \frac{2762\cdot8}{92\cdot3} = 29\cdot95$$

by (I,9) $R = \dfrac{1\cdot985 \times 778}{29\cdot95}$

$$= 51\cdot6 \text{ ft.lb. per lb. } °F. \quad \text{Ans.}$$

2. *Define the mol and the universal gas constant.*

A cylinder contains a mixture of CH_4 and the theoretical minimum air required for complete combustion.   Determine :

(a) *the volumetric analysis of the mixture, i.e. the percentage, CH_4, O_2 and N_2;*

(b) *the apparent " molecular weight " of the mixture ;*

(c) *if the volume occupied at 14 lb. per sq. in. and 100° C. (212° F.) is 1·5 cu. ft., find the weight of mixture in the cylinder.*

Universal Gas Content = 2,779 ft.lb. per lb.mol per ° C. (or 1,544 ft.lb. per lb.mol per ° F.).

Assume that air contains 20·9% O_2 by volume.

(U.L.C.I.)

The lb.mol may be defined as a unit volume of a gas, occupying 358·7 cu. ft. at 14·7 lb. per sq. in. and 32° F. and having a mass equal to the molecular weight expressed in lb.

The universal gas constant may be defined as the product of the molecular weight of a gas and the characteristic constant of the gas. Alternatively, the universal gas constant represents the amount of work done at S.T.P. to heat a lb.mol of gas through one degree of temperature at constant pressure over and above the work required to do this at constant volume (cf. equation I,6a).

For theoretically complete combustion, in lb.mols,

$$1[CH_4] + 2[O_2] \; + 2 \times \frac{79 \cdot 1}{20 \cdot 9}[N_2] \rightarrow 1[CO_2] + 2[H_2O] + 7 \cdot 565[N_2]$$

i.e. $1 \ldots + 2 \ldots + 7 \cdot 565 \ldots \rightarrow$

(a) CH_4, by vol. $= \dfrac{1}{10 \cdot 565} \times 100 = 9 \cdot 46\%$

O_2, by vol. $= \dfrac{2}{10 \cdot 565} \times 100 = 18 \cdot 92\%$ }Ans.

N_2, by vol. $= \dfrac{7 \cdot 565}{10 \cdot 565} \times 100 = 71 \cdot 6\%$

(b) Mean molecular weight $= \dfrac{(1 \times 16) + (2 \times 32) + (7 \cdot 565 \times 28)}{1 + 2 + 7 \cdot 565}$

$$= \frac{292}{10 \cdot 565} = \underline{27 \cdot 63.} \quad \text{Ans.}$$

(c) By (I,9)

Characteristic constant $R = \dfrac{1,544}{27 \cdot 63} = 55 \cdot 85$ ft.lb. per lb. ° F.

By (I,7) $w = \dfrac{PV}{RT} = \dfrac{14 \times 144 \times 1 \cdot 5}{55 \cdot 85 \times 672}$

$$= \underline{0 \cdot 0806 \text{ lb.}} \quad \text{Ans.}$$

3. *The exhaust from an engine has the "weight" analysis shown.*

Gas	% by weight	Molecular weight	Molecular C_v B.T.U. per lb.mol	Universal gas constant
CO_2 . . .	15·6	44	9·08	1·985
O_2	4·3	32	5·25	
N_2	73·35	28	5·25	
H_2O . . .	6·75	18	6·60	

The gas is passed through a heat exchanger at 15 lb. per sq. in. for heating a building, the inlet temperature being 1,050° F.

Find :

(a) *the partial pressure of the H_2O in the hot exhaust gas ;*

(b) *the heat given up per lb. of gas in cooling to 150° F. (U. Lond.)*

We know from (I,13) that the partial pressure is proportional to the number of lb.mols, i.e.

$$\frac{\text{p.p. of } H_2O}{\text{total pressure}} = \frac{\text{lb.mols of } H_2O}{\text{total no. of lb.mols}}$$

$$\text{p.p. of } H_2O = 15 \times \frac{\dfrac{6·75}{18}}{\dfrac{15·6}{44} + \dfrac{4·3}{32} + \dfrac{73·35}{28} + \dfrac{6·75}{18}}$$

$$= 15 \times \frac{0·3750}{0·3546 + 0·1344 + 2·6200 + 0·3750}$$

$$= 15 \times \frac{0·3750}{3·4840} = \underline{1·615 \text{ lb. per sq. in.}} \quad \text{Ans. (a).}$$

By (I,6a) $\qquad C_{p \, mol} = 1·985 + C_{v \, mol}.$

Heat given up in heat exchanger at constant pressure per lb. of gas

$$= \Sigma \text{lb. stuff per lb. gas} \times \frac{C_{p \, mol}}{\text{molecular weight}} \times (1,050 - 150), \text{ cf. (I,10) for } C_p$$

$$= \left[\frac{0·156}{44}(9·08 + 1·985) + \left(\frac{0·043}{32} + \frac{73·35}{28} \right)(5·25 + 1·985) \right.$$

$$\left. + \frac{0·0675}{18}(6·60 + 1·985) \right] \times (1,050 - 150)$$

$$= [(0·003546 \times 11·065) + (0·02754 \times 7·235) + (0·00375 \times 8·58)] \times 900$$

$$= 0·2706 \times 900 \qquad\qquad = \underline{243·5 \text{ B.T.U. per lb. of gas.}} \quad \text{Ans. (b).}$$

Note : This method is permissible for the heat given up by the H_2O, since the saturation temperature at the partial pressure of the steam is approximately 118° F. (see steam tables), so that at 150° F. the steam is still superheated.

A.T.E. L

4. *The combustion at constant volume of 1 lb.mol of benzene* (C_6H_6) *with the necessary* O_2 *liberates 1,403,000 B.T.U. if both* C_6H_6 *and the resulting* H_2O *are in liquid form at 60° F.*

(a) *Given that* $R = 1·985$ *and that the latent heat of benzene at 60° F. and constant pressure is 14,600 B.T.U. per lb.mol, find the heat released at constant volume if the* C_6H_6 *were originally in the form of vapour at 60° F. and the* H_2O *again in the liquid form.*

(b) *Given that the latent heat of* H_2O *at 60° F. and constant pressure is 1,060 B.T.U. per lb., how much heat would be released at constant volume if the* C_6H_6 *were originally in the form of vapour at 60° F. and the* H_2O *also in the vapour form at 60° F. ?*   (U. Lond.)

The information contained in the question may be conveniently written in the form of a combustion equation, thus

$$1[C_6H_6] \text{ liqu. at } 60° \text{F.} + 7·5[O_2] + \ldots \xrightarrow[\substack{\text{const.}\\\text{vol.}}]{}$$

$$6[CO_2] + 3[H_2O] \text{ liqu. at } 60° \text{F.} + 1,403,000 \text{ B.T.U.}$$

(a) In this case the fuel is to be supplied in the form of *vapour* at 60° F. ; ∴ available heat will be greater by the amount of the latent heat which the fuel already contains and which will therefore not have to be supplied by the combustion process.   Also, the combustion is to take place at constant volume so that we shall require the latent heat at constant volume, viz.

L.H.$_V$ = L.H.$_P$ — Heat Units required to change the volume at constant pressure.

At 60° F., $\text{L.H.}_V = 14,600 - \dfrac{P(V - V_L)}{J}$

And neglecting the relatively small volume of the liquid V_L,

by (I,7a) $\dfrac{PV}{J} = mR_{mol}T$

$$= 1 \times 1·985 \times 520 = 1,030 \text{ B.T.U. per lb.mol.}$$
$$\therefore \text{ L.H.}_V = 14,600 - 1,030 = 13,570 \text{ B.T.U. per lb.mol.}$$

Hence,

$$1[C_6H_6] \text{ } vap. \text{ at } 60° \text{F.} + 7·5[O_2] \ldots \xrightarrow[\substack{\text{const.}\\\text{vol.}}]{}$$

$$6[CO_2] + 3[H_2O] \text{ liqu. at } 60° \text{F.} + 1,403,000 + 13,570$$

i.e.   Heat released = 1,416,570 B.T.U. per lb.mol.   Ans.

(b) If the H_2O is in the form of vapour at 60° F., less heat will be available by the amount of latent heat required at constant volume to change 3 lb.mols from liquid at 60° F. into vapour at 60° F.

$$\text{L.H.}_\text{V} \text{ of } H_2O = \text{L.H.}_\text{P} - \frac{PV}{J}.$$

Now, 1 lb.mol $H_2O = 18$ lb., and $\dfrac{PV}{J} = 1{,}030$ B.T.U. per lb.mol at 60° F., as before.

∴ L.H.$_\text{V}$ of $H_2O = 18 \times 1{,}060 - 1{,}030 = 18{,}050$ B.T.U. per lb.mol.

Hence, $1[C_6H_6]$ *vap.* at 60° F. $+ 7\cdot5[O_2]$ . . . $\xrightarrow[\substack{\text{const.}\\ \text{vol.}}]{}$

$$6[CO_2] + 3[H_2O] \text{ *vap.* at } 60° F. + 1{,}416{,}570 - 3 \times 18{,}050$$

i.e.   Heat released $= 1{,}362{,}420$ B.T.U. per lb.mol.   Ans.

5. *A gas has the following percentage composition by volume: Hydrogen, 29; CH_4, 2; CO, 11; CO_2, 16; Nitrogen, 42.*

Calculate the volume of air theoretically sufficient for the complete combustion of 1 cu. ft. of this gas, and the volume of the " dry " products of combustion at the same temperature and pressure as the gas and air. Calculate also the lower calorific value of the gas, given that the calorific value of CO is 342 B.T.U. per cu. ft., and the lower calorific values of hydrogen and CH_4 are 291 and 963 B.T.U. per cu. ft. respectively.

(Air contains 21% of oxygen by volume.)

(*I.Mech.E.*)

Working in volumes, for theoretically complete combustion,

$$29[H_2] + 2[CH_4] + 11[CO] + 16[CO_2] + 0\cdot21x[O_2] + (42 + 0\cdot79x)[N_2] \rightarrow$$
$$a[CO_2] + b[H_2O] + (42 + 0\cdot79x)[N_2]$$

where x is the air-fuel ratio by volume (per 100 vols. of gas).

For carbon balance, $2 + 11 + 16 = a$,   i.e. $a = 29$.
For hydrogen balance, $29 + (2 \times 2) = b$,   i.e. $b = 33$.

For oxygen balance, $\dfrac{11}{2} + 16 + 0\cdot21x = 29 + \dfrac{33}{2}$

$$\therefore x = \frac{24\cdot0}{0\cdot21} = 114\cdot3$$

i.e.   1·143 cu. ft. of air are theoretically sufficient per cu. ft. of gas.   Ans.

The " dry " products per 100 vols. of gas are 29 vols. CO_2 and 132·3 vols. of N_2. At the same temperature and pressure as the gas and air we have

$$\frac{29 + 132\cdot3}{100} = 1\cdot613 \text{ cu. ft. dry products.} \quad \text{Ans.}$$

L.C.V. of the gas $= (291 \times 0\cdot29) + (963 \times 0\cdot02) + (342 \times 0\cdot11)$
$$= 84\cdot4 + 19\cdot3 + 37\cdot6 = 141\cdot3 \text{ B.T.U. per cu. ft.} \quad \text{Ans.}$$

6. *Find the weight of hexane* C_6H_{14}, *which would be required to saturate 1 lb. of dry air at 32° F., if the pressure of the mixture is 14·7 lb. per sq. in., and the vapour pressure of the hexane at this temperature is 1·965 in. of mercury. When the mixture is chemically correct for complete combustion, what is the percentage of full saturation?*

Calculate the higher and the lower calorific values of the chemically correct mixture per cu. ft. at 32° F. and 14·7 lb. per sq. in.

$R_{mol} = 1,544$ *ft.lb. F. units. H.C.V. of hexane* $= 20,750$ *B.T.U. per lb.*

(*R for air* $= 53·3$ *ft.lb. F. units.*)

(*U. Lond.*)

Saturation Pressure of hexane at 32° F. $= 1·965 \times 0·49 = 0·963$ lb. per sq. in. (cf. list of constants (p. vii) for 0·49).

$$\therefore \text{ p.p. of air} = 14·7 - 0·963 = 13·737 \text{ lb. per sq. in.}$$

By (I,9) and using the figure of 1,544 for R_{mol} in ft.lb. units as quoted in the question,

$$R \text{ for hexane} = \frac{1,544}{(72 + 14)} = 17·98 \text{ ft.lb. per lb. } °F.$$

By (I,7) the specific volume of hexane at 32° F. and a pressure of 0·963 lb. per sq. in. is

$$V = \frac{wRT}{P} = \frac{17·98 \times 492}{0·963 \times 144} = 63·9 \text{ cu. ft. per lb. hexane}$$

But also for dry air,

$$V = \frac{wRT}{P} = \frac{53·3 \times 492}{13·737 \times 144} = 13·2 \text{ cu. ft. per lb. of dry air.}$$

But Dalton's Law of Partial Pressures also tells us that, for a mixture of gases, each separate gas occupies the *whole* volume, so that the hexane vapour C_6H_{14} will also occupy 13·2 cu. ft. when associated with 1 lb. of dry air.

$$\therefore \text{ Weight of hexane per lb. of dry air} = \frac{13·2}{63·9} = \underline{0·207 \text{ lb.}} \quad \text{Ans.}$$

This is the weight of hexane to saturate 1 lb. of dry air, as it is the largest quantity which could associate with 1 lb. of air at the prevailing temperature and pressure. Students not familiar with this application of Dalton's Law should turn to chapter XI.

For chemically correct combustion, we have this volumetric equation

$$1[C_6H_{14}] + 9\tfrac{1}{2}[O_2] + \ldots [N_2] \rightarrow 6[CO_2] + 7[H_2O] + \ldots [N_2]$$

i.e. 86 lb. $+ 9·5 \times 32$ lb. $+ \ldots \rightarrow \ldots + 7 \times 18$ lb. $+ \ldots$

$\therefore$ 1 lb. hexane needs $\dfrac{304}{86}$ lb. O_2, i.e. $\dfrac{304}{86} \times \dfrac{100}{23 \cdot 1} = 15 \cdot 33$ lb. of air.

Weight of hexane per lb. of air $= \dfrac{1}{15 \cdot 33} = 0 \cdot 0652$ lb., for chemically correct mixture.

$$\therefore \ 100 \times \dfrac{0 \cdot 0652}{0 \cdot 207} = 31 \cdot 4\% \text{ of full saturation.} \quad \text{Ans.}$$

Since the chemically correct mixture is not saturated, and the total pressure is still 14·7 lb. per sq. in., the partial pressure of the hexane is directly proportional to the degree of saturation. This follows from the relation $P = \dfrac{w\mathrm{R}T}{V}$, for a common value of T ($= 492°$ F. here), R being a constant for hexane under all conditions and V the volume occupied by the hexane, i.e. the volume occupied by 1 lb. of air. We already know that p.p. $= 0 \cdot 963$ lb. per sq. in. at $32°$ F. and that $0 \cdot 207$ lb. of hexane are then required to saturate 1 lb. of air. If w is now reduced to $0 \cdot 314$ of $0 \cdot 207$, then P must be reduced in the same ratio for the equation to remain correct,

i.e.   New p.p. of hexane $= 0 \cdot 963 \times 0 \cdot 314 = 0 \cdot 302$ lb. per sq. in.

$\therefore$ New p.p. of air $= 14 \cdot 7 - 0 \cdot 302 = 14 \cdot 398$ lb. per sq. in.

By (I,7) for air, $V = \dfrac{15 \cdot 33 \times 53 \cdot 3 \times 492}{14 \cdot 398 \times 144} = 194 \cdot 0$ cu. ft. for the 15·33 lb. of air per lb. of hexane contained in the chemically correct mixture, and this is also the volume occupied by this 1 lb. of hexane in the mixture.

$$\therefore \ \underline{\text{H.C.V.}} = \dfrac{20,750}{194} = \underline{107 \text{ B.T.U. per cu. ft. of mixture.}} \quad \text{Ans.}$$

The above combustion equation shows that $7 \times 18 = 126$ lb. of H_2O are produced for 86 lb. of hexane, i.e. $\dfrac{126}{86}$ lb. of H_2O per lb. of hexane, and this steam also occupies 194·0 cu. ft. per lb. of hexane.

$$\therefore \ \text{L.C.V.} = 107 - \dfrac{126}{86} \times \dfrac{1,055}{194}$$

$$= 107 - 7 \cdot 9$$

$$= \underline{99 \cdot 1 \text{ B.T.U. per cu. ft. of mixture.}} \quad \text{Ans.}$$

The meaning of the figure 1,055 B.T.U. per lb. H_2O has been explained in example 7, chapter VII.

7. *A closed vessel contains a mixture of dry air and hexane vapour* (C_6H_{14}), *the proportions being those necessary for complete combustion. The pressure of the mixture is 20 lb. per sq. in. and the temperature 212° F. What is the volume per lb. of the mixture?*

After complete combustion, the temperature is allowed to fall until condensation of the water vapour just commences. Find the temperature and pressure when this will occur.

(*Air contains 23·1% oxygen by weight.*)

(*U. Lond.*)

The reaction will take place according to the relation for chemically correct combustion,

$$1[C_6H_{14}] + 9 \cdot 5[O_2] + 9 \cdot 5 \times \frac{0 \cdot 792}{0 \cdot 208}[N_2] \rightarrow 6[CO_2] + 7[H_2O] + 36 \cdot 2[N_2]$$

where   % O_2 in air by vol. $= \dfrac{\dfrac{23 \cdot 1}{32}}{\dfrac{23 \cdot 1}{32} + \dfrac{76 \cdot 9}{28}} \times 100 = 20 \cdot 8\%$.

Total mols in mixture $= 1 + 9 \cdot 5 + 36 \cdot 2 = 46 \cdot 7$.

By (I,13)

$$\left.\begin{array}{l} \text{p.p. of } C_6H_{14} = \dfrac{1}{46 \cdot 7} \times 20 = 0 \cdot 428 \text{ lb. per sq. in.} \\[3mm] \text{,, ,, } \quad O_2 = \dfrac{9 \cdot 5}{46 \cdot 7} \times 20 = 4 \cdot 07 \text{ lb. per sq. in.} \\[3mm] \text{,, ,, } \quad N_2 = \dfrac{36 \cdot 2}{46 \cdot 7} \times 20 = 15 \cdot 50 \text{ lb. per sq. in.} \end{array}\right\} \Sigma \text{p.p.} = 20.$$

From (I,7) and (I,9)

$$w = \frac{P}{RT} = \frac{P \times \text{mol. wt.}}{1 \cdot 985 \times 778 \times 672} \text{ lb. per cu. ft.}$$

Weight of $C_6H_{14} = \dfrac{0 \cdot 428 \times 86 \times 144}{1,038,000} = 0 \cdot 00510$ lb. per cu. ft.,

and ,,   ,, $O_2 = \dfrac{4 \cdot 07 \times 144 \times 32}{1,038,000} = 0 \cdot 01806$ lb. per cu. ft.,

and ,,   ,, $N_2 = \dfrac{15 \cdot 50 \times 144 \times 28}{1,038,000} = 0 \cdot 06020$ lb. per cu. ft.,

∴ Total weight per cu. ft. of mixture $= 0 \cdot 08336$ lb.

∴ Volume per lb. of mixture $= \dfrac{1}{0 \cdot 08336} = 11 \cdot 99$ cu. ft.   Ans.

Note that Dalton's Law tells us that *each* gas occupies the *whole* volume ; i.e. the weight per cu. ft. of a certain gas at a given p.p. is the same as the weight of that same gas at the same p.p. per cu. ft. of the mixture.

When condensation occurs, the steam is just dry saturated, i.e. the volume per lb. of products is also the specific volume of steam, V_s at the appropriate partial pressure.

Now, total weight of products $= 6 \times 44 + 7 \times 18 + 36 \cdot 2 \times 28$
$$= 264 + 126 + 1{,}014$$
$$= 1{,}404 \text{ lb., containing 126 lb. of } H_2O.$$

By conservation of mass,
actual lb. of saturated H_2O per cu. ft. of mixture (i.e. of H_2O)

$$= 0 \cdot 08336 \times \frac{126}{1{,}404} = 0 \cdot 007485$$

$$\therefore \quad \frac{1}{0 \cdot 007485} = 133 \cdot 5 \text{ cu. ft. per lb. of dry steam.}$$

The steam tables give these data :

P_s	t_s	V_s
2·6	135·9	135·8
2·8	138·8	126·7

By interpolation, $V_s = 133 \cdot 5$ when $P_s = 2 \cdot 651$ and $t_s = 136 \cdot 6$,

i.e. <u>Condensation will commence at $136 \cdot 6°$ F.</u> Ans.

The simplest way to find the total pressure of the products is to remember that p.p.'s are proportional to the number of lb.mols (cf. I, 13), or

$$\frac{\text{p.p. of A}}{\text{Total pressure}} = \frac{m_A}{\Sigma m}$$

$$\therefore \quad \text{Total pressure} = (6 + 7 + 36 \cdot 2) \times \frac{2 \cdot 651}{7}$$

$$= \frac{49 \cdot 2 \times 2 \cdot 651}{7}$$

$$= \underline{18 \cdot 65 \text{ lb. per sq. in.}} \quad \text{Ans.}$$

8. *The lower calorific value of benzene C_6H_6 is 9,640 C.H.U. per lb. Find the volumetric heat in C.H.U. per cu. ft. of air-benzene mixture at S.T.P. when in the proportion giving chemically correct combustion. Neglect the volume occupied by the fuel. What is the percentage change of volume on combustion ?*

(*R for air = 96.*)   (*U. Manch.*)

9,640 C.H.U. per lb. $\equiv$ 17,350 B.T.U. per lb.

For chemically correct combustion,

$$1[C_6H_6] + 7\cdot5[O_2] + 7\cdot5 \times \frac{79}{21}[N_2] \rightarrow 6[CO_2] + 3[H_2O] + 28\cdot2[N_2],$$

taking the percentage of O_2 in air as 21% by vol.; i.e. $(1 + 7\cdot5 + 28\cdot2)$ lb.mols have the calorific value of 1 lb.mol of benzene, viz. $(17,350 \times 78)$ B.T.U.

$$\therefore \text{ Heat Value of 1 lb.mol of correct mixture} = \frac{17,350 \times 78}{36\cdot7}$$

$$= 36,900 \text{ B.T.U.}$$

But we know that 1 lb.mol of any gas, or gaseous mixture, occupies 358·7 cu. ft. at S.T.P.

$$\therefore \text{ Heat Value of 1 cu. ft. of correct mixture at S.T.P.} = \frac{36,900}{358\cdot7}$$

$$= \underline{102\cdot8 \text{ B.T.U.}} \quad \text{Ans.}$$

Mols of mixture before combustion $= 1 + 7\cdot5 + 28\cdot2 = 36\cdot7$
Mols of products after combustion $= 6 + 3 \quad + 28\cdot2 = 37\cdot2$

$$\therefore \text{ Percentage Change} = \frac{37\cdot2 - 36\cdot7}{36\cdot7} \times 100 = \underline{1\cdot36\%} \text{ (increase).} \quad \text{Ans.}$$

Note, the use of the term " volumetric heat " in the question is not in accordance with the definition given on page 10 and as used throughout this book. However, the question suggests that the heat value is required, as evaluated above.

9. *An alcohol fuel which may be considered as C_2H_6O has a latent heat of 365 B.T.U. per lb., and a net calorific value of 12,690 B.T.U. per lb. of liquid. The air supply is preheated by a muff on the engine exhaust manifold before being carburetted.*

Estimate (a) *the gross and net calorific values per cu. ft. of chemically correct mixture in the induction system if the pressure is 14 lb. per sq. in. and the temperature 65° F., the fuel being completely vaporized, and* (b) *the temperature to which the air must be heated so as to maintain the induction temperature at 65° F., the liquid fuel being also supplied at 65° F.*

Air contains 23·1% O_2 by weight, and C_p for air is 0·24. (*U. Lond.*)

For a chemically correct mixture, in volumes,

$$1[C_2H_6O] + 3[O_2] + 3 \times \frac{0.792}{0.208}[N_2] \rightarrow 2[CO_2] + 3[H_2O] + 11.42[N_2]$$

where   % O_2 in air by vol. $= \dfrac{\dfrac{23.1}{32}}{\dfrac{23.1}{32} + \dfrac{76.9}{28}} \times 100 = 20.8\%.$

1 lb.mol occupies 358·7 cu. ft. at 32° F. and 14·7 lb. per sq. in., $\therefore$ at 65° F. and 14 lb. per sq. in.,

$$1 \text{ lb.mol} = 358.7 \times \frac{14.7}{14} \times \frac{525}{492} = 402.0 \text{ cu. ft.}$$

Total lb.mols in mixture $= 1 + 3 + 11.42 = 15.42.$

Since the fuel is already vaporized in the induction system, the L.C.V. must include its latent heat which has already been added by the preheated air,

i.e.   L.C.V. of fuel $= (12,690 + 365) \times 46$ B.T.U. per lb.mol of fuel,

$\because$ molecular wt. of fuel $= 24 + 6 + 16 = 46.$

$$\therefore \text{ Required L.C.V.} = \frac{13,055 \times 46}{15.42 \times 402.0}$$

$$= 96.9 \text{ B.T.U. per cu. ft. of mixture.} \text{ Ans.}$$

$$\text{H.C.V.} = 13,055 + 9 \times \frac{6}{46} \times 1,055 = 13,055 + 1,238$$

$$= 14,293 \text{ B.T.U. per lb.}$$

$$\therefore \text{ Required H.C.V.} = 96.9 \times \frac{14,293}{13,055}, \quad \text{or} \quad \frac{14,293 \times 46}{15.42 \times 402.0}$$

$$= 106.0 \text{ B.T.U. per cu. ft. of mixture.} \text{ Ans.}$$

Note, $9 \times \dfrac{6}{46} =$ lb. of H_2O produced per lb. of fuel, and 1,055 is the latent heat of water taken at 60° F. in accordance with standard practice (cf. page 137).

Since the mean molecular weight of air is 28·9,

lb. of air supplied per lb. of fuel $= \dfrac{(3 + 11.42)28.9}{46} = 9.06.$

Hence, neglecting heat losses in the muff,

$$9.06 \times 0.24 \times (t - 65) = 365 \times 1$$

$$t = 65 + \frac{365}{9.06 \times 0.24} = 65 + 167.8,$$

i.e. Temp. of preheated air $= 232.8°$ F.   Ans.

EXAMPLES

1. A combustible mixture of air and octane vapour (C_8H_{18}), the air being 15% in excess of that required for chemically correct combustion, is compressed adiabatically through a volume ratio of 6 to 1. The temperature at the start of compression is 120° F.

Given that the volumetric heats of octane vapour and air are 40 and 5·2 B.T.U. per lb.mol respectively, find :

(a) the value of the adiabatic index for the mixture,

(b) the work required per lb. during the compression only.

Air contains 21% O_2 by volume. $R_{mol} = 1·985$.   (*U. Lond.*)

[With 15% excess air, 14·38 lb.mols of O_2 and 54·1 lb.mols of N_2 are supplied per lb.mol of C_8H_{18} ; mean $C_{v\,mol} = 5·70$; $\gamma = \underline{1·348}$; mean mol. wt. $= 30·1$; R for mixture $= 51·25$ ft.lb. per lb. ° F. ; by (I,17) $T_2 = 1,084°$ F. abs. ; $\underline{W.D.}$ per lb. $= 74,200$ ft.lb.]

2. A volatile fuel, formula C_7H_{16}, is mixed with the correct amount of air required for its complete combustion. Calculate (a) the volume (at 14·7 lb. per sq. in. and 32° F.) of mixture formed per lb. of fuel, (b) the mean molecular weight and the mean gas constant for the mixture before and after combustion. Take the universal gas constant as 1,545 ft.lb. per lb.mol × deg. F. and the composition of air as $23O_2$ to $77N_2$ by weight or $21O_2$ to $79N_2$ by volume. Atomic weights : carbon, 12 ; hydrogen, 1 ; oxygen, 16 ; nitrogen, 14.   (*I.Mech.E.*)

[lb. of mixture per lb. of fuel $= 16·13$; mean R before comb. $= 51·2$ ft.lb. per lb. ° F. ; (a) $\underline{192\text{ cu. ft}}$; (b) before : $\underline{30·2}$, $R = \underline{51·2}$; after : $\underline{28·6}$, $R = \underline{54·0}$.]

3. The molecular weight of a certain combustible gas is 24·8. What is the weight of 0·79 cu. ft. of this gas at 0° C. and 14·7 lb. per sq. in. ?   (Universal Gas Constant $= 2,779$ ft.lb. per lb.mol per ° C.)

This weight of gas is contained in 0·49 lb. of a gas-air mixture. Taking the molecular weight of air as 28·9, estimate the proportion by volume of gas to air.

If the specific heat at constant pressure for this mixture is 0·24, what is the value of γ, the index for adiabatic compression ?   (*U.L.C.I.*)

[R for gas $= 62·2$ ft.lb. per lb. ° F. ; lb. of gas $= \underline{0·0547}$; $\underline{\text{gas to air}}$ ratio $= 1 : \underline{6·85}$; mean mol. wt. of mixture $= 28·4$; R for mixture $= 54·4$ ft.lb. per lb. ° F. ; $\gamma = \underline{1·41}$.]

4. A mixture of octane C_8H_{18} and ethyl alcohol C_2H_5OH, in the proportions of 1 molecule of octane to 2 molecules of alcohol, is completely burnt in a supply of air 20% in excess of that required for complete combustion. Determine the volumetric analysis of the *dry* exhaust products.

For air, volumetric analysis, oxygen $= 20·9\%$, nitrogen $79·1\%$.   (*I.C.E.*)

[18·5 lb.mols of O_2 from air for complete combustion ; answers : $\underline{12\%\ CO_2}$, $\underline{3·7\%\ O_2}$, $\underline{84·3\%\ N_2}$.]

5. One cu. ft. of methane at S.T.P. is burnt completely at constant volume with the chemically correct amount of air. Calculate the maximum temperature and pressure attained, neglecting dissociation and heat loss to walls, given that the lower Calorific Value of methane is 961 B.T.U. per cu. ft.

The volumetric heats of CO_2, H_2O and N_2 are respectively :

$6·55 + 0·00187T$
$5·35 + 0·00142T$ }heat units per mol.
$4·73 + 0·00056T$

T is in ° F. abs.   (*U. Dur.*)

[Assume air contains 21% O_2 by vol. ; comb. equation shows that there is no molecular increase or decrease (10·52 lb.mols per lb.mol of CH_4) ; $C_{v \, mol}$ for mixture = 5·02 + 0·000848T ; mean $C_{v \, mol}$ for mixture between $T_1°$ F. abs. and 492° F. = 5·229 + 0·000424T_1 ;   L.C.V. = 344,800 B.T.U. per lb.mol. of fuel = 32,750 B.T.U. per lb.mol of mixture ; $T_1 = 4,960°$ F. abs. ; $t = 4,500°$ F. ; $P_1 = 148$ lb. per sq. in.]

6. Assuming that a petrol is pure hexane (C_6H_{14}), calculate :

(a) the weight of petrol required to saturate 1 lb. of air at S.T.P. (32° F. and 14·7 lb. per sq. in.),

(b) the degree of saturation if an air-petrol mixture contains 30% more air than the minimum for chemically complete combustion.

Assume vapour pressure of hexane to be 1·97 in. Hg at 32° F.   Universal gas constant = 1·985.   Equivalent molecular weight of air = 28·9.   (*U. Lond.*)

[(a) Partial pressure of air = 13·735 lb. per sq. in. ; volume per lb. of air = 13·30 cu. ft. by I,7 ; again, by (I,7), lb. of petrol per lb. of air = 0·209.

(b) Chemically correct combustion : 15·3 lb. of air per lb. of petrol ; with 30% excess air, there are 0·050 lb. of petrol per lb. of air ; i.e. 24% of saturation.]

7. Explain carefully why the calorific value of a fuel measured in a constant volume bomb calorimeter may differ from the calorific value realized in burning the fuel at constant pressure, the initial and final temperature being the same in both cases.

The combustion of 1 lb.mol of liquid benzene at constant volume and 64° F. is represented by the equation :

C_6H_6 (liqu.) + 7·5O_2 = 6CO_2 + 3H_2O (liqu.) + 1,404,000 B.T.U.

The latent heats of benzene and steam at constant pressure and 64° F. are 14,650 and 18,900 B.T.U. per lb.mol respectively.

Determine the heat of combustion of benzene at 64° F. under the following conditions :

(i) C_6H_6 (vap.) + 7·5O_2 = 6CO_2 + 3H_2O (liqu.) $\Big\}$ at constant volume.
(ii) C_6H_6 (vap.) + 7·5O_2 = 6CO_2 + 3H_2O (vap.)

(iii) C_6H_6 (liqu.) + 7·5O_2 = 6CO_2 + 3H_2O (liqu.) $\Big\}$ at constant pressure.
(iv) C_6H_6 (vap.) + 7·5O_2 = 6CO_2 + 3H_2O (vap.)

(*U. Lond.*)

[Fuel, L.H. at constant vol. = 13,610 B.T.U. per lb.mol ; H_2O ditto = 17,860 ; (i) 1,417,610 ;   (ii) 1,364,030 ;   (iii) 1,402,960 ;   (iv) 1,361,950, all in B.T.U. per lb.mol of fuel.]

CHAPTER IX

GAS PRODUCERS

1. *Give a short account of the reactions which may take place in a suction-gas producer supplied with carbon, air and water.*

Carbon in the form of coke with 12% ash, is used as a fuel in a gas producer. Water is supplied at 60° F., and the resulting reactions of both the water and the air with the carbon produce CO, there being no CO_2 in the gas produced. The generation of the steam and its subsequent dissociation together absorb 94% of the heat liberated by the partial combustion of the carbon with the air.

Estimate the weights of air and water required per lb. of coke, and find the volumetric composition of the gas produced.

The gross or higher calorific value of hydrogen is 62,000 B.T.U. per lb., and the heat produced by burning 1 lb. carbon to CO is 4,450 B.T.U. per lb. Air contains 23·1% oxygen by weight, and the temperature of the gas may be neglected. (*U. Lond.*)

The action of a gas producer consists in producing a gas having the greatest possible CO and H_2 contents, i.e. the greatest calorific value, consistent with practical considerations affecting the production and handling.

The primary reactions which usually take place are

$$C + O_2 = CO_2 + \text{Heat}$$
$$CO_2 + C = 2CO - \text{Heat}.$$

These equations represent the burning of carbon to CO_2, and the subsequent reduction of the latter into CO. The net amount of heat liberated by these two events is about 4,400 B.T.U. per lb. of carbon burnt and this would tend to produce a temperature in the producer so high that the reactions could not continue without resulting in damage to the producer. In order to absorb this surplus heat a controlled amount of water is usually supplied to the producer; this water enters into a secondary reaction with the incandescent carbon either according to

$$C + 2H_2O = CO_2 + 2H_2 - \text{Heat}$$
or
$$C + H_2O = CO + H_2 - \text{Heat},$$

depending on the prevailing temperatures and the amount of oxygen available. By controlling the supply of water per lb. of carbon, the temperature may be kept within the required limits. Further details may be found in the standard textbooks.

156

In this example,
$$2C + O_2 = 2CO$$
i.e.
$$1 \text{ lb. } C + \frac{4}{3}O_2 = \frac{7}{3}CO + 4,450 \text{ B.T.U.,}$$

$\therefore$ Heat absorbed by steam generation and dissociation per lb. of C
$$= 0.94 \times 4,450 = 4,183 \text{ B.T.U.}$$

Since no CO_2 is to be produced, the H_2O reacts as
$$C + H_2O = CO + H_2$$
i.e. 12 lb. C+18 lb. H_2O = 28 lb. CO+2 lb. $H_2-2\times 62,000+12\times 4,450$

(Note, the H.C.V. for hydrogen is taken since the H_2O is supplied in the form of water and must be evaporated before dissociation.)

i.e. 12 lb. C and 18 lb. H_2O absorb $(124,000 - 53,600) = 70,600$ B.T.U.

$\therefore \left(12 \times \dfrac{4,183}{70,600}\right)$ lb. C and $\left(18 \times \dfrac{4,183}{70,600}\right)$ lb. H_2O absorb 4,183 B.T.U.

i.e.   0·711   lb. C and   1·066   lb. H_2O absorb 4,183 B.T.U.

whence for primary and secondary reactions to balance,

$$(1 + 0.711) \text{ lb. } C + \left(\frac{4}{3} \text{ lb.}\right)O_2 + \left(\frac{4}{3} \times \frac{76\cdot9}{23\cdot1}\right) \text{ lb. } N_2 + 1.066 \text{ lb. } H_2O$$

$$= \left(\frac{7}{3} + 28 \times \frac{4,183}{70,600}\right) \text{ lb. } CO + \left(2 \times \frac{4,183}{70,600}\right) \text{ lb. } H_2 + \left(\frac{4}{3} \times \frac{76\cdot9}{23\cdot1}\right) \text{ lb. } N_2$$

i.e. 1·711 lb. C + 5·772 lb. of air + 1·066 lb. H_2O
$$= 3\cdot99 \text{ lb. } CO + 0\cdot119 \text{ lb. } H_2 + 4\cdot439 \text{ lb. } N_2$$

$\therefore$ 1 lb. C needs 3·37 lb. of air and 0·623 lb. H_2O,
and   1 lb. of coke needs only 88% of these quantities as it contains 12% ash

$\therefore$ 2·96 lb. of air and 0·548 lb. of water are needed per lb. of coke.   Ans.

The products are :

Stuff	Proportional weights	Molecular weights	Proportional volumes	% vol.	
CO	3·99	28	0·1426	39·55	Ans.
H_2 . . .	0·119	2	0·0595	16·45	
N_2 . . .	4·439	28	0·1585	43·95	

$$\Sigma = 0\cdot3606$$

2. *The following results were obtained during a test on a suction-gas producer and gas engine plant :*

Coal consumption, 48·7 lb. per hour, of calorific value 14,000 B.T.U. per lb. ; volumetric composition of gas, CO, 18 ; H_2, 10 ; CH_4, 3·3 ; N_2, 68·7 ; volume ratio of air to gas, 1·5 to 1 ; indicated m.e.p., 68 lb. per sq. in. ; explosions per minute, 120. The engine is single-acting, with bore 14 in., stroke 21 in., and works on the four-stroke cycle. Take calorific values (B.T.U. per standard cu. ft.) CO, 342 ; H_2, 347 ; CH_4, 1,073 ; assume a volumetric efficiency 0·8 for the engine, based on S.T.P. conditions ; and calculate (a) volume of gas per lb. of fuel, (b) thermal efficiency of producer, (c) thermal efficiency of engine. (*I.Mech.E.*)

$$\text{Heat input to producer} = \frac{48\cdot7}{60} \times 14{,}000 = 11{,}360 \text{ B.T.U. per min.}$$

$$\text{C.V. of gas} = (0\cdot18 \times 342) + (0\cdot10 \times 347) + (0\cdot033 \times 1{,}073)$$
$$= 61\cdot6 + 34\cdot7 + 35\cdot4 = 131\cdot7 \text{ B.T.U. per S.C.F.}$$

$$\text{Swept volume of engine} = \frac{\pi}{4} \times \frac{196}{144} \times \frac{21}{12} = 1\cdot87 \text{ cu. ft.}$$

$$\text{Volume of mixture aspirated} = 1\cdot87 \times 0\cdot8 \times 120 = 179\cdot5 \text{ S.C.F. per min.}$$

$$\text{Volume of gas aspirated} = \frac{1}{1\cdot5 + 1} \times 179\cdot5 = 71\cdot8 \text{ S.C.F. per min.}$$

(*a*) $$\text{Volume of gas, at S.T.P.} = \frac{71\cdot8 \times 60}{48\cdot7}$$

$$= \underline{88\cdot4 \text{ cu. ft. per lb. of fuel.}} \text{ Ans.}$$

(*b*) $$\text{Thermal efficiency of producer} = \frac{131\cdot7 \times 71\cdot8}{11{,}360} \times 100$$

$$= \underline{83\cdot2\%.} \text{ Ans.}$$

(*c*) $$\text{W.D. by engine} = 68 \times 1\cdot87 \times 144 \times 120 \times \frac{1}{778}$$

$$= 2{,}824 \text{ B.T.U. per min.}$$

$$\text{Thermal efficiency of engine} = \frac{2{,}824}{71\cdot8 \times 131\cdot7} \times 100$$

$$= \underline{29\cdot9\%.} \text{ Ans.}$$

It should be noted that ans. (*b*) refers to what is known as the " cold " efficiency of the producer since it is based on the C.V. of the cold gases. If the sensible heat in the hot gases leaving the producer were allowed for, a value for the " hot " efficiency would be obtained and this would approach 100%, neglecting losses, and in practice may reach 90 to 95%.

3. *The gas from a producer, obtained by drawing air and steam through incandescent anthracite, consists of hydrogen, carbon monoxide and nitrogen only. The analysis of the anthracite is 94% carbon, 6% ash by weight.*

Determine the weight of steam and air required per lb. of anthracite burnt and the volumetric analysis of the producer gas. Neglect all heat interchanges except those in the chemical reactions.

$$C.V. \text{ of } H_2 = 51,800 \text{ B.T.U. per lb. } (lower)$$
$$C.V. \text{ of } CO = 4,390 \text{ B.T.U. per lb.}$$
$$C.V. \text{ of } C = 14,550 \text{ B.T.U. per lb.}$$
$$Heat \text{ given to steam} = 1,120 \text{ B.T.U. per lb.}$$

(Air contains 23·1% O_2 by weight and 21% O_2 by volume.)

(U. Lond.)

The C.V. of carbon is 14,550 B.T.U. per lb. if completely burnt to CO_2. If, however, the carbon is burnt to CO first and then the CO to CO_2, the heat released by both these combustions together will be 14,550 B.T.U.

If 1 lb. C burned to CO, it would have produced $\dfrac{28}{12}$ lb. CO, and this

CO, if burned to CO_2, would have released $\dfrac{28}{12} \times 4,390$ B.T.U.

$\therefore$ C.V. of C burning to CO $= 14,550 - \dfrac{28}{12} \times 4,390$ B.T.U.

$$= 14,550 - 10,250 = 4,300 \text{ B.T.U. per lb. C.}$$

Let the primary reaction be denoted by (*a*) and the secondary by (*b*),

(*a*) $\qquad 2C + O_2 \rightarrow 2CO + \text{Heat}$

i.e. 24 lb. C + 32 lb. $O_2 \rightarrow$ 56 lb. CO + $(24 \times 4, 300) = 103,200$ B.T.U.

(*b*) $\qquad C + H_2O \rightarrow CO + H_2 - \text{Heat}$

i.e. 12 lb. C + 18 lb. $H_2O \rightarrow$ 28 lb. CO + 2 lb. $H_2 + \ldots - \ldots$

where
12 lb. C combine with 16 lb. O_2 and liberate $12 \times 4,300 = 51,600$ B.T.U.
and where
18 lb. H_2O are evaporated and superheated, and absorb
$$18 \times 1,120 = 20,160 \text{ B.T.U.}$$
and where
18 lb. H_2O are dissociated into 2 lb. H_2 and absorb
$$2 \times 51,800 = 103,600 \text{ B.T.U.}$$

$\therefore$ Net absorption in (*b*) $= 123,760 - 51,600 = 72,160$ B.T.U.

i.e. $\qquad$ 12 lb. C + 18 lb. $H_2O \rightarrow \ldots - 72,160$ B.T.U.
so that

$$\left(12 \times \frac{103,200}{72,160} \right) \text{ lb. C} + \left(18 \times \frac{103,200}{72,160} \right) \text{ lb. } H_2O \rightarrow \ldots - 103,200$$

17·14 lb. C + 25·75 lb. H_2O absorb 103,200 B.T.U.

and from (a)   24 lb. C + 32 lb. O_2 liberate 103,200 B.T.U.

$$\therefore \quad \frac{25·75}{17·14 + 24} = 0·625 \text{ lb. } H_2O \text{ are required per lb. C}$$

i.e. $0·625 \times 0·94 = \underline{0·587 \text{ lb. } H_2O \text{ per lb. of anthracite.}}$ Ans.

Also,

$$\frac{32}{17·14 + 24} \times 0·94 \times \frac{100}{23·1} = \underline{3·16 \text{ lb. of air per lb. of anthracite.}} \quad \text{Ans.}$$

The products are :

$$CO, \ 56 + 28 \times \frac{103,200}{72,160} = 56 + 40·1 = 96·1 \text{ lb.} \equiv 3·43 \text{ lb.mols}$$

$$H_2, \ 2 \times \frac{103,200}{72,160} = 2·86 \text{ lb.} \quad\quad\quad\quad\quad\quad \equiv 1·43 \text{ lb.mols}$$

$$N_2, \ \frac{76·9}{23·1} \times 32 = 106·5 \text{ lb.} \quad\quad\quad\quad\quad\quad \equiv 3·77 \text{ lb.mols}$$

$$\varSigma = 8·63$$

$$\therefore \text{ \% by vol., } \underline{CO = 39·75\%, \ H_2 = 16·56\%, \ N_2 = 43·7\%.} \quad \text{Ans.}$$

EXAMPLES

1. What is the essential difference between the " hot " and " cold gas " efficiency of a gas producer ?

The main and secondary reactions in a producer are :

$$2C + O_2 \longrightarrow 2CO + 4,370 \text{ B.T.U. per lb. of C.}$$
$$C + 2H_2O \longrightarrow CO_2 + 2H_2 - 6,160 \text{ B.T.U. per lb. of C.}$$

Assuming that the correct quantity of water is supplied and that the fuel is pure carbon of calorific value 14,540 B.T.U. per lb., find the efficiency of the producer, given that R for H_2 is 770 ft.lb. per lb. ° F.

Gas	Calorific value, B.T.U. per cu. ft. at N.T.P.	Molecular weight
CO	343	28
H_2 . . .	292	2

(*U. Lond.*)

[For thermal balance and per lb. C, we have 1·365 lb. CO and 0·1385 lb. H_2; i.e. 17·5 cu. ft. CO and 24·8 cu. ft. H_2, assuming N.T.P. refers to 32° F. ; $\eta = 91·0\%$.]

2. The fuel used in a gas producer is anthracite consisting of 92% carbon and the remainder ash. The steam passing through the fire is generated by the producer and absorbs 1,050 B.T.U. per lb. The amounts of air and steam used are the minimum quantities for the reduction of the carbon to carbon monoxide, the reactions being $C + H_2O = CO + H_2$ and $2C + O_2 = 2CO$.

Assuming the reactions are thermally balanced, and there are no losses, estimate :

(a) the weight of steam required per lb. of fuel ;

(b) the volume of gas at 14·7 lb. per sq. in. and 60° F. produced per lb. of fuel ;

(c) the net calorific value per cu. ft. of gas under the above conditions.

Net C.V. of hydrogen, 52,000 B.T.U. per lb. ; C.V. of carbon burning to CO, 4,450 B.T.U. per lb. ; and to CO_2, 14,500 B.T.U. per lb. Air contains 23·1% O_2 by weight. (*U. Lond.*)

[(a) H_2O per lb. of fuel, 0·599 lb. ; (b) CO, 29·1 cu. ft. ; H_2, 12·6 cu. ft. ; N_2, 31·1 cu. ft. ; total volume per lb. of fuel, 72·8 cu. ft. ; (c) 175 B.T.U.]

3. In a gas engine producer plant the volumetric analyses of the producer gas and of the engine exhaust gas were as follows :

	CO	H_2	CH_4	C_2H_4	CO_2	O_2	N_2
Producer gas %	20·5	12·5	3·0	0·5	7·5	0·2	55·8
Exhaust gas %	—	—	—	—	10·7	8·3	81·0

Find : (i) the chemically correct volumetric air-fuel ratio for the producer gas ; (ii) the percentage excess air supplied to the gas engine.

What do you understand by the term " cold efficiency " of a gas producer ? Air contains 21% of oxygen by volume. (*U. Lond.*)

[Per 100 lb.mol of fuel : (i) $32[CO_2]$ and $19·5[H_2O]$, requiring $23·80[O_2]$, whence vol. air-fuel ratio = 1·134 ; (ii) by O_2 balance $24·8[O_2]$ in flue, whence excess air = 1·18 lb.mol, % = 105 approx.

N.B. N_2 balance gives about 108%.]

CHAPTER X

INTERNAL COMBUSTION TURBINES

Introduction

1. The thermodynamic principles underlying the I.C. turbine are naturally similar to those of the steam turbine and many similarities of treatment will be found between questions in this chapter and the chapters on General Steam Turbine Performance, Steam Nozzles, and also on Compressors. Nevertheless, since the subject is becoming increasingly important in practice, the separate treatment of problems in connection with I.C. turbines and jet-propulsion units seems appropriate. The simplest I.C. turbine plant consists of a rotary compressor, centrifugal or axial, a combustion chamber, usually a number of separate ones, in parallel, a set of nozzles, a turbine which may be mounted on the same shaft as the compressor impeller, and often a heat exchanger to utilize some of the heat in the exhaust gas to preheat the air.

2. A few words of comment would appear appropriate on the term "adiabatic efficiency" in connection with the rotary type of compressor used in I.C. turbine units. A definition of this term was given earlier (cf. equation (III,11)), viz.

$$\eta_{\text{ad}} = \frac{\text{adiabatic isentropic temp. rise}}{\text{actual temp. rise}}.$$

If the compression is adiabatic, as it is in most high-speed rotary compressors providing the compressor is uncooled, then we know from (III,10)

$$\text{W.D.} = C_p \text{ (final temp.} - \text{initial temp.) per lb. of air}$$

i.e. $$= C_p \times \text{actual temp. rise.}$$

It follows that $$\text{W.D.} = C_p \times \frac{\text{adiabatic isentropic temp. rise}}{\text{adiabatic efficiency}}$$

or, $$\text{Actual W.D.} = \frac{\text{adiabatic isentropic W.D.}}{\text{adiabatic efficiency}}.$$

This is correct providing the adiabatic isentropic work is found from (III,3), with γ substituted for n.

i.e. $$\text{ad. isent. W.D. per lb. of air} = \frac{\gamma}{\gamma - 1} RT_1 \left[\left(\frac{P_2}{P_1} \right)^{\frac{\gamma - 1}{\gamma}} - 1 \right].$$

$$= C_p \times \text{ad. isent. temp. rise.}$$

If, however, (III,3) were used to find the actual W.D. with the actual mean value of n for the compression, where $n > \gamma$, then a false answer would be obtained, because

162

$$\eta_{ad} \times \frac{n}{n-1}RT_1\left[\left(\frac{P_2}{P_1}\right)^{\frac{n-1}{n}} - 1\right] \neq \frac{\gamma}{\gamma-1}RT_1\left[\left(\frac{P_2}{P_1}\right)^{\frac{\gamma-1}{\gamma}} - 1\right]$$

in general. The reason is to be found in the P–V and T–ϕ diagrams, fig. X,1.

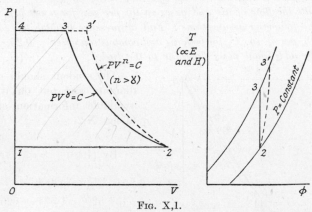

FIG. X,1.

The increase in area of the P–V diagram 1 2 3′ 4 over 1 2 3 4 takes account only of the increase in the value of the index and therefore of the increased volumes, but neglects the effect on the phase work from 2 to 3′ of the heat generated within the air mainly by friction between the molecules. This results in a rise of temperature, gain of entropy and, of course, of internal energy as shown by the T–ϕ diagram, the temperature scale being proportional to an E and H scale (cf. equations (I,19) and (I,20)). Thus the W.D. is influenced not only by the volumes, but also by the entropy change within the air. This is a case where the external W.D. is no longer given by the area of the P–V diagram, i.e. $\int P\,dV$, because the friction effect is " unresisted ". It should be noted also that 2–3 and 2–3′ are both assumed adiabatic, but only 2–3 is isentropic.

To conclude, the term adiabatic efficiency is defined uniquely by the ratio of isentropic to actual temperature rise and the definition holds good in terms of temperatures only. An extension of the definition to the ratio of isentropic W.D. to actual W.D. is satisfactory only if the isentropic W.D. is calculated from (III,3) or (III,10) and the actual W.D. deduced from it. The extension is unsatisfactory if an attempt were made to calculate the actual W.D. from (III,3) directly. It is therefore to be recommended that the adiabatic efficiency should always be given in accordance with the definition (III,11), and this is in keeping with the bulk of current practice. The authors wish to add that the use of the term " adiabatic temperature efficiency " would, in their opinion, remove the misunderstanding which sometimes arises.

1. *A simple gas turbine takes in air at 14·7 lb. per sq. in. and 60° F. and compresses it through a pressure ratio of 5 : 1, the adiabatic efficiency of compression being 85%. The air passes to the combustion chamber, and after combustion the gases enter the turbine at a temperature of 1,000° F. and expand to 14·7 lb. per sq. in., the turbine efficiency being 80%.*

Estimate the flow of air and gases in lb. per sec. for a net h.p. of 2,000, making the following assumptions : Fall of pressure through the combustion system 1 lb. per sq. in., C_p for both air and combustion gases = 0·25, $\gamma = 1·40$. Neglect the additional mass flow due to the fuel. (U. Lond.)

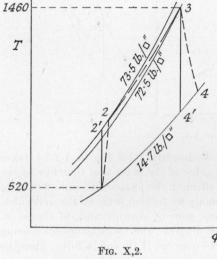

FIG. X,2.

The student should draw the diagram and put on it all the available information as shown in fig. X,2.

By (I,18)

$$T_{2'} = 520 \times 5^{\frac{0·4}{1·4}}$$

$$= 520 \times 1·584 = 825° \text{ F. abs.}$$

∴ Isentropic temp. rise $= 305°$ F.

Actual temp. rise $= \dfrac{305}{0·85} = 359°$ F.

By (III,10)

W.D. in compressor $= 0·25 \times 359 = 89·75$ B.T.U. per lb. of air.

Since there is a fall of pressure of 1 lb. per sq. in. through the combustion system, i.e. from (2) to (3), we now have an expansion ratio of $\dfrac{72·5}{14·7} = 4·93$.

∴ again by (I,18) $\quad T_{4'} = \dfrac{1,460}{4·93^{0·286}} = 928°$ F. abs.

Isentropic temp. drop $= 1,460 - 928 = 532°$ F.

∴ Actual temp. drop $= 0·8 \times 532 = 426°$ F.

By (III,10)

W.D. in turbine $= 0·25 \times 426 = 106·5$ B.T.U. per lb. of air.

Of this, 89·75 B.T.U. are absorbed in driving the compressor

∴ Net W.D. $= 106·5 - 89·75 = 16·75$ B.T.U. per lb. of air

i.e. $\quad 2,000$ h.p. $= w$ lb. per sec. $\times 16·75 \times \dfrac{778}{550}$

$$\underline{w = 84·4 \text{ lb. of air per sec.}} \quad \text{Ans.}$$

2. *Air is expanded in a suitably shaped nozzle from a pressure of 100 lb. per sq. in. to 14·7 lb. per sq. in., the initial temperature being 200° F. Given that the critical pressure ratio for air is 0·527 when γ = 1·4, and that the area at the throat is 0·35 sq. in., find the weight of air passing through the nozzle per sec.*

Assuming that there is no frictional loss before the throat, but that there is a 5% frictional loss in the divergent part of the nozzle, find the velocity and temperature of the air at exit. The velocity of approach to the nozzle inlet may be neglected. (*U. Lond.*)

For frictionless (i.e. isentropic) adiabatic expansion, the W.D. is the same as that in the Rankine Cycle, or the reversed compressor-type cycle,

i.e.
$$\text{W.D.} = H_1 - H_2 = \frac{\gamma}{\gamma - 1} RT_1 \left[1 - \left(\frac{P_2}{P_1} \right)^{\frac{\gamma - 1}{\gamma}} \right] \text{ per lb.}$$

$$\therefore \text{ W.D. to throat} = \frac{1 \cdot 4}{0 \cdot 4} \times 53 \cdot 3 \times 660 \left[1 - 0 \cdot 527^{\frac{0 \cdot 4}{1 \cdot 4}} \right]$$

$$= 3 \cdot 5 \times 53 \cdot 3 \times 660 \times 0 \cdot 1673$$

$$= 20{,}600 \text{ ft.lb. per lb. of air.}$$

Velocity at throat[1] $= \sqrt{2g \times 20{,}600} = 8 \cdot 03 \sqrt{20{,}600}$

$$= 1{,}152 \text{ ft. per sec.}$$

Since there are no losses up to the throat, the entire W.D. is converted to K.E.

$$\text{Vol. per lb. at throat} = \frac{RT}{P} = \frac{53 \cdot 3 \times \left(660 \times 0 \cdot 527^{\frac{1}{3 \cdot 5}} \right)}{144 \times (100 \times 0 \cdot 527)} = 3 \cdot 86 \text{ cu. ft.}$$

$$\left(\text{Note, from (I,18) T at throat} = 660 \times 0 \cdot 527^{\frac{0 \cdot 4}{1 \cdot 4}} = 660 \times 0 \cdot 8327. \right)$$

$$\therefore \text{ Weight passing per sec.} = \frac{\text{Area} \times \text{Velocity}}{\text{Spec. vol.}}, \text{ for continuous flow,}$$

$$= \frac{0 \cdot 35}{144} \times \frac{1{,}152}{3 \cdot 86} \qquad = 0 \cdot 726 \text{ lb. \quad Ans.}$$

Again, Isentropic W.D. per lb., inlet to exit

$$= \frac{1 \cdot 4}{0 \cdot 4} \times 53 \cdot 3 \times 660 \left[1 - \left(\frac{14 \cdot 7}{100} \right)^{\frac{1}{3 \cdot 5}} \right] \text{ ft.lb.}$$

$$= 51{,}750 \text{ ft.lb.}$$

$\therefore$ Isentropic W.D. per lb., throat to exit $= 51{,}750 - 20{,}600 = 31{,}150$ ft.lb.

$\therefore$ Frictional loss, ,, ,, ,, $= 0 \cdot 05 \times 31{,}150 = 1{,}557$ ft.lb.

---

[1] The general method of dealing with expansions through nozzles is explained in chapter XV, which should be studied first in case of difficulty.

Net W.D. per lb. converted to K.E., inlet to exit

$$= 51,750 - 1,557 = 50,193 \text{ ft.lb.}$$

$$\therefore \text{ Exit velocity} = \sqrt{2g \times 50,193} = 1,800 \text{ ft. per sec.}$$

By (I,18) Isentropic temp. at exit

$$= 660 \times \left(\frac{14\cdot7}{100}\right)^{\frac{1}{3\cdot5}} = 660 \times 0\cdot578 = 381° \text{ F. abs.}$$

But the friction loss of 1,557 ft.lb. per lb. reappears as heat, thereby raising the final temp. at the constant pressure of 14·7 lb. per sq. in.

i.e.   degrees of re-heat $= \dfrac{1,557}{778 \times 0\cdot24} = 8\cdot4° \text{ F.}$

$$\text{Actual final temp.} = 389\cdot4° \text{ F. abs.}\quad \text{Ans.}$$

3. *A group of nozzles is required to expand the gas in a gas turbine from 100 lb. per sq. in. and 480° F. to 70 lb. per sq. in.*

Given that $C_p = 0\cdot240$ and $C_v = 0\cdot1702$, calculate the required area of discharge per lb. per sec. of gas flowing if the nozzle efficiency is 0·8, i.e., K.E. at discharge = 0·8 adiabatic heat drop.   (*U. Lond.*)

$$R = 778(0\cdot24 - 0\cdot1702) = 54\cdot3, \text{ by (I,6)}$$
and $\gamma = 1\cdot41, \text{ by (I,14)}$.

Fig. X,3.

Now, by (I,7) $V_1 = \dfrac{1 \times 54\cdot3 \times 940}{100 \times 144} = 3\cdot544$ cu. ft. per lb.

If the point 2 is the point corresponding to adiabatic isentropic expansion according to $PV^\gamma = $ constant, then

$$V_2 = V_1\left(\frac{P_1}{P_2}\right)^{\frac{1}{\gamma}} = 3\cdot544 \times \left(\frac{100}{70}\right)^{\frac{1}{1\cdot41}} = 4\cdot564 \text{ cu. ft. per lb.}$$

Isentropic $\text{W.D.}_{1-2} = \dfrac{\gamma}{\gamma-1}(P_1V_1 - P_2V_2)$, by (III,1) reversed

$$= \frac{1\cdot41}{0\cdot41} \times 144(100 \times 3\cdot544 - 70 \times 4\cdot564)$$

$$= 17,290 \text{ ft.lb. per lb.}$$

$\therefore$ K.E. at exit, i.e. at $3 = 0\cdot8 \times 17,290$ ft.lb. per lb.

in accordance with information given in the question. Neglecting the velocity of approach, as is usual,

$$v_3 = \sqrt{2g \times 0\cdot8 \times 17,290} = 943 \text{ ft. per sec.}$$

Now, $0\cdot2 \times 17,290$ ft.lb. of work are wasted in friction and reappear in the form of heat, i.e. in re-heating the gas from (2) to (3) at constant pressure.

But, by (I,7) $$\frac{P_1V_1}{T_1} = \frac{P_2V_2}{T_2}$$

$$\therefore T_2 = 940 \times \frac{70}{100} \times \frac{4\cdot564}{3\cdot544} = 847° \text{ F. abs.}$$

$$\therefore \frac{0\cdot2 \times 17,290}{778} = 1 \times 0\cdot24 \times (T_3 - 847)$$

whence $$T_3 = 865\cdot5° \text{ F. abs.}$$

Also at constant pressure,

$$V_3 = V_2\frac{T_3}{T_2} = 4\cdot564 \times \frac{865\cdot5}{847} = 4\cdot66 \text{ cu. ft. per lb.}$$

$\therefore$ Discharge Area per unit rate of mass flow

$$= \frac{\text{spec. volume}}{\text{velocity}} = \frac{4\cdot66}{943} = 0\cdot004945 \text{ sq. ft.}$$

$$= \underline{0\cdot712 \text{ sq. in.}} \quad \text{Ans.}$$

4. *In a jet-propulsion unit, air is compressed by means of an uncooled rotary compressor, the pressure at delivery being 3½ times that at entrance, and the temperature rise during compression is 1·15 times that for frictionless adiabatic compression. The air is then led to a combustion chamber where the fuel is burned under constant pressure conditions. The products of combustion at 900° F. pass through a turbine which drives the compressor. The exhaust gases from the turbine are expanded in a nozzle down to atmospheric pressure. The atmospheric pressure is 14·7 lb. per sq. in., and the temperature is 50° F.*

Assuming that the values of R and γ after combustion remain the same as for air, estimate (a) *the power required to drive the compressor per lb. of air per sec.,* (b) *the air-fuel ratio if the calorific value of the fuel is 18,750 B.T.U. per lb., and* (c) *the thrust developed per lb. of air per sec. The velocity of approach may be neglected, and the gases are expanded isentropically in both the turbine and the nozzle.*

(*R for air* = 53·3 *ft.lb.* ° *F. units.* γ = 1·4 *for air.*)

(*U. Lond.*)

By (I,18) $T_2 = 510 \times 3·5^{\frac{0·4}{1·4}} = 510 \times 1·430 = 729·3°$ F. abs.

Isentropic temperature rise = 219·3° F.

∴ Actual temperature rise = 219·3 × 1·15 = 251° F.

∴ $T_{2'}$ = 762° F. abs. = actual temp. leaving compressor.

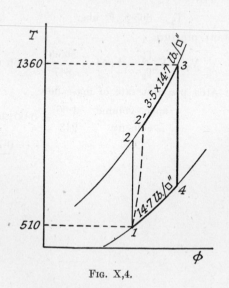

Fig. X,4.

Since the compressor is uncooled,

W.D. per lb. $= C_p(T_{2'} - T_1)$, cf. (III,10)

$= 0.24(762 - 510) = 60.5$ B.T.U.

$\therefore$ h.p. absorbed by compressor per lb. per sec.

$$= \frac{1 \times 60.5 \times 60}{42.4} = \underline{85.5}. \quad \text{Ans. } (a).$$

[Note, $C_p = 0.24$, since $53.3 = 778(C_p - C_v)$ and $1.4 = \dfrac{C_p}{C_v}$. Also,

42.4 B.T.U. per min. $= \dfrac{33,000}{778}$ is the equivalent of 1 h.p.]

Heat required to raise temp. to $1,360°$ F. abs. $= 0.24(1,360 - 762)$

$= 143.7$ B.T.U. per lb. of air

$\therefore 18,750 = x \times 143.7$

$x = \underline{131.8}$ lb. of air per lb. of fuel. Ans. (b).

In view of the high air-fuel ratio, the mass of the fuel is customarily neglected.

Again, by (I,18) $T_4 = \dfrac{1,360}{\dfrac{0.4}{3.5^{1.4}}} = \dfrac{1,360}{1.430}$

$= 951°$ F. abs.

$\therefore$ Work developed in turbine and nozzle (isentropically)

$= 0.24(1,360 - 951)$, by (III,10)

$= 98.2$ B.T.U. per lb.

Of this, 60.5 B.T.U. are absorbed to drive the compressor,

$\therefore 98.2 - 60.5 = 37.7$ B.T.U. are available for K.E. in the nozzle,

$$778 \times 37.7 = \frac{v_4^2}{2g}$$

$v_4 = 8.03\sqrt{37.7 \times 778} = 1,370$ ft. per sec.

Thrust $=$ Rate of Change of Momentum

Thrust $= \dfrac{1,370 - 0}{32.2} = \underline{42.5}$ lb. per lb. of air per sec. Ans. (c).

5. *A gas turbine set takes in air at 60° F., the pressure ratio is 4 : 1, and the maximum temperature is 1,040° F. Assuming efficiencies of 0·86 and 0·83 for the turbine and compressor respectively, determine the overall efficiency :*

    (a) *without heat exchange ;*

    (b) *with heat exchanger making use of 75% of the heat available.*

Assume that pressure drops in the connecting pipes, etc. can be neglected and that the specific heats of air are constant.

If such a set is used to drive an alternator, state how it can be governed.

(U. Melb.)

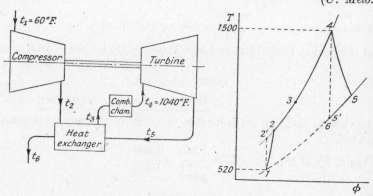

FIG. X,5.

Final temperature after turbine if the expansion were isentropic, by (I,18)

$$T_{5'} = T_4\left(\frac{P_5}{P_4}\right)^{\frac{\gamma-1}{\gamma}} = 1{,}500 \times \left(\frac{1}{4}\right)^{\frac{0·4}{1·4}}$$

$$T_{5'} = \frac{1{,}500}{1·485} = 1{,}010° \text{ F. abs.}$$

Isentropic temp. drop through turbine = 490° F., and for constant specific heats, this is proportional to the W.D.

$$\therefore \text{ Actual temp. drop} = 0·86 \times 490 = 421·5° \text{ F.}$$

i.e. $T_5 = 1{,}500 - 421·5 = 1{,}078° \text{ F. abs.}$

Similarly, $T_{2'} = 520 \times 1·485 = 772° \text{ F. abs.}$

$$T_{2'} - T_1 = 772 - 520 = 252° \text{ F.}$$

$$\therefore T_2 - T_1 = \frac{252}{0·83} = 303° \text{ F.}, \quad \text{and} \quad T_2 = 823° \text{ F. abs.}$$

Available heat in exchanger $= C_p(T_5 - T_2)$

$$= 255 C_p \text{ B.T.U. per lb.}$$

$$\therefore 0·75 \times 255 C_p = C_p(T_3 - 823)$$

$$T_3 = 823 + 191 = 1{,}014° \text{ F. abs.}$$

$$T_4 - T_3 = 486° \text{ F.}$$

(*a*) Without heat exchanger, the temperature rise $T_4 - T_2$ is due entirely to injected fuel in the combustion chamber.

$$\therefore \text{ Heat supplied} = C_p(1,500 - 823) = 677C_p$$
$$\text{Turbine W.D.} = 421 \cdot 5C_p$$
$$\text{Compressor W.D.} = 303C_p$$
$$\text{Net W.D.} = 118 \cdot 5C_p$$

$$\text{Overall } \eta = \frac{118 \cdot 5}{677} = \underline{17 \cdot 5\%}. \quad \text{Ans.}$$

(*b*) With heat exchanger, the air is preheated from 2 to 3 and fuel is only supplied to raise the temperature from 3 to 4, i.e.

$$\text{Heat supplied} = 486C_p$$
$$\text{Net W.D.} = 118 \cdot 5C_p, \text{ as before.}$$

$$\text{Overall } \eta = \frac{118 \cdot 5}{486} = \underline{24 \cdot 4\%}. \quad \text{Ans.}$$

Governing could be carried out by controlling the quantity of fuel injected. More recently, this is being assisted by by-passing the combustion chamber with a portion of the air, although this is more useful when working on the " closed " cycle where the air at 6 is returned to the compressor at 1.

EXAMPLES

1. In an aeroplane power unit, the gas expands through a turbine to an intermediate pressure and on leaving the turbine it expands from the intermediate pressure to the back pressure, generating kinetic energy for the jet. All the power of the turbine is absorbed in driving the associated compressor.

In such a plant, the gas enters the turbine at 65 lb./in.^{2} and 800° C. and expands therein to 25 lb./in.^{2}. The turbine absorbs 75% of the available adiabatic heat drop. Expansion occurs through the jet from the exhaust condition of the turbine to 14·7 lb./in.^{2}.

Calculate the temperature of the gas entering the jet and the velocity leaving the jet.

The following assumptions may be made :

Velocities of gas entering the turbine and entering the jet are negligible. There are no heat losses. Conversion to kinetic energy in jet is 100% of the available adiabatic drop. ($C_p = 0 \cdot 25$; $C_v = 0 \cdot 181$.) (*U. Sheff.*)

[$\gamma = 1 \cdot 38$; temp. entering jet = 1,136° F. ; K.E. generated = 42,200 ft.lb. per lb. ; $v = 1{,}650$ ft. per sec.]

2. In the theoretical cycle for a jet-propulsion unit both the compression and the expansion are considered isentropic, and the heat is supplied at constant pressure. Show that the thrust developed per lb. of air per second when the velocity of approach is neglected is

$$\left[\frac{2J}{g} \cdot C_p \cdot T(q-1)(r^{\gamma-1}-1) \right]^{\frac{1}{2}},$$

where q is the ratio of the absolute temperatures after and before combustion, r is the *volume* compression ratio, and T is the absolute temperature of the atmosphere.

If the compression ratio is 3·5 by volume and the air-fuel ratio by weight is 150, the fuel having a calorific value of 19,500 B.T.U. per lb., and the initial temperature is 60° F., estimate the theoretical thrust developed per lb. of fuel per sec. when the velocity of approach is 500 ft. per sec. (*U. Lond.*)

$\left[\dfrac{v^2}{2g\mathrm{J}} \right.$ = K.E. = W.D. in turbine − W.D. in compressor ; use (III,10) for

W.D. ; thrust = $\dfrac{\text{change in vel.}}{g}$ lb. per lb. of air per sec. In numerical part,

K.E. produced = 39,800 ft.lb. per lb. of air ; jet velocity = 1,680 ft. per sec. ;
thrust = 5,500 lb. The mass of the fuel is neglected throughout.]

3. A gas turbine plant works between the fixed absolute temperature limits 300° C. and 900° C., the absolute pressure limits being 15 lb./in.² and 60 lb./in.². The internal or adiabatic efficiency of the blower is 0·80 and that of the turbine is 0·85.

Estimate the actual thermal efficiency of the plant, and the horse-power available for driving an external load if the fuel consumption is 1 lb. per sec.
Take the following values of the constants :
γ for air and combustion products = 1·4 ; C_p for air and products = 0·25 ;
J = 1,400 ft.lb./C.H.U. ; C.V. of fuel = 10,000 C.H.U./lb. (*U. Syd.*)

[Temp. at end of compression = 868° F. abs. ; at end of expansion = 1,170° F. abs. ; turbine W.D. = 112·6 ; compressor W.D. = 82 B.T.U./lb. air ; $\eta = 16\cdot3\%$; lb. air/lb. fuel = 95·8 ; h.p. = 4,150.]

4. (*a*) A gas turbine set draws in atmospheric air at 14·7 p.s.i.a. and 60° F. ; there are two pressure stages with intercooler, and the total pressure ratio is 8 : 1. The maximum temperature of the cycle is 1,100° F., and there is one turbine for expansion. A regenerator is used and recovers 60% of the available heat. Determine the efficiency and the ratio of the useful work to turbine work. The turbine and compressor efficiencies may be taken as 0·86 and 0·83 respectively. R = 53·3 ft.lb. per lb. ° F. and $\gamma = 1\cdot4$.

(*b*) Explain briefly the idea of the closed gas turbine system and discuss its merits and demerits. (*U. Melb.*)

[Take " ideal " intercooler conditions ; $C_p = 0\cdot240$; isentropic temp. ratio per compr. stage = 1·346 ; total comp. W.D. per lb. = 104·2 B.T.U. ; actual temp. leaving turbine = 959° F. abs. ; turbine W.D. per lb. = 144·3 B.T.U. ;
ratio $\dfrac{\text{useful W.D.}}{\text{turbine W.D.}} = 0\cdot278$. Available heat in regenerator = 222 × C_p B.T.U. ;
actual temp. rise of pre-combustion air = 133° F. ; external heat supp. per lb. = 165·6 B.T.U. ; $\eta = 24\cdot2\%$.]

5. Sketch diagrammatically the arrangement of an internal combustion turbine to work on a closed cycle with two-stage compression and expansion of the working substance and regenerative heating after compression.

If the total pressure ratio is 5, the maximum cycle temperature is 1,100° F., minimum 70° F., compression and expansion are adiabatic and the intercooler and regenerative heater are each 70% efficient, find the ideal thermal efficiency of the cycle.

If the efficiency ratios of the turbine and compressor units are each 0·75, what is the maximum thermal efficiency that may be expected from the turbine ? (*U. Manch.*)

[(*a*) Take $\gamma = 1\cdot4$. Temperatures, in order, round the cycle (all in ° F. abs.) : 530, 667, 571, 719, 1083, 1560, 1239, 1560, 1239, 875 ; comp. W.D. = 285C_p ; turb. W.D. = 642C_p ; heat supp. = 798C_g ; $\eta = 44\cdot7\%$. (*b*) ditto, T° F. abs. : 530, 713, 585, 786, 1159, 1560, 1319, 1560, 1319, 946 ; comp. W.D. = 384C_p ; turb. W.D. = 482C_p ; heat supp. = 642C_p ; $\eta = 15\cdot0\%$.]

CHAPTER XI

PARTIAL PRESSURES; HUMIDITY OF ATMOSPHERE

Introduction

Questions involving partial pressures arise in many fields of application of Thermodynamics and examples of these will be found in other chapters of this book, notably chapter VIII on combustion of fuels. The fundamental theory is simple, yet the detailed application is usually a source of difficulty to the student. Apart from a knowledge of the characteristic gas equation (I,7) and a working knowledge of the steam tables, Dalton's Law should be known and appreciated. This is given in article 6, section B, chapter I, and it should be emphasized that it is commonly assumed to hold for a mixture of gases and vapours as well as for a mixture of gases only. The validity of this assumption depends on the type of vapour, and its state, but it is known to be a reasonably true statement as far as H_2O at low partial pressures is concerned.

The following definitions should be known,

Absolute humidity (A.H.) of air = actual lb. of H_2O vapour per lb. of *dry* air

$$\% \text{ A.H.} = \frac{\text{Actual lb. of } H_2O \text{ vapour per lb. of dry air}}{\text{lb. of } H_2O \text{ vapour required to saturate 1 lb. of dry air at the same temp.}} \times 100$$

% Relative humidity (R.H.)

$$= \frac{\text{Actual lb. of } H_2O \text{ per cu. ft. of air}}{\text{lb. of } H_2O \text{ required to saturate 1 cu. ft. of air at the same temp.}} \times 100$$

$$= \frac{\text{A.H. for given condition}}{\text{A.H. at saturation}} \times 100,$$

and this can be shown to be equal (very nearly) to the further definition which is the most useful one and should be remembered,

$$\% \text{ R.H.} = \frac{\text{Partial pressure of steam actually present}}{\text{Partial pressure of steam if it were saturated at the same temp.}}$$

173

1. Briefly state the effect of air leakage into a condenser.

What do you understand by " partial pressures", and what is the law connecting them?

A closed vessel of 24 cu. ft. capacity contains saturated water vapour and air at a temperature of 40·5° C. and a pressure of 1·6 lb. per sq. in. Due to air leakage into the vessel, the pressure rises to 3·2 lb. per sq. in. and the temperature falls to 36·8° C.

Calculate the weight of air which has leaked in. (Take the characteristic constant for air as 96 ft.lb. per lb.)   *(U.L.C.I.)*

The most important effects of air leakage into a condenser are :

    (i) an increase in the condenser pressure which limits the useful heat drop in the turbine or engine ;

    (ii) a lowering of the partial pressure of the steam and of the (saturation) temperature along with it ; this means that the latent heat increases and therefore more cooling water is required and undercooling of the condensate is likely to be more severe with a resulting lower overall efficiency.

The second part of the question is answered in chapter I, section B, article 6.

$$40\cdot5° \text{ C.} \equiv \left(40\cdot5 \times \frac{9}{5} + 32\right)° \text{ F.} = 104\cdot9° \text{ F.}$$

$$36\cdot8° \text{ C.} \equiv 98\cdot2° \text{ F.}$$

$$96 \text{ ft.lb. } ° \text{ C. units} \equiv \frac{96}{1\cdot8} = 53\cdot3 \text{ ft.lb. } ° \text{ F. units.}$$

Initially, at 109·4° F., p.p. of steam = 1·25 lb. per sq. in., from steam tables.

$$\therefore \text{ p.p. of air} = 1\cdot6 - 1\cdot25 = 0\cdot35 \text{ lb. per sq. in.}$$

By (I,7)   Weight of air present $= \dfrac{PV}{RT} = \dfrac{0\cdot35 \times 144 \times 24}{53\cdot3 \times 565}$

$$= 0\cdot0402 \text{ lb.}$$

Finally, at 98·2° F., p.p. of steam = 0·90 lb. per sq. in., from steam tables.

$$\therefore \text{ p.p. of air} = 3\cdot2 - 0\cdot9 = 2\cdot3 \text{ lb. per sq. in.}$$

New weight of air present $= \dfrac{2\cdot3 \times 144 \times 24}{53\cdot3 \times 558}$

$$= 0\cdot2672 \text{ lb.}$$

$$\therefore \underline{\text{Air Leakage}} = 0\cdot2672 - 0\cdot0402 = \underline{0\cdot227 \text{ lb.}} \quad \text{Ans.}$$

2. *A vessel of 81 cu. ft. capacity contains a mixture of two gases whose molecular weights are 32 and 16. The ratio of the partial pressures is 1 to 3, and the temperature of the mixture is 27° C.*

If the weight of the mixture is 22·5 lb., find :
   (a) *the weight of each gas present in the mixture ;*
   (b) *the pressure in the vessel ;*
   (c) *the partial pressures when the temperature is raised to 102° C.*

(U.L.C.I.)

Let the two gases be A and B respectively. Then, by (I,13) the partial pressures are proportional to the number of lb.mols and also to the product of (wR). Also, by (I,9) R is inversely proportional to the molecular weight. Hence

$$\frac{P_A}{P_B} = \frac{m_A}{m_B} = \frac{1}{3} . \qquad \qquad \text{(i)}$$

and

$$\frac{R_A}{R_B} = \frac{16}{32} = \frac{1}{2} . \qquad \qquad \text{(ii)}$$

(a) Again,

$$\frac{P_A}{P_B} = \frac{w_A R_A}{w_B R_B}, \text{ i.e. } \frac{w_A}{w_B} = \frac{1}{3} \times 2$$

but

$$w_A + w_B = 22·5.$$

$$\therefore w_B = \frac{22·5}{1·667} = \underline{13·50 \text{ lb.}}$$

$$\text{and } \underline{w_A = 9·0 \text{ lb.}} \quad \text{Ans.}$$

(b) $27° \text{ C.} \equiv (27 \times 1·8 + 32)° \text{ F.} = 80·6° \text{ F.}$

We may now proceed *either* by assuming the value of 1·985 for the universal gas constant, whence

by (I,9) $R_A = \dfrac{1·985 \times 778}{32} = 48·3$ ft.lb. per lb. ° F.

$\therefore$ by (I,7) $P_A \times 144 \times 81 = 9·0 \times 48·3 \times 540·6$

$$P_A = 20·13 \text{ lb. per sq. in.}$$

from (i) above, $P_B = 60·39$ lb. per sq. in.

$$\underline{\text{Pressure in vessel} = 80·5 \text{ lb. per sq. in.}} \quad \text{Ans.}$$

or we may assume the value of 358·7 S.C.F. per lb.mol of any gas.
   For,

The mean molecular weight of mixture $= \dfrac{\Sigma(m \times \text{molecular weight})}{\Sigma m}$

$$= \frac{(1 \times 32) + (3 \times 16)}{1 + 3} = 20$$

∴ Specific weight of mixture $= \dfrac{20}{358 \cdot 7}$ lb. per cu. ft. at 32° F. and 14·7 lb.

per sq. in.

But actually we have $\dfrac{22 \cdot 5}{81}$ lb. per cu. ft. at 80·6° F. and P lb. per sq. in.

By (I,7) the pressure is proportional to $\dfrac{w}{V}$ and the absolute temperature,

i.e.
$$\frac{P}{14 \cdot 7} = \frac{\dfrac{22 \cdot 5}{81} \times 540 \cdot 6}{\dfrac{20}{358 \cdot 7} \times 492}$$

i.e.
$$P = 14 \cdot 7 \times \frac{22 \cdot 5}{20} \times \frac{358 \cdot 7}{81} \times \frac{540 \cdot 6}{492}$$

$$= \underline{80 \cdot 5 \text{ lb. per sq. in.}} \quad \text{Ans.}$$

(c) $102°$ C. $\equiv (102 \times 1 \cdot 8 + 32)°$ F. $= 215 \cdot 6°$ F.

The volume of the vessel remains constant for our purposes

∴ New total pressure $= 80 \cdot 5 \times \dfrac{675 \cdot 6}{540 \cdot 6} = 100 \cdot 5$ lb. per sq. in.

But (i) above tells us that we have a ratio of 1 : 3 for the number of lb.mols of A and B respectively; and in the absence of any chemical action, the number of lb.mols must remain the same (which implies that the mean molecular weight and the gas constant of the mixture also remain the same).

∴ new $P_A = \frac{1}{4} \times 100 \cdot 5 = 25 \cdot 1$ lb. per sq. in.⎫
     new $P_B = \frac{3}{4} \times 100 \cdot 5 = 75 \cdot 4$ lb. per sq. in.⎭ $\underline{\text{Ans.}}$

3. *A boiler drum is partly charged with water, the space above the water being filled with moist air of relative humidity 0·9 at 90° F. and 14·7 lb. per sq. in.*

The pressure in the drum is now raised by heating to 390° F. with the stop-valve closed.

Determine, neglecting the change of volume of the water on heating, the original and final ratios by weight of air to water vapour, also the final pressure in the boiler. (U. Lond.)

At 90° F., the partial pressure of the steam in the air above the water surface would be 0·7 lb. per sq. in. (from steam tables), if the air were saturated with vapour.

Since the relative humidity is 0·9,

$$\text{Actual p.p. of steam} = 0.7 \times 0.9 = 0.63 \text{ lb. per sq. in.}$$

By Dalton's Law, p.p. of air $= 14.7 - 0.63 = 14.07$ lb. per sq. in.

Now, from the tables, at 0·7 lb. per sq. in., the vol. per lb. of saturated steam is 466·6 cu. ft.

i.e.   1 cu. ft. of space may hold $\dfrac{1}{466.6}$ lb. of saturated steam.

$\therefore$ 1 cu. ft. of space actually holds $\dfrac{0.9}{466.6} = 0.00193$ lb. of steam

of 0·9 relative humidity.

But, from (I,7), per cu. ft. of space there are $\dfrac{14.07 \times 144 \times 1}{53.3 \times 550} = 0.0692$ lb.

of air at the partial pressure of 14·07 lb. per sq. in. and 90° F.

$$\therefore \text{Original ratio} \frac{\text{lb. of air}}{\text{lb. of water vapour}} = \frac{0.0692}{0.00193}$$

$$= \underline{35.9}. \quad \text{Ans.}$$

If the stop valve remains closed, we have a *constant volume* operation. Hence, the partial pressure of the air component is increased in the ratio of the absolute temperatures, i.e.

$$\text{New p.p. of air} = 14.07 \times \frac{850}{550} = 21.75 \text{ lb. per sq. in.}$$

The mass of air per cu. ft. of space will remain constant under these conditions, a fact which is easily checked by substituting again in $PV = wRT$,

i.e. $\dfrac{21.75 \times 144 \times 1}{53.3 \times 850} = 0.0692$ lb. per cu. ft. of space.

If the air is saturated after heating, an assumption which *must* now be made, and which is reasonable in view of the high initial humidity and the probable evaporation of the water,

New p.p. of steam $= 220$ lb. per sq. in., at 390° F., from steam tables,

and also 1 cu. ft. of space holds $\dfrac{1}{2.089} = 0.478$ lb. of vapour, if the air is saturated.

$$\therefore \text{New ratio} \frac{\text{lb. of air}}{\text{lb. of steam}} = \frac{0.0692}{0.478} = \underline{0.145}. \quad \text{Ans.}$$

$$\text{Final Pressure in boiler} = 21.75 + 220$$
$$= \underline{241.75} \text{ lb. per sq. in.} \quad \text{Ans.}$$

4. *What do you understand by the term " Vacuum Efficiency " of a condensing plant ? On what factors does this efficiency depend ?*

In a condenser test the following observations were made : Vacuum, 27·6 in. of mercury ; barometer, 30·05 in. ; mean temperature of condensation, 95° F. ; hot well temperature, 84·2° F. ; weight of cooling water, 102,000 lb. per hr. ; inlet temperature, 62·2° F. ; outlet temperature, 88·1° F. ; weight of condensate per hr., 2,620 lb.

Find :

(a) *the weight of air present per cu. ft. of condenser volume ;*
(b) *the state of the steam entering the condenser ;*
(c) *the Vacuum Efficiency.*

(*U. Lond.*)

$$\text{Vacuum Efficiency} = \frac{\text{Vacuum produced at steam inlet}}{\text{Barometer} - \text{Absolute Press. corresponding to temperature of condensation}}.$$

If the partial pressure of the steam during condensation were equal to the absolute condenser pressure, this efficiency would be 100%. In fact, there will always be some air present in a condenser due to leakage and due to dissolved gases in the incoming steam ; this air exerts its own partial pressure and therefore lowers the p.p. of the steam during condensation. The value of the efficiency thus depends on the effectiveness of cooling the air and of removing it with an air pump.

(*a*)   Absolute pressure in condenser $= 0{\cdot}49 \times (30{\cdot}05 - 27{\cdot}6)$
$$= 1{\cdot}20 \text{ lb. per sq. in.}$$

p.p. of steam at condensation temp. of 95° F. $= 0{\cdot}816$ lb. per sq. in. by interpolation of the steam tables.

$$\therefore \text{ p.p. of air} = 1{\cdot}20 - 0{\cdot}816 = 0{\cdot}384 \text{ lb. per sq. in.}$$

By (I,7), per cu. ft. of condenser volume,

$$\text{Weight of air} = \frac{PV}{RT} = \frac{0{\cdot}384 \times 144 \times 1}{53{\cdot}3 \times 555}$$

$$= 0{\cdot}00187 \text{ lb.} \quad \text{Ans.}$$

(*b*)   Heat to coolant per lb. of steam $= \dfrac{102{,}000 \times 25{\cdot}9}{2{,}620} = 1{,}009$ B.T.U.

Heat given up by 1 lb. of steam of dryness x in condensing at 95° F., i.e. 0·816 lb. per sq. in., and in being undercooled from 95° F. to 84·2° F.

$$= 1{,}040x + 10{\cdot}8$$

$$\therefore \text{ Neglecting losses, } 1{,}009 = 1{,}040x + 10{\cdot}8$$

$$x = \frac{998}{1{,}040} = 0{\cdot}959. \quad \text{Ans.}$$

(c) We already know that the absolute pressure of the steam at the condensation temperature of 95° F. is 0·816 lb. per sq. in., i.e.

$$\frac{0·816}{0·49} = 1·665 \text{ in. of Hg.}$$

$$\therefore \text{ Vacuum } \eta = \frac{27·6}{30·05 - 1·665} \times 100 = \underline{97·3\%}. \quad \text{Ans.}$$

5. *A vessel of 190 cu. ft. capacity initially contains a mixture of air and saturated water vapour at a temperature of 107·9° F. and a vacuum of 26 in. (barometer 30 in.). In a given time 0·325 lb. of vapour condenses and 2·5 lb. of air leak in. Find the new values of vacuum and temperature.*

(R for air, 53·3 ft.lb. per lb. × ° F.   1 in. Hg. = 0·491 lb. per sq. in.)

(U. Glas.).

Initial absolute pressure = 0·491(30 − 26) = 1·964 lb. per sq. in.
At 107·9° F., p.p. of steam = 1·2 lb. per sq. in., from steam tables.
$$\therefore \text{ p.p. of air} = 1·964 - 1·2 = 0·764 \text{ lb. per sq. in.}$$

By (I,7)   Weight of air in 190 cu. ft. $= \dfrac{0·764 \times 144 \times 190}{53·3 \times 568} = 0·691 \text{ lb.}$

Weight of saturated H_2O in 190 cu. ft. $= \dfrac{190}{281·1} = 0·676 \text{ lb.}$

where 281·1 = V_s at 1·2 lb. per sq. in.
Due to condensation, final weight of H_2O = 0·676 − 0·325 = 0·351 lb.
Due to leakage, final weight of air = 0·691 + 2·5 = 3·19 lb.
Assuming that the vapour remains saturated as condensation proceeds and its partial pressure therefore falls, we now have

$$\frac{190}{0·351} = 541 \text{ cu. ft. per lb. of vapour.}$$

From the steam tables, this corresponds to a p.p. of 0·6 lb. per sq. in. and a temperature of 85° F. approximately.

$$\therefore \underline{\text{New temp. of mixture} = 85° \text{ F.}} \quad \text{Ans.}$$

But for air, $P = \dfrac{wRT}{V} = \dfrac{3·19 \times 53·3 \times 545}{190 \times 144}$

$$= 3·39 \text{ lb. per sq. in.}$$

new pressure = 3·39 + 0·6 = 4 lb. per sq. in., nearly.

$$\underline{\text{New vacuum} = 30 - \frac{4}{0·491} = 20·9 \text{ in. Hg., nearly.}} \quad \text{Ans.}$$

6. *A condenser receives wet steam at 1 lb. per sq. in. (abs.), and the temperatures of the air-vapour mixture and condensate leaving the condenser are 97° F.*

The rate of condensation is 5,200 lb. per hr., and air leakage is estimated at 40 lb. per hr. If the cooling water flows through the condenser tubes at a rate of 2,500 lb. per min. with a temperature rise of 32° F., calculate :

(a) *the weight of water vapour drawn from the condenser per min. by the air pump ;*

(b) *the steam conditions entering the condenser.*

$$(U.\ Manch.)$$

(*a*) The temperature at the air extraction is given as 97° F.

$\therefore$ at air pump, p.p. steam = 0·868 lb. per sq. in., by interpolation of the steam tables.

$$\therefore \text{ p.p. air} = 1 - 0{\cdot}868 = 0{\cdot}132 \text{ lb. per sq. in.}$$

By (I,7), per 100 cu. ft. of space,

$$\text{Weight of air withdrawn} = \frac{PV}{RT} = \frac{0{\cdot}132 \times 144 \times 100}{53{\cdot}3 \times 557} = 0{\cdot}064 \text{ lb.}$$

If we make the usual assumption that the vapour is saturated when extracted, we also have per 100 cu. ft. of space at 0·868 lb. per sq. in., $\frac{100}{381{\cdot}5} = 0{\cdot}262$ lb. of dry steam, where $V_s = 381{\cdot}5$ by interpolation of the steam tables.

$$\therefore \frac{0{\cdot}262}{0{\cdot}064} = 4{\cdot}09 \text{ lb. of vapour are withdrawn per lb. of dry air.}$$

Assuming the moisture in the air leaking into the condenser to be negligible,

$$4{\cdot}09 \times \frac{40}{60}$$

$$= 2{\cdot}73 \text{ lb. of vapour are lost per min.} \quad \text{Ans.}$$

(*b*) Heat entering the condenser per min.

$$= \frac{5{,}200}{60}(69{\cdot}7 + 1036{\cdot}1x) + 2{,}500(t_1 - 32).$$

Heat leaving the condenser per min.

$$= \left(\frac{5{,}200}{60} - 2{\cdot}73\right)(97 - 32) + 2{,}500(t_2 - 32).$$

Neglecting losses, and collecting terms

$$86{\cdot}7(69{\cdot}7 + 1{,}036x) = [2{,}500 \times 32] + (86{\cdot}7 - 2{\cdot}7) \times 65$$
$$69{\cdot}7 + 1{,}036x = 924 + 63$$

$$x = \frac{917}{1{,}036} = 0{\cdot}884. \quad \text{Ans.}$$

7. *In a boiler for a steam turbine plant, the feed water is to be taken as completely saturated with air at 16° C., the dissolved air content reckoned at 0° C. and 14·7 lb. per sq. in. then being 2% by volume. Find the ratio of air to steam by weight in the steam supplied to the turbine.*

The B.E.A.M.A. rule for air-removing capacity of air pumps for a turbine plant using 120,000 lb. of steam per hr., gives 63 lb. of air per hr. Compare this figure with the maximum air content that can be carried into the system from the feed water, as above. What does this comparison suggest about air leakage into turbine spaces under vacuum? (I.C.E.)

$$16° \text{C.} = \left(16 \times \frac{9}{5} + 32\right)° \text{F.} = 61° \text{F., nearly.}$$

Taking R for air as 53·3 ft.lb. ° F., by (I,7), at 61° F. and 14·7 lb. per sq. in.,

$$\text{Volume per lb. of air} = \frac{53·3 \times 521}{14·7 \times 144} = 13·11 \text{ cu. ft.}$$

Volume of water at 32° F. = 0·016 cu. ft. per lb. (cf. I,30).

$$\therefore \text{Volume of dissolved air} = \frac{2}{100} \times 0·016 = 0·00032 \text{ cu. ft. per lb. of water.}$$

$$\therefore \frac{\text{lb. of air}}{\text{lb. of water}} \text{ (at 61° F.)} = \frac{0·00032}{13·11}$$

$$= 0·0000244 = \frac{1}{41,000}. \text{ Ans.}$$

B.E.A.M.A. rule gives a corresponding ratio of air to steam of

$$\frac{63}{120,000} = \frac{1}{1,905}$$

i.e. this rule allows for an air pump capable of dealing with more than 20 times the weight of air per lb. of steam due to dissolved air in the feed water. This suggests that, for the high vacua employed in turbine plants, the bulk of the air extracted at the condenser air pump is derived from air leakage into the system and only a smaller part is due to dissolved air in the feed water, according to the figures used in this example.

It should be added, however, that the above rule allows a good safety margin, the actual proportions being less than 20 to 1. Further, the actual amount of air dissolved in the feed water depends largely on the success of a method of de-aeration of the make-up water. Without such auxiliary plant, the dissolved air content would soon increase to unmanageable proportions.

8. *Describe either* (a) *an arrangement suitable for reducing the vapour loss at the air extraction of a condenser, or* (b) *a de-aerator, explaining how it is incorporated into the circuit.*

The vacuum in the condenser of a steam plant is 27·5 in. of mercury with the barometer standing at 29·30 in. The temperature of the exhaust steam at the entrance to the condenser is 92·3° F., and condensation takes place at this temperature. The air is extracted at 79·6° F. What is the weight of air associated with each lb. of steam which is 0·8 dry at the entrance to the condenser, and what weight of dry vapour is withdrawn per lb. of air at the air extraction ?

$$(R \ for \ air \ is \ 53·3 \ ft.lb. \ °\ F. \ units.)$$

$$(U. \ Lond.)$$

For part (a) the student should give a description of the usual cooling arrangements made at the air extraction of a condenser. Part (b) requires a description of de-aerator, such as the one made by G. & J. Weir Ltd. of Glasgow, and used to reduce the dissolved air content in the boiler feed.

Absolute Pressure in condenser = $0·49(29·30 - 27·5) = 0·882$ lb. per sq. in.

At *entrance to condenser*,

$t = 92·3°$ F., $\therefore$ p.p. of steam = $0·75$ lb. per sq. in. from steam tables.

$$\therefore \ \text{p.p. of air} = 0·882 - 0·75 = 0·132 \ \text{lb. per sq. in.}$$

But the steam is 0·8 dry at entrance to the condenser and at 0·75 lb. per sq. in.

$$\therefore \ \text{Per cu. ft. of space we have} \ \frac{1}{0·8 \times 437·3} \ \text{lb. of steam.}$$

By (I,7)

Per cu. ft. of space we also have $\dfrac{0·132 \times 144 \times 1}{53·3 \times 552·3} = 0·000646$ lb. of air.

$$\therefore \ \frac{\text{lb. of air}}{\text{lb. of steam}} \ \text{(at entrance to condenser)} = 0·8 \times 437·3 \times 0·000646$$

$$= 0·226. \ \text{Ans.}$$

At the *air extraction*, the temperature has been reduced to 79·6° F. to reduce vapour losses. This means that the new p.p. of the steam is now 0·5 lb. per sq. in. from the steam tables, and thus the new p.p. of the air is $0·882 - 0·5 = 0·382$ lb. per sq. in.

$$\therefore \ \text{By (I,7)} \quad \text{Weight of air per cu. ft. of space} = \frac{0·382 \times 144 \times 1}{53·3 \times 539·6}$$

$$= 0·00191 \ \text{lb.}$$

But the vapour is now taken to be dry, giving a weight of $\frac{1}{643}$ lb. of steam per cu. ft. of space.

$$\therefore \ \frac{\text{lb. of dry vapour}}{\text{lb. of air}} \ \text{(at air extraction)} = \frac{1}{643} \times \frac{1}{0·00191}$$

$$= 0·814. \ \text{Ans.}$$

9. *In the open cooling system of a gas engine the jacket water is cooled by evaporation in a cooling tower. The weight of water supplied to the top of the tower is 40,000 lb. per hr. at a temperature of 125° F. The air entering the bottom of the tower at the rate of 30,000 lb. per hr. is moist, having a relative humidity of 50% at a temperature of 70° F. The air leaves the top of the tower at 110° F. in a saturated condition.*

Find the temperature to which the jacket water is reduced, and estimate the loss of jacket water per hr. The atmospheric pressure is 14·7 lb. per sq. in., and in the table below the properties of steam at low pressures are given, the symbols having their usual significance :

t_{sat} ° F.	P_{sat}	V_s	H_s
50·5	0·1815	1,674	1,083·9
70·0	0·3630	—	—
110·0	1·275	265·4	1,109·5

(U. Lond.)

At the bottom of the tower :

At 70° F., if the steam saturated the air, the p.p. of the steam would be 0·3630 lb. per sq. in. Hence, for a relative humidity of 50% at 70° F. the actual p.p. of the steam is $0·5 \times 0·3630 = 0·1815$ lb. per sq. in. and the dew-point (when condensation would commence) is at 50·5° F.

$\therefore$ p.p. of air $= 14·7 - 0·1815 = 14·5185$ lb. per sq. in.

Working at the dew-point (50·5° F.), since we only know the specific volume of this steam under saturation conditions, not for the superheat region,

$$\text{Volume of air per lb. of air} = \frac{w\text{RT}}{\text{P}} = \frac{1 \times 53·3 \times 510·5}{14·52 \times 144} = 13·14 \text{ cu. ft.}$$

And by Dalton's Law this is also the volume of the steam component per lb. of air. But we have 1,674 cu. ft. of steam per lb. of steam at dew-point conditions (see above table)

$\therefore \dfrac{13·14}{1,674} = 0·00785$ lb. of steam are associated with 1 lb. of *dry* air at the air admission at the bottom of the tower. Now, 30,000 lb. of moist air are supplied to the tower per hr., if x is the weight of *dry* air per hr.,

$$30,000 = x + 0·00785x$$

whence, $x = \dfrac{30,000}{1·00785} = 29,766$ lb. of *dry* air per hr.

Also, $29,766 \times 0·00785 = 234$ lb. of vapour per hr.

Although this has been evaluated for $t = 50·5°$ F., the ratio of the *mass* of steam and air must be the same at any *higher* temperature (the steam being then superheated), but not at a lower temperature than 50·5° F., when the steam would condense.

At the top of the tower :

The air leaves at 110° F. and is saturated, i.e. the dew-point is 110° F. and the p.p. of the steam 1·275 lb. per sq. in.

$$\therefore \text{ p.p. of air} = 14\cdot7 - 1\cdot275 = 13\cdot425 \text{ lb. per sq. in.}$$

Proceeding as before,

$$\text{Volume per lb. of air} = \frac{1 \times 53\cdot3 \times 570}{13\cdot425 \times 144} = 15\cdot716 \text{ cu. ft.}$$

$$\therefore \frac{15\cdot716}{265\cdot4} = 0\cdot0595 \text{ lb. of steam per lb. of } dry \text{ air.}$$

$\therefore$ Water evaporated by air passing up the tower $= 0\cdot0595 - 0\cdot00785$

$$= 0\cdot05165 \text{ lb. per lb. of dry air}$$

$\therefore$ <u>Loss per hr.</u> $= 0\cdot05165 \times 29,766 = \underline{1,536 \text{ lb.}}$ (i.e. 3·8%). Ans.

Also, $29,766 \times 0\cdot0595 = 1,770$ lb. of vapour per hr. are leaving the top of the tower.

To find the final temperature of the jacket water, we shall have to draw up a heat balance, bearing in mind that the steam component will always be superheated at temperatures above the dew-point. No values for the specific heat of superheated steam are given in the question, so that we shall have to make a reasonable assumption, say 0·5. Actually, C_p will probably be less at the low p.p. of the steam, but as there are only a few degrees of superheat the error involved will be small. The student should also recall that the datum for steam tables is always 32° F. and therefore the sensible heat of water, at moderate temperatures, is very nearly $(t - 32)$ B.T.U. per lb. and the total heat of dry air is

$$C_p(t - 32) = 0\cdot24(t - 32) \text{ B.T.U. per lb.}$$

reckoned from the same datum.

Heat entering the tower = Heat in dry air at bottom
+ Heat in vapour at bottom + Heat in warm engine water at top

$$= \big[29,766 \times 0\cdot24 \times (70 - 32)\big] + \big[234(1083\cdot9 + 0\cdot5 \times 19\cdot5)\big]$$
$$+ \big[40,000(125 - 32)\big].$$

Similarly, Heat leaving the tower

$$= \big[29,766 \times 0\cdot24 \times (110 - 32)\big] + \big[1,770 \times 1,109\cdot5\big] + \big[38,464(t - 32)\big].$$

$\therefore$ Neglecting losses, and collecting up terms,

$$\big[234 \times 1,093\cdot7\big] + \big[40,000 \times 93\big] = \big[29,766 \times 0\cdot24 \times 40\big]$$
$$+ \big[1,770 \times 1,109\cdot5\big] + \big[38,464(t - 32)\big]$$
$$256 + 3,720 = 286 + 1,965 + 38\cdot464(t - 32)$$
$$t - 32 = \frac{1,725}{38\cdot5} = 44\cdot8 \qquad \underline{t = 77° \text{ F.}} \text{ approx. Ans.}$$

10. *A volume of 10,000 cu. ft. of moist air is at 14·7 lb. per sq. in. and 45° F. and its relative humidity is 0·705. It is required to heat the air at constant pressure to 65° F.*

Find :

    (a) *the heat to be supplied, if C_p for air = 0·24 and C_p for steam = 0·475;*

    (b) *the relative humidity after heating.*

° F.	P lb. per sq. in.	Heat per lb.		Specific vol. cu. ft. per lb.
		h	L	
36	0·1040	4·03	1,073·2	2,837
45	0·1475	13·07	1,068·1	2,037
65	0·3060	33·08	1,056·8	1,022

(U. Lond.)

The p.p. of the vapour at 45° F., if the air is saturated = 0·1475 lb. per sq. in.

∴ actual p.p. of vapour at 45° F., rel. humidity 0·705 = 0·1475 × 0·705
$$= 0·1040 \text{ lb. per sq. in.}$$

The saturation temperature at this pressure is 36° F., according to the extracts from extended steam tables provided with the question. As we do not know the law of variation of the specific volume of superheated steam in the air, it will now be necessary to carry out an imaginary cooling operation to 36° F. with the 10,000 cu. ft., so that the air will be saturated. Then, knowing V_s for steam, we can calculate the mass of steam associated with the air.

∴ Cooling 10,000 cu. ft. of air from 45° F. to 36° F. at constant total pressure reduces the volume of the air to

$$10,000 \times \frac{496}{505} = 9,820 \text{ cu. ft.}$$

This new volume is saturated with steam, having $V_s = 2,837$ cu. ft. per lb. and thus contains

$$\frac{9,820}{2,837} = 3·46 \text{ lb. of steam.}$$

But the p.p. of the air component at 36° F.

$$= 14·7 - 0·104 = 14·596 \text{ lb. per sq. in.}$$

∴ Weight of dry air in 9,820 cu. ft. and at 36° F.

$$= \frac{PV}{RT} = \frac{144 \times 14·596 \times 9,820}{53·3 \times 496} = 782 \text{ lb.}$$

The weights of steam and air thus found will, of course, be the same at any temperature above 36° F., due to the principle of conservation of mass.

(a) At any temperature above 36° F. the steam is superheated, so that the heating from 45° F. to 65° F. is a superheating operation for the steam component, taking place at constant pressure.

$$\therefore \text{ Heat given to steam} = 3 \cdot 46 [H_{sup_2} - H_{sup_1}] \backsimeq 3 \cdot 46 \times C_p \times (t_2 - t_1)$$
$$= 3 \cdot 46 \times 0 \cdot 475 \times (65 - 45) = 32 \cdot 9$$
$$\text{Heat given to air} = 782 \times 0 \cdot 24 \times (65 - 45)$$
$$= 3{,}754$$

$$\text{Net Heat supplied} = 3{,}787 \text{ B.T.U. \quad Ans.}$$

(b) 10,000 cu. ft. of air at 45° F. become $10{,}000 \times \dfrac{525}{505} = 10{,}400$ cu. ft.

on heating to 65° F.; or 9,820 cu. ft. of air at 36° F. become $9{,}820 \times \dfrac{525}{496} = 10{,}400$ cu. ft. at 65° F.

The information provided in the above table tells us that 10,400 cu. ft. of air (and $\therefore$ of steam) could hold $\dfrac{10{,}400}{1{,}022} = 10 \cdot 18$ lb. of steam.

But the actual weight of steam has remained constant at 3·46 lb., since none is condensed.

$$\therefore \text{ New relative humidity} = \frac{3 \cdot 46}{10 \cdot 18}$$
$$= 0 \cdot 34. \quad \text{Ans.}$$

EXAMPLES

1. A vessel of 10 cu. ft. capacity contains a mixture of C_6H_6 vapour and air, the air being 15% in excess of that required for complete chemical combination. The pressure of the mixture is 25 lb. per sq. in. at 180° F. Find the partial pressures and masses of the C_6H_6, O_2 and N_2 present, given that air contains 23·1% by weight of O_2 and that R = 1·985 B.T.U. per lb.mol.   (*U. Lond.*)

[$C_6H_6 : O_2 : N_2 = 1 : 8 \cdot 625 : 32 \cdot 8$ by vol.; p.p.'s in same order 0·59, 5·08, 19·33 lb. per sq. in.; R's ditto 19·80, 48·25, 55·20 ft.lb. per lb. ° F.; w's ditto 0·067, 0·237, 0·788 lb.]

2. A mixture of steam, 0·90 dry, and air is contained in a cylinder at 180° F. and 20 lb. per sq. in. The contents are now compressed to one-fifth of the original volume, when the temperature becomes 273·1° F.

Determine, neglecting the volume of any water present:

(a) the resulting pressure in the container;
(b) the final dryness of the steam.   (*U. Lond.*)

[Take R for air = 53·3 ft.lb. per lb. ° F.; p.p. steam = 7·5 lb. per sq. in. initially and 44 lb. per sq. in. finally; by (I,7), 0·526 lb. of air per 10 initial cu. ft. of space, and $\therefore$ final p.p. air = 71·4 lb. per sq. in. Ans. (a) 115·4 lb. per sq. in. For (b) $0 \cdot 9V_{s_1} = 5 \times x_2 V_{s_2}$, $x_2 = 0 \cdot 943$.]

3. A fuel consisting of 84% carbon and 16% hydrogen is burned completely, the air supplied being 50% in excess of the chemically correct requirement. Find :

    (*a*) the partial pressure of the water vapour in the products of combustion if the pressure is 15 lb. per sq. in. and the temperature is 450° F. ;

    (*b*) the Total Heat per lb. of the products, taking 32° F. as datum ;

    (*c*) the weight of 1 cu. ft. of the products at 450° F.

Air contains 23·1% O_2 by weight, and the mean specific heat of the dry gases is 0·24.   (*U. Lond.*)

[(*a*) 1·44 lb. per sq. in. ; (*b*) H steam from chart 1,264 B.T.U. per lb. ; total heat in D.F.G. = 2,250 and in H_2O = 1,820 B.T.U. per lb. of fuel ; total heat per lb. of products = 170 B.T.U. ; mean R for products = 53·8 ft.lb. per lb. ° F. ; w = 0·0441 lb. per cu. ft.]

4. Explain carefully the importance of a low vacuum in steam turbine practice.

The vacuum at the air extraction pipe in a condenser is 28 in. of mercury (barometer 30 in.) and the temperature 35·77° C. (96·3° F.). The air leakage into the condenser is 4 lb. per 10,000 lb. of steam. Determine :

    (*a*) the volume of air to be dealt with by the dry air pump per lb. of steam entering the condenser ;

    (*b*) the weight of water vapour associated with this air.

Take R for air = 96 ft.lb. per lb. per ° C. = 53·3 ft.lb. per lb. per ° F.

                                        (*U.L.C.I.*)

[p.p. air = 0·13 lb. per sq. in. ; (*a*) 0·634 cu. ft. of air per lb. of steam ; 0·245 lb. of air per lb. of vapour ; (*b*) 0·00163 lb. of vapour per lb. of steam.]

5. Show that, in a mixture of gases contained in a closed vessel, if the percentage by volume of any constituent is *a* and the total pressure P, then the partial pressure of that constituent is $\dfrac{aP}{100}$; whereas, if its percentage by weight is *m* and its molecular weight M, the partial pressure of that constituent is given by $\dfrac{\frac{mP}{M}}{\Sigma\frac{m}{M}}$, the denominator being the sum of terms such as $\dfrac{m}{M}$.

A closed vessel contains a mixture of hydrogen and air in the volumetric proportions of 20% to 80%, the pressure and temperature in the vessel being 15 lb. per sq. in. and 15° C. respectively. The mixture is exploded and the hydrogen completely burnt. Show that, after explosion, dew would form in the vessel at a temperature just under 65° C. and find the total pressure in the vessel at 60° C.

For air : analysis by volume, oxygen 20·9%, nitrogen 79·1%. (*U. Camb.*)

[$H_2O : O_2 : N_2 = 20 : 6\cdot7 : 63\cdot3$, by vol. ; $\dfrac{P_2}{T_2} = 0\cdot0260$ lb. per sq. in. × ° F. allowing for 10% mol. decrease ; $\dfrac{\text{p.p. } H_2O}{T_2} = 0\cdot00578$; from steam tables by interpolating $\dfrac{P_s}{T_s}$, p.p. $H_2O = 3\cdot51$ lb. per sq. in., $t_s = 147\cdot7°$ F. ; at 140° F., $V_s = 123\cdot1$ cu. ft. per lb. ; $x = 0\cdot832$, giving 16·64 lb.mols of H_2O instead of 20 ; $P_s = 2\cdot89$ lb. per sq. in. ; $P_2 = 15\cdot05$ lb. per sq. in.]

6. An air-conditioning plant is to deliver air at a temperature of 20° C. and with a relative humidity of 43%. For this purpose a steady stream of air is cooled, saturated with water vapour and then heated up to 20° C.

Estimate the temperature at which saturation must take place and the heat supplied in raising the temperature per 1,000 cu. ft. delivered.

The pressure of the air and steam may be taken each to remain constant, the total being 15 lb. per sq. in. The mean specific heat of the steam may be taken as 0·5.

For air : $K_p = 0·240$, R = 96 ft.lb. C. units.   (*U. Camb.*)

[Use the following data, abstracted from extended steam tables : P_s at 68° F. = 0·3390 lb. per sq. in. ; t_s and V_s at 0·146 lb. per sq. in. = 45° F. and 2,036 cu. ft. per lb.   Then, 1,000 cu. ft. at 68° F. contain 76·0 lb. of air and equal 957 cu. ft. at 45° F. which hold 0·470 lb. H_2O ; $\therefore$ Q = 420 + 5·4 = 425 B.T.U.]

7. Explain why the relative humidity of the atmosphere may be expressed for practical purposes as the ratio of the saturation pressure at the dew-point to the saturation pressure at the actual temperature of the air.

Air at a pressure of 14·69 lb. per sq. in. and a temperature of 75° F. has a relative humidity of 80%. If this air is compressed to 30 lb. per sq. in. and a temperature of 85° F., and is saturated under these conditions, find the weight of vapour which will have been condensed per lb. of *dry* air.

68	.	.	.	0·3390	925·9
69	.	.	.	0·3509	896·3
75	.	.	.	0·4298	740·0
85	.	.	.	0·5959	543·5

(*U. Lond.*)

[Initial p.p. of vapour = 0·3438, $\therefore$ t_s = 68·4° F. (dew-point) ; at 68·4° F., vol. per lb. of dry air = 13·62 cu. ft. ; lb. of vapour per lb. of dry air = 0·0149 ; new p.p. of air = 29·404 lb. per sq. in. ; new vol. per lb. of dry air = 6·87 cu. ft. containing 0·0126 lb. of vapour ; Ans. = 0·0023 lb.]

8. A surface condenser, fitted with separate air and water extraction pumps, has a portion of the tubes near the air-pump suction screened off from the steam so that the air is cooled below the condensate temperature. The steam condensed per hr. is 5,000 lb. and the air leakage is 4 lb. per hr.   The inlet temperature of the steam is 38° C., the temperature at entrance to the air cooler is 37° C. and at the air-pump suction is 31° C.   The properties of steam at these temperatures may be taken as follows :

Temperature, ° C.	.	.	.	.	38	37	31
Vapour pressure, in Hg.	.	.	.		1·94	1·84	1·32
Specific volume, cu. ft. per lb.	.	.			344	365	500

Assuming a constant vacuum throughout the condenser, find

(*a*) The weight of steam condensed in the air cooler per minute ;
(*b*) The volume of air to be dealt with by the air pump per minute.

(*U. Lond.*)

[Assume, 5,000 lb. per hr. is the *dry* steam component entering condenser ; R = 96 ft.lb. per lb. × ° C. for air ; *at inlet to condenser* : p.p. air = 0·000483, $\therefore$ condenser pressure = 0·951 lb. per sq. in. abs., vol. of air per min. = vol. of steam per min. = 28,650 cu. ft. ; *at entrance to cooler* : air p.p. = 0·049 lb. per sq. in., vol. of air per min. = 281 cu. ft., associated steam = 0·771 lb. ; *at air-pump suction* : air p.p. = 0·304 lb. per sq. in., vol. of air per min. = 44·4 cu. ft., associated steam = 0·088 lb. ; $\therefore$ condensed steam per min. = 0·683 lb.]

CHAPTER XII

PROPERTIES OF STEAM

Introduction

The student should familiarize himself with the use of the steam tables [1] and observe the following :

Information available on the first and last pages of the steam tables :

J = 778 ft.lb. per B.T.U.

$a = 1/5\cdot4$ (cf. chapter I, page 1)

The standard barometric pressure is 30 in. of mercury at 62° F.

    = 14·696 lb. per sq. in.

1 in. of mercury = 0·49 lb. per sq. in.

Volume per lb. of water = 0·01602 + 0·000023G. cu. ft.

Volume per lb. of superheated steam $= \dfrac{1\cdot253(H - 835)}{P}$ cu. ft.

    where P is in lb. per sq. in.

1 h.p.-hr. = 2,546 B.T.U. ; 1 h.p.-min. = 42·4 B.T.U.

1 k.W.-hr. = 3,413 B.T.U.

Table I

This is tabulated in *absolute* pressures, and in examination papers pressures are usually quoted as absolute ; if they are not, then they are expressed as *gauge* pressures. The second column giving either the vacuum in in. of mercury or the gauge pressure, is based on the standard barometric height of 30 in., and for barometric heights other than 30 in. the appropriate correction must be added or subtracted.

The temperature is the saturation temperature, and the values for the liquid heat " h " refer only to water at saturation pressure and temperature, i.e. boiling water.

The use of G (Gibbs' Function) is demonstrated in various examples.

The values of h, L and H_s are self-explanatory ; but it should be noted that only the liquid entropy and the total entropy of the dry saturated vapour are given. If the increase in entropy due to the latent heat is required, then a subtraction is needed (cf. I,25).

The volume per lb. of dry saturated steam is given in the last column but one.

The values of st_o and Factor Π are not generally of interest to the engineering student.

Tables II and III

It is essential that these tables always be consulted when the values

[1] " *Abridged Callendar Steam Tables*, Fahrenheit Units ", fourth edition, Edward Arnold & Co.

of the total heat or entropy of superheated steam is required. Often this entails an interpolation for both pressure and temperature, a typical example being explained in question 4 of this chapter.

From Table II, the mean value of the specific heat over any given range of temperature can be obtained, and this method should be adopted whenever possible, in preference to using some arbitrary value such as 0·5.

In order to obtain values of H, V and ϕ for wet steam, see (I,24), (I,31) and (I,26).

1. *It is desired to estimate the condition of the steam entering a surface condenser ; describe briefly how this could be done without taking a sample of the steam, and what major assumptions would be made.*

10,000 lb. of steam enter a surface condenser per hr. with a pressure 1 lb. per sq. in. abs. ; 70,000 gal. of cooling water are passed through the tubes per hr. and its temperature rises from 82·5° F. to 95° F. The condensed steam leaves the condenser with a temperature 90° F. ; what is the condition of the steam entering the condenser ? (I.Mech.E.)

The major assumptions to be made are :

    (a) the heat losses by radiation, etc., are negligible, and

    (b) the actual *steam* pressure is 1 lb. per sq. in., i.e. there is no air present.

The errors introduced by making these assumptions are not great, especially when compared with the accuracy of measurement of the circulating water quantity and temperature rise.

Since 1 gal. of water weighs 10 lb.,

Weight of cooling water per lb. of steam = 70 lb.

Heat removed by this quantity of cooling water

$$= 70(95 - 82·5) = 875 \text{ B.T.U.}$$

If the dryness of the exhaust steam be x, then the total heat of this steam will be $h + xL$ (I,24)

$$= 69·7 + x.1036·1.$$

The liquid heat of the condensate will be very nearly

$$(90 - 32) = 58 \text{ B.T.U.}$$

∴ Heat removed by the cooling water per lb. of steam, the pressure of the steam remaining constant,

$$= 69·7 + x.1036·1 - 58.$$

Equating this to 875 B.T.U. we have,

$$x = \frac{863·3}{1036·1} = \underline{0·833 \text{ dry.}} \quad \text{Ans.}$$

2. *Steam at 250 lb. per sq. in. and 0·95 dry is throttled to 200 lb. per sq. in. and passed to an engine which expands it adiabatically to 4 lb. per sq. in. and exhausts at this pressure.*

Calculate, using the steam tables :

(a) *the entropy per lb. of steam entering the engine ;*
(b) *the steam consumption of the engine in lb. per h.p.-hr. ;*
(c) *the internal energy per lb. of steam leaving the boiler.*

(*U. Lond.*)

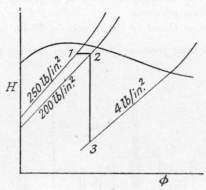

Fig. XII,1.

The throttling process is shown as 1 to 2 on the diagram, the total heat being constant.

(a) $\qquad H_1 = 1{,}202 \cdot 1 - 0 \cdot 05 \times 826 \cdot 0 = 1{,}160 \cdot 8$ B.T.U.
$\qquad\quad H_2 = 355 \cdot 5 + x_2 \times 844.$

Equating H_1 and H_2 gives $x_2 = 0 \cdot 954.$

$$\therefore \phi_2 = 0 \cdot 5437 + 0 \cdot 954(1 \cdot 5466 - 0 \cdot 5437)$$
$$= 1 \cdot 5005. \quad \text{Ans.}$$

(b) $\qquad \phi_3 = \phi_2 = 0 \cdot 2199 + x_3(1 \cdot 8632 - 0 \cdot 2199)$
$\qquad\quad \therefore x_3 = 0 \cdot 779.$
$\qquad\quad \therefore H_3 = 121 \cdot 0 + 0 \cdot 779 \times 1{,}006 \cdot 7 = 905 \cdot 2$ B.T.U.

By (I,37), the work done is equal to the heat drop in this case.

$$\therefore \text{Heat drop} = 255 \cdot 6 \text{ B.T.U. per lb.} = \text{W.D.}$$

$$\therefore \text{Consumption} = \frac{2{,}546}{255 \cdot 6} = 9 \cdot 96 \text{ lb. per h.p.-hr.} \quad \text{Ans.}$$

(c) $\qquad \dfrac{P_1 V_1}{J} = \dfrac{250 \times 144 \times 0 \cdot 95 \times 1 \cdot 844}{778} = 81 \cdot 0$ B.T.U. per lb.

$\therefore$ By (I,1) $\qquad$ Internal Energy $= 1{,}160 \cdot 8 - 81 \cdot 0$
$$= 1{,}079 \cdot 8 \text{ B.T.U.} \quad \text{Ans.}$$

3. *State the principle of the throttling calorimeter. Why is it necessary, under certain conditions, to incorporate a separator with a throttling calorimeter?*

In a test on a combined separating and throttling calorimeter the following data were obtained:

Pressure of steam before throttling   = 200 lb. per sq. in.
Pressure of steam after throttling   = 15 lb. per sq. in.
Temperature of steam after throttling = 273° F.
Discharge from separator   = 0·4 lb. per min.
Discharge from throttling calorimeter = 20 lb. per min.

Determine the dryness fraction of the steam entering the separator.

(U.L.C.I.)

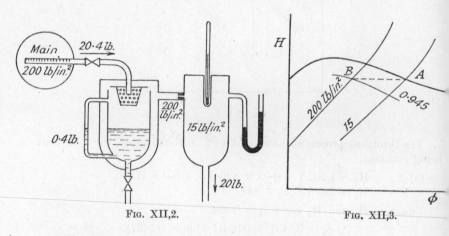

Fig. XII,2.   Fig. XII,3.

Throttling is an operation of constant total heat or enthalpy.

If the dryness of the steam to be throttled is less than a certain value there will be no superheating after throttling and so the total heat of the throttled steam cannot be estimated. Under these conditions it would be necessary to use a combined separating and throttling calorimeter arranged as in fig. XII,2. The water collected in the separator is measured under the mains pressure, for if this water were drained from the separator, a certain proportion would "flash" into steam at the lower pressure. At 200 lb. per sq. in., the liquid heat is 355·5 B.T.U., whereas at 15 lb. per sq. in. this is only 181·2 B.T.U. So if this high-pressure water were discharged to the atmosphere it would become very wet steam, the dryness fraction of which would be given by

$$355\cdot5 = 181\cdot2 + x.970$$
$$x = 0\cdot179.$$

Nearly 18% would immediately evaporate into steam, leaving only 82% as water.

For the limiting case when a throttling calorimeter alone may be used, the throttled steam would be just dry saturated at A on the total heat-entropy diagram. The point B at 200 lb. per sq. in. and at the same total heat would represent the state of the steam before throttling, giving a dryness of 0·945.

In the problem, the degrees of superheat after throttling are

$$273 - 213 = 60° \text{ F.},$$

and by reference to Table II the total heat is 1,180·5 B.T.U. per lb. If it had been assumed that the specific heat of the steam were 0·5, the value would have been 1,181·2 B.T.U. The error would have been much greater at higher pressures and temperatures, and it is better to use Tables II and III for the properties of superheated steam.

Equating the total heat before throttling to that after throttling:

$$1,180·5 = 355·5 + x.844$$
$$x = 0·978 \text{ dry.}$$

If 20 lb. of steam per min. are discharged from the throttling calorimeter, the weight of water in the high-pressure steam entering must have been $20(1 - 0·978) = 0·44$ lb. Thus if 20·4 lb. of steam flows from the main, 0·4 lb. of water collected in the separator and 0·44 lb. of water entering the throttling calorimeter, the dryness of the steam in the main is

$$\frac{20·4 - (0·4 + 0·44)}{20·4} = \underline{0·959.} \quad \text{Ans.}$$

However, if the weight of water discharged from the separator under atmospheric conditions had been 0·4 lb., the actual weight of water removed by the separator would have been $\dfrac{0·4}{0·821} = 0·488$ lb., giving a dryness of 0·945.

As we are only interested in the dryness fraction of the steam entering the separator and not in the dryness fraction of the steam entering the throttling calorimeter, we could proceed as follows in place of the above:

Total heat in mains steam − Sensible heat of separated water
= Total heat of throttled steam

$$20·4(355·5 + 844x) - 0·4 \times 355·5 = 20 \times 1,180·5$$
$$20 \times 355·5 + 20·4 \times 844 \times x = 20 \times 1,180·5$$

$$x - \frac{16,500}{17,220} = \underline{0·959.} \quad \text{Ans.}$$

This solution assumes, of course, that the 0·4 lb. of water is collected at mains pressure. This is the usual assumption to make, as it corresponds to the practical method.

A.T.E.   O

4. *The expansion of the steam in a cylinder follows the law $PV^{1.1} = $ constant. The state at the commencement is 0·9 dry at 40 lb. per sq. in., and the expansion is continued until the volume is four times that at the commencement. Estimate the quantity of heat which must pass into or out of 1 lb. of steam during the expansion.* (*U. Lond.*)

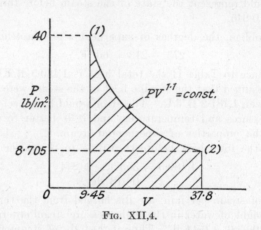

FIG. XII,4.

This is a " non-flow " process or one " phase " of a cycle.

The work done during the expansion according to the law $PV^n = $ constant is given by $\dfrac{P_1V_1 - P_2V_2}{n-1}$ (I,4) and is represented by the shaded area in the diagram.

At 40 lb. per sq. in. $V_s = 10·5$ cu. ft. per lb.

$$\therefore xV_s = 9·45 \text{ cu. ft. per lb.}$$

$$\therefore \text{ Final volume} = 4 \times 9·45 = 37·8 \text{ cu. ft.}$$

The pressure at the end of expansion is obtained from

$$\frac{40}{P} = 4^{1.1} = 4·595$$

whence $P = 8·705$ lb. per sq. in.

Also, we have $\dfrac{P_1V_1}{J} = \dfrac{40 \times 144 \times 9·45}{778} = 70·0$ B.T.U.

and $\dfrac{P_2V_2}{J} = \dfrac{8·705 \times 144 \times 37·8}{778} = 60·9$ B.T.U.

$$\therefore \frac{P_1V_1 - P_2V_2}{J} = 9·1 \text{ B.T.U.}$$

and W.D. $= \dfrac{9·1}{n-1} = 91·0$ B.T.U. by (I,4).

Using Table I of the steam tables and interpolating to find the values for a pressure of 8·7 lb. per sq. in. :

p	h	L	V_s
8·5	153·8	986·8	44·73
9·0	156·5	985·2	42·40

−0·5	−2·7	1·6	2·33 for −0·5 lb. per sq. in.
0·2	1·1	−0·6	−0·93 ,, 0·2 ,, ,, ,, ,,

8·7	154·9	986·2	43·60 ,, 8·7 ,, ,, ,, ,,

The dryness at the end of expansion is $\dfrac{37·8}{43·6} = 0·866$.

Since $E = H - \dfrac{PV}{J}$ (I,1) we can find the Internal Energy at points (1) and (2).

$$H_1 = 236·1 + 0·9 \times 934·4 = 1{,}077 \text{ B.T.U.}$$
$$H_2 = 154·9 + 0·866 \times 986·2 = 1{,}009 \text{ B.T.U.}$$
$$\therefore H_2 - H_1 = -68 \text{ B.T.U.}$$

$$\therefore E_2 - E_1 = (H_2 - H_1) - \left(\frac{P_2 V_2 - P_1 V_1}{J}\right)$$

$$= -68 + 9·1$$
$$= -58·9 \text{ B.T.U.}$$

Also by (I,2a) $Q = (E_2 - E_1) + \text{W.D.}_{1-2}$
$$= -58·9 + 91$$
$$= +32·1 \text{ B.T.U. flowing into the cylinder.   Ans.}$$

The steam gives up 91 B.T.U. of work ; the Internal Energy supplies only 58·9 B.T.U., leaving 32·1 B.T.U. to be supplied from an outside source which, in this case, would probably be the steam jacket.

5. *Explain how the Internal Energy of 1 lb. of steam may be calculated. Steam at a pressure of 80 lb. per sq. in. and with 40° F. of superheat, is expanded adiabatically and without loss in a cylinder to 15 lb. per sq. in. Using the steam tables, calculate the work done per lb. of steam during the expansion and deduce the mean adiabatic index of expansion over this range.*

(*U. Lond.*)

Because the expansion represents a phase or non-flow operation, is frictionless (without loss) and adiabatic the work done will equal the change in Internal Energy numerically (cf. I,2). The initial volume per lb. is deduced from the expression $\dfrac{1 \cdot 253(H - 835)}{P}$. H is taken from Table II and is 1,205·6 B.T.U. giving a volume of $\dfrac{1 \cdot 253}{80}(1{,}205 \cdot 6 - 835) = 5 \cdot 803$ cu. ft.

From Table III the entropy at the start of the expansion is 1·6488, and equating this to the total entropy of the wet steam after expansion, we have, using suffices 1 and 2 to represent the initial and the final states,

$$1 \cdot 6488 = 0 \cdot 3137 + x_2 \times 1 \cdot 4419$$

whence $\qquad x_2 = 0 \cdot 926$ dry.

∴ Total heat after expansion, $H_2 = 181 \cdot 2 + 0 \cdot 926 \times 970$
$$= 1{,}079 \cdot 4 \text{ B.T.U.}$$

By (I,1), $E_1 = H_1 - \dfrac{P_1 V_1}{J} = 1{,}205 \cdot 6 - \dfrac{80 \times 144 \times 5 \cdot 803}{778}$

$$= 1{,}205 \cdot 6 - 85 \cdot 9 = 1{,}119 \cdot 7 \text{ B.T.U.}$$

$$E_2 = 1{,}079 \cdot 4 - \frac{15 \times 144 \times 0 \cdot 926 \times 26 \cdot 28}{778}$$

$$= 1{,}079 \cdot 4 - 67 \cdot 6 = 1{,}011 \cdot 8 \text{ B.T.U.}$$

∴ $E_2 - E_1 = -107 \cdot 9$ B.T.U.

hence the W.D. per lb. of steam is $+107 \cdot 9$ B.T.U., since the value of Q is zero in the equation (I,2) $Q = \varDelta E + \text{W.D.}$ Ans.

Also $\qquad\qquad \text{W.D.} = \dfrac{P_1 V_1 - P_2 V_2}{n - 1}$

where n is the mean adiabatic index over this range.

Thus $\qquad\qquad 107 \cdot 9 \times 778 = \dfrac{(85 \cdot 9 - 67 \cdot 6)}{n - 1} \times 778$

or $\qquad\qquad n - 1 = \dfrac{18 \cdot 3}{107 \cdot 9}$ and $n = 1 \cdot 17$, nearly. Ans.

6. *A mass of 60 lb. of H_2O is contained in a closed vessel of 6 cu. ft. capacity*
at 800 lb. per sq. in., there being nothing but H_2O present. Find the amount
of heat required to raise the pressure to 1,000 lb. per sq. in., assuming that any
steam present is dry saturated and given that the specific volumes of boiling
water at 800 and 1,000 lb. per sq. in. are 0·0209 and 0·0216 cu. ft. per lb.
respectively. (*U. Lond.*)

When heat is supplied to any fluid in a closed vessel there is no change
in total volume, and so no external work is performed. The heat supplied
increases the Internal Energy only (cf. I,2). The volumes per lb. of water
are given, because the value 0·01602 + 0·000023G as quoted in the steam
tables is only valid as far as 450° F., the saturation temperatures at 800 and
1,000 lb. per sq. in. being above this. In view of the high pressures and
therefore the low values of V_s, the specific volume of water is not negligible
here.

At 800 lb. per sq. in. $V_s = 0·569$ cu. ft.

Let there be x lb. of liquid and $(60 - x)$ lb. of *dry* steam.

Then $\qquad\qquad x \times 0·0209 + (60 - x)0·569 = 6$

whence $\qquad x = 51·33$ lb., $\therefore$ 8·67 lb. of *dry* steam,

and   Total Heat $= 51·33 \times 509·9 + 8·67 \times 1,199·6 = 36,580$ B.T.U.

also $\qquad\qquad \dfrac{PV}{J} = \dfrac{144 \times 800 \times 6}{778} = 888$ B.T.U.

$\therefore$ By (I,1) Original Internal Energy $= 35,692$ B.T.U.

At 1,000 lb. per sq. in. $V_s = 0·446$.

Let there be y lb. of liquid and $(60 - y)$ lb. of dry steam.

$$y \times 0·0216 + (60 - y)0·446 = 6$$

whence $\qquad y = 48·9$ lb., $\therefore$ 11·1 lb. of dry steam,

and   Total Heat $= 48·9 \times 542·6 + 11·1 \times 1,192·8 = 39,780$ B.T.U.

also $\qquad\qquad \dfrac{PV}{J} = \dfrac{144 \times 1,000 \times 6}{778} = 1,110$ B.T.U.

$\therefore$ Final Internal Energy $= 38,670$ B.T.U.

$\therefore$ By (I,2a) Heat supplied $=$ change in Internal Energy $+$ W.D.

$\qquad\qquad\qquad\qquad = 38,670 - 35,692 + 0$

$\qquad\qquad\qquad\qquad\qquad = \underline{+\ 2,978\ \text{B.T.U.}}$ Ans.

7. *What is the final condition of the steam in each of the following operations, if the initial condition in each case is 0·95 dry, pressure 120 lb. per sq. in. ?*

    (i) *The steam loses 35 C.H.U. per lb. at constant pressure ;*

    (ii) *its temperature is reduced at constant volume to 165° C. ;*

    (iii) *it does 55 C.H.U. of work per lb. in a turbine stage and leaves at 40 lb. per sq. in. ;*

    (iv) *it receives 20 C.H.U. per lb. at constant pressure, and is then throttled to a pressure 50 lb. per sq. in.*

(U.L.C.I.)

(i)   35 C.H.U. = 63 B.T.U.

At constant pressure, the loss in heat will increase the wetness. The latent heat at 120 lb. per sq. in. is 878·9 B.T.U.

$\therefore$ Increase in wetness due to the removal of 63 B.T.U. $= \dfrac{63}{878\cdot9} = 7\cdot16\%.$

$\therefore$ Final dryness $= 95 - 7\cdot16 = \underline{87\cdot8\%}.$ Ans.

(ii)   165° C. = 329° F.

Since the saturation temperature at 120 lb. per sq. in. is 341·3° F., the reduction in temperature will lower the pressure to the saturation pressure at 329° F. By interpolation using Table I, this pressure is 101·7 lb. per sq. in.

The specific volumes at 120 and 101·7 lb. per sq. in. are 3·729 and 4·364 cu. ft. per lb. respectively.

Let x be the dryness at 101·7 lb. per sq. in. Then since the volume remains constant we have :

$$0\cdot95 \times 3\cdot729 = x \times 4\cdot364$$

$$\underline{x = 0\cdot812 \text{ dry.}}\quad \text{Ans.}$$

(iii)   55 C.H.U. = 99 B.T.U.

The total heat at commencement $= 312\cdot5 + 0\cdot95 \times 878\cdot9$
$$= 1{,}147\cdot6 \text{ B.T.U.}$$

The W.D. in the turbine, 99 B.T.U., is the only expenditure of energy, there being no other losses, the total heat at 40 lb. per sq. in. will be

$$1{,}147\cdot6 - 99 = 1{,}048\cdot6 \text{ B.T.U. (cf. I,37).}$$

$\therefore$ Dryness at 40 lb. per sq. in. $= \dfrac{1{,}048\cdot6 - 236\cdot1}{934\cdot4} = \underline{0\cdot870}.$ Ans.

This result implies a decrease in entropy (cf. chart), which is rather unlikely to occur in practice.

(iv)   20 C.H.U. = 36 B.T.U.

The total heat will be increased to 1,147·6 + 36 = 1,183·6 B.T.U.

and by reference to the tables, the steam is still wet.

Since the throttling process is at constant total heat, the total heat at

50 lb. per sq. in. must also be 1,183·6, which is greater than that for dry saturated steam.

Therefore reference must be made to Table II, where by interpolation the degrees of superheat may be found as follows :

Mean specific heat between 0° and 20° of superheat

$$= \frac{1,185\cdot5 - 1,174\cdot8}{20} = 0\cdot535$$

$$\therefore \text{ Degrees of superheat} = \frac{1,183\cdot6 - 1,174\cdot8}{0\cdot535} = \underline{16\cdot5° \text{ F.}} \quad \text{Ans.}$$

The student is advised to locate all these answers on a total heat–entropy diagram for the sake of practice.

8. *Steam at 100 lb. per sq. in. and 0·90 dry expands in a cylinder according to PV = constant to 40 lb. per sq. in. Find the interchange of heat between steam and cylinder walls per lb. of steam, stating its direction.*

Give a sketch of the corresponding line on a total heat–entropy diagram.

(*U. Lond.*)

It should be noted that when the expansion is hyperbolic, $P_1V_1 = P_2V_2$ and thus the change in Internal Energy equals the change in total heat. This is, however, *only* true when the expansion is hyperbolic.

Since $P_1V_1 = P_2V_2$, we have

$$V_2 = \frac{100 \times 0\cdot9 \times 4\cdot434}{40} = 9\cdot98 \text{ cu. ft. per lb.}$$

$$\therefore \text{ dryness at 40 lb. per sq. in.} = \frac{9\cdot98}{10\cdot50} = 0\cdot950$$

$$H_2 - H_1 = (236\cdot1 + 0\cdot950 \times 934\cdot4) - (298\cdot5 + 0\cdot9 \times 889\cdot7)$$

thus $$E_2 - E_1 = + 25\cdot5 \text{ B.T.U.}$$

$$\text{W.D.} = \frac{144 \times 100 \times 0\cdot9 \times 4\cdot434}{778} \log_e 2\cdot5, \text{ by (I,5)}$$

$$= + 67\cdot7 \text{ B.T.U.}$$

Thus the heat received by the steam from the cylinder walls from (I,2) is

$$Q = + 25\cdot5 + 67\cdot7 = \underline{93\cdot2 \text{ B.T.U. per lb.}} \quad \text{Ans.}$$

The student should plot the initial and final states of the steam on the total heat–entropy diagram and observe that the Heat Drop is not the W.D. per lb. of steam because,

    (*a*) we are dealing only with the phase of expansion, not with the whole cycle ; and

    (*b*) even in a cycle the W.D. is only equal to $\varDelta H$ if the expansion phase is truly adiabatic (cf. chapter I, pages 3 and 21).

9. *A vessel having a capacity of 30 cu. ft. contains steam at 150 lb. per sq. in. and 0·92 dry. Steam is blown-off until the pressure drops to 75 lb. per sq. in. The valve is then closed and the vessel cooled until the pressure is 60 lb. per sq. in. Assuming that the total heat per lb. of steam in the vessel remains constant during the blowing-off period, determine :*

   (a) *the weight of steam blown off ;*
   (b) *the dryness of the steam in the vessel after cooling ;*
   (c) *the heat lost by the steam per lb. during cooling.*

(U. Lond.)

(*a*) Since H_1 is to be equal to H_2, during the blowing-off period,
per lb. of steam, $H_1 = 330\cdot6 + 0\cdot92 \times 864\cdot5$, at 150 lb. per sq. in.
               $= 1{,}126\cdot6$ B.T.U.

Now at 75 lb. per sq. in., by interpolation from the steam tables,
     $h = 277\cdot5, \quad L = 905\cdot3, \quad \text{and} \quad V_s = 5\cdot817$

$$\therefore H_2 = 277\cdot5 + 905\cdot3x_2 = 1{,}126\cdot6$$

$$x_2 = \frac{849\cdot1}{905\cdot3} = 0\cdot938.$$

But the volume of the vessel remains constant at 30 cu. ft.
so that $30 = 0\cdot92 \times 3\cdot015 \times w_1, \quad \therefore w_1 = 10\cdot81$ lb.
and $30 = 0\cdot938 \times 5\cdot817 \times w_2, \quad \therefore w_2 = 5\cdot50$ lb.

           Weight blown off $= 10\cdot81 - 5\cdot50 = \underline{5\cdot31}$ lb.   **Ans.**

(*b*) At 60 lb. per sq. in., $30 = 5\cdot50 \times 7\cdot175 \times x_3; \quad x_3 = \underline{0\cdot761}$ **Ans.**

(*c*) By (I,1) $E_2 = 1{,}126\cdot6 - \dfrac{75 \times 0\cdot938 \times 5\cdot817}{5\cdot4}$

             $= 1{,}126\cdot6 - 75\cdot7 = 1{,}050\cdot9$ B.T.U. per lb.

and $E_3 = (262\cdot2 + 0\cdot761 \times 916\cdot2) - \dfrac{60 \times 0\cdot761 \times 7\cdot175}{5\cdot4}$

             $= 959\cdot2 - 60\cdot6 = 898\cdot6$ B.T.U. per lb.

By (I,2), since no external work is done during the cooling operation which takes place at constant volume,

$$Q_{2\text{-}3} = E_3 - E_2 = 898\cdot6 - 1{,}050\cdot9 = -\underline{152\cdot3}. \quad \textbf{Ans.}$$

i.e. 152·3 B.T.U. are lost (negative sign) per lb. of steam during cooling.

10. *A boiler contains water and steam at atmospheric pressure, all air having been expelled and the stop valve closed. Find the quantity of heat required to convert 1 lb. of water from this condition into dry saturated steam at 100 lb. per sq. in., the stop valve being still closed.*

When the stop valve is open and the boiler is supplying dry saturated steam at 100 lb. per sq. in. pressure, how much additional heat is required per lb. of steam formed, from feed water at 120° F. ?   (*U. Lond.*)

When steam exists in contact with water at a given pressure, 14·7 lb. per sq. in. here, the steam must be wet and the temperature must be the saturation temperature at the given pressure, 212° F. in this case. We thus know that the conditions of the water are those corresponding to saturation conditions.

$\therefore$ For 1 lb. water, by (I,1) $E_1 = h_1 - \dfrac{P_1 V_1}{J}$

$$= 180 \cdot 1 - \frac{14 \cdot 7 \times 144 \times 0 \cdot 01670}{778}$$

$$= 180 \cdot 1, \text{ to one place of decimals.}$$

(Note, V_1 = vol. of water = $0 \cdot 01602 + 0 \cdot 000023 \times 29 \cdot 4 = 0 \cdot 01670$ cu. ft. per lb., where $G = 29 \cdot 4$ at 212° F.)

For 1 lb. dry steam at 100 lb. per sq. in.,

$$E_2 = 1,188 \cdot 2 - \frac{100 \times 144 \times 4 \cdot 434}{778}$$

$$= 1,188 \cdot 2 - 82 \cdot 1 = 1,106 \cdot 1.$$

Since the stop valve remains closed, the operation is one of constant volume and the external W.D. = 0.

$\therefore$ By (I,2) $Q = 1,106 \cdot 1 - 180 \cdot 1$

$$= \underline{\underline{926 \text{ B.T.U. per lb.}}}   \text{Ans.}$$

The safest course is now to repeat the above procedure for the second part of the question ; thus

New $E_1 = 120 - 32 = 88$ B.T.U. per lb., very nearly,

since the volume of the water is now even smaller than before and $\dfrac{PV}{J}$ is again of a negligible order.

Also, $E_2 = 1,106 \cdot 1$, as before.

The operation is now one of constant pressure,

$\therefore$ W.D. = $100 \times 144 \times (V_s - V_w)$ ft.lb. per lb.

Now $V_s = 4 \cdot 434$, and as this figure is given in the tables to three places of decimals, the initial volume of the water may not be entirely negligible. By (I,30) $V_w = 0 \cdot 01602 + 0 \cdot 000023 \times 7 \cdot 4 = 0 \cdot 01619$ cu. ft. per lb., where $G = 7 \cdot 4$ at 120° F.

i.e.   W.D. $= \dfrac{100 \times 144}{778} \times (4{\cdot}434 - 0{\cdot}016) = 81{\cdot}8$ B.T.U. per lb.

$\therefore$ By (I,2) $\begin{aligned} Q &= (1{,}106{\cdot}1 - 88) + 81{\cdot}8 \\ &= 1{,}100, \text{ nearly.} \end{aligned}$

$\therefore$ Additional heat $= 1{,}100 - 926 = \underline{174 \text{ B.T.U. per lb.}}$ Ans.

It is possible to solve the second part of the question rather more quickly, if it is remembered that $Q = \varDelta H$ at constant pressure ; this was demonstrated in chapter I, equations (I,1a) and (I,2a).

Now, $H_1 = h_1 = 88$
    $H_2 = 1{,}188{\cdot}2$

$\therefore Q = 1{,}188{\cdot}2 - 88 = 1{,}100$ B.T.U. per lb., nearly.

The greatest caution should be exercised when using such " short cuts " to an answer. It cannot be over-emphasized that $Q = \varDelta H$, only if the *pressure is constant* and in no other case. The student may be better advised to use $Q = \varDelta E + \text{W.D.}$ in all cases, as this is always correct for a non-flow process, even if it does involve a little extra work at times.

11. *Distinguish clearly between the total heat (or enthalpy) and the internal energy of superheated steam.*

A vessel of 50 cu. ft. capacity is full of steam at a pressure of 200 lb. per sq. in., its dryness fraction being 0·85. Water at 59° F. is injected under a constant head of 500 ft. How much water will it be necessary to inject in order to reduce the pressure in the vessel to 30 lb. per sq. in., and what will be the final percentages of water and dry steam, respectively, in the vessel?

Assume that there are no radiation and conduction losses.

(U. Lond.)

The distinction between H and E is given in chapter I.
The original weight of steam in the vessel will be

$$\frac{50}{0{\cdot}85 \times 2{\cdot}29} = 25{\cdot}69 \text{ lb.}$$

Let W lb. of water be injected. Then, neglecting the volume occupied by the water in the wet steam at 200 lb. per sq. in., and assuming that there are A lb. of water and B lb. of *dry* saturated steam in the vessel finally, i.e. final $x = \dfrac{B}{A + B}$, we have :

$$A \times 0{\cdot}017 + B \times 13{\cdot}73 = 50$$

(The vol. per lb. of water $= 0{\cdot}01602 + 0{\cdot}000023 \times 42{\cdot}4 = 0{\cdot}017$ cu. ft.)

Also $$A + B = 25 \cdot 69 + W$$

$$\therefore\ 0 \cdot 017A + 13 \cdot 73(25 \cdot 69 + W - A) = 50$$

$$\therefore\ A = 22 \cdot 07 + 1 \cdot 001W\ .\qquad .\qquad .\qquad .\qquad \text{(i)}$$

and $$B =\ 3 \cdot 61 + 0 \cdot 001W\ .\qquad .\qquad .\qquad .\qquad \text{(ii)}$$

$$E_1 = 355 \cdot 5 + 0 \cdot 85 \times 844 - \frac{200 \times 0 \cdot 85 \times 2 \cdot 29}{5 \cdot 4}$$

$$= 355 \cdot 5 + 717 \cdot 4 - 72 \cdot 0$$
$$= 1{,}000 \cdot 9\ \text{B.T.U. per lb.}$$

$$\therefore\ \text{Total } E_1 = 25{,}710\ \text{B.T.U.}$$

500 ft. head of water $= 216 \cdot 5$ lb. per sq. in.

$$\therefore\ \text{Total Energy per lb. of water} = 27 + \frac{216 \cdot 5 \times 0 \cdot 016}{5 \cdot 4}\ \text{(cf. below)}$$

$$= 27 \cdot 64\ \text{B.T.U.}$$

Also, the total Internal Energy finally,

$$E_2 = 219A + \left(1{,}164 \cdot 6 - \frac{30 \times 13 \cdot 73}{5 \cdot 4}\right)B$$

$$= 219A + 1{,}088 \cdot 3B.$$

Since $Q = E_2 - E_1$ under constant volume conditions (I,2),

$$27 \cdot 64W = 219A + 1{,}088 \cdot 3B - 25{,}710,$$

and by substitution from (i) and (ii),

$$\underline{W = 89 \cdot 0\ \text{lb.}}\quad \text{Ans.}$$

$$\therefore\ A = 111 \cdot 2\ \text{lb. water,}\qquad \text{i.e. } \underline{97 \cdot 1\%.}$$

$$B =\ 3 \cdot 3\ \text{lb. dry steam, i.e. } \underline{2 \cdot 9\%.}\quad \text{Ans.}$$

In this type of question the arithmetic can be troublesome and cumulative errors arise from equations such as (i) and (ii).

The term $\dfrac{216 \cdot 5 \times 0 \cdot 016}{5 \cdot 4}$ in the total energy of the injected water represents the work of introduction of the water over and above that which is in any case included in $h = 59 - 32 = E + \dfrac{PV}{J}$. That amount which is automatically included in the 27 B.T.U. is, however, the PV term at *saturation* conditions at 59° F. only, so that if P' represents the saturation pressure at 59° F., the additional PV term is really given by $\dfrac{(216 \cdot 5 - P') \times 0 \cdot 016}{5 \cdot 4}$.

P' is, of course, very small and would not affect the answer to any extent.

12. *A mass dW lb. of dry saturated steam, of specific volume V cu. ft. per lb. and total heat H B.T.U. per lb., is condensed in an accumulator containing W lb. of boiling water, thereby raising the pressure.*

The equation for the process is

$$W\left(h - \frac{Pv}{J}\right) + dW\left(H - \frac{PV}{J}\right) + dW \times \frac{P}{J}(V - v)$$

$$= (W + dW)\left\{\left(h - \frac{Pv}{J}\right) + d\left(h - \frac{Pv}{J}\right)\right\}.$$

Explain the meaning of each of the three groups of symbols in the upper line of the equation.

Prove that $\log_e \dfrac{W \; end}{W \; start} = \displaystyle\int \frac{dh}{L}$ *if v is small.*

Determine the weight of dry saturated steam per 100 lb. of boiling water at 60 lb. per sq. in. required to raise the pressure to 120 lb. per sq. in. (Squared paper may be used for approximate integration.)

(U. Lond.)

Steam accumulators are used for the same purpose as electrical accumulators. The principal use of steam accumulators is in conjunction with mixed pressure turbines where high-pressure steam is constantly supplied and low-pressure steam is available via the accumulator from the exhaust of an engine working intermittently in regular cycles.

When the engine exhausts more L.P. steam than the turbine requires, the surplus steam is condensed in a large quantity of boiling water thereby raising its temperature and pressure. When the engine supply is deficient, the turbine demand causes a drop in pressure in the accumulator; this results in steam evaporation due to the lower saturation temperature. This steam is then available for the turbine.

In the question, v refers to the specific volume of boiling water at the pressure P. With the nomenclature given:

1st term = Total internal energy of boiling water in the accumulator, initially.

2nd term = Total internal energy of the added steam.

3rd term = Total work of introduction given up by the added steam in collapsing from dry steam having a specific volume V to boiling water having a specific volume v.

It should be noted that the right-hand side of the equation represents the final total internal energy; this may be more readily recognized in the form

$$(W + dW)\left\{(h + dh) - \frac{(P + dP)(v + dv)}{J}\right\},$$

which is the same as the R.H.S. of the equation when the second order term is neglected.

Neglecting v as small,

$$\mathrm{W}h + d\mathrm{WH} = (\mathrm{W} + d\mathrm{W})(h + dh).$$

Neglecting the second order term,

$$d\mathrm{W}(\mathrm{H} - h) = \mathrm{W}\, dh, \quad \text{and } \mathrm{H} - h = \mathrm{L}$$

$$\int_{\mathrm{W_1}}^{\mathrm{W_2}} \frac{d\mathrm{W}}{\mathrm{W}} = \int \frac{dh}{\mathrm{L}}$$

$$\underline{\log_e \frac{\mathrm{W \ end}}{\mathrm{W \ start}} = \int \frac{dh}{\mathrm{L}}.} \quad \text{Q.E.D.}$$

We shall have to plot $\dfrac{1}{\mathrm{L}}$ against h from 60 to 120 lb. per sq. in. It will be found that the resulting graph is very nearly straight, giving an area of $\frac{1}{2} \times (0 \cdot 001092 + 0 \cdot 001138) \times 50 \cdot 3 = 0 \cdot 05606$.

$$\therefore \ 2 \cdot 303 \log_{10} \frac{100 + \varDelta \mathrm{W}}{100} = 0 \cdot 05606$$

$$\log_{10} \frac{100 + \varDelta \mathrm{W}}{100} = \log_{10} 1 \cdot 0576$$

$$\underline{\varDelta \mathrm{W} = 5 \cdot 76 \text{ lb.}} \quad \text{Ans.}$$

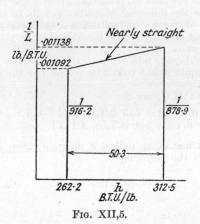

FIG. XII,5.

EXAMPLES

1. A boiler generates 10,000 lb. of steam per hr. at a pressure of 110 lb./in.^{2} abs. from feed water at 180° F. A sample of this steam is throttled to 20 lb./in.^{2} abs. when its temperature is found to be 258° F. The coal consumed amounts to 1,200 lb./hr. and has a C.V. of 13,200 B.T.U./lb. Find the dryness fraction of the steam generated, the boiler efficiency and the equivalent evaporation per lb. of fuel from and at 212° F. (*U. Glas.*)

$[x = 0.980$; $\eta = 64.6\%$; equ. evap. from and at 212° F.

$$= \frac{\text{lb. of steam per lb. of fuel} \times \text{Heat given to steam}}{\text{Latent Heat at 212° F.}} = 8.79 \text{ lb. per lb. of fuel.}]$$

2. In a steam plant the steam leaves the boiler at a pressure of 200 lb. per sq. in., superheated to 500° F. It is throttled to a pressure of 150 lb. per sq. in. and then expanded adiabatically to 15 lb. per sq. in.

Using the steam tables find, by calculation, the heat drop for the expansion, and the final dryness of the steam.

Assuming the expansion to follow a law $PV^n = $ a constant, determine the value of the index n. (*U. Lond.*)

$[H_1 = H_2 = 1,268.3$ B.T.U. ; $\phi_2 = 1.6532$; $x_3 = 0.930(\phi_2 = \phi_3)$; $H_3 = 1,083.2$, $\Delta H = 185.1$ B.T.U. per lb. ; $V_2 = 3.62$ cu. ft. ; $V_3 = 24.45$ cu. ft. ; $n = 1.205$.]

3. The volume of a certain quantity of dry saturated steam at 50 lb. per sq. in. is 2.5 cu. ft. Find the amount of heat given out if this steam is cooled to 212° F. (*a*) at constant pressure ; (*b*) at constant volume. (*U. Lond.*)

$[w = 0.294$ lb. ; (*a*) $Q = h_2 - H_1 = \underline{- 292 \text{ B.T.U.}}$; (*b*) $P_2 = 14.7$ lb. per sq. in. ; $x = 0.318$; $Q = E_2 - E_1 = \underline{- 185 \text{ B.T.U.}}$]

4. A substance has the physical properties given below at a pressure of 120 lb. per sq. in. Calculate the following quantities per lb. of the substance.

Total heats, internal energies, and entropies of the liquid and vapour at 200° C. The total heat and entropy of the liquid are to be taken as 0 at 0° C.

Ebullition temperature, 200° C.

Volume per lb. of liquid, 0.15 cu. ft. ; of dry saturated vapour, 5 cu. ft.

Specific heat of liquid $(0.8 + 0.0002T)$, where T is the absolute temperature Centigrade.

Latent Heat, 300 C.H.U. per lb. (*I.C.E.*)

[Liquid : h, e, ϕ in order = 315 B.T.U., 311.7 B.T.U., 0.479 ; Vapour : H, E, ϕ in order = 855 B.T.U., 744 B.T.U., 1.113.]

5. The expansion line of an indicator diagram taken from the cylinder of a steam engine shows the following :

P in lb. per sq. in.	150	85	50	28	20
Vol. in cu. ft.	1.08	2.4	4.2	7.2	10

(*a*) Obtain the best value of n, the index of the expansion line.

(*b*) Assuming that the quantity of stuff expanding in the cylinder is 0.6 lb., set out the corresponding values of T and ϕ. (*W.S.S.*)

[Plot log P against log V ; $n = 0.90$ nearly ; T's in order 818, 776, 741, 706, 688° F. abs., and ϕ's in order 1.144, 1.356, 1.437, 1.462, 1.496.]

6. (a) A superheater receives steam at 280 lb. per sq. in. abs., $98 \cdot 5\%$ dry, and discharges it at 270 lb. per sq. in. with $200°$ F. ($93 \cdot 3°$ C.) superheat. Calculate the heat added to the steam per lb., also the change of entropy of the steam.

(b) A closed vessel contains 50 cu. ft. of steam, originally at 270 lb. per sq. in. abs. with $200°$ F. superheat. The steam is allowed to cool slowly at constant volume. At what temperature does condensation begin and what amount of heat is given out in cooling to this temperature ?   (*I.Mech.E.*)

[(a) This is a flow-process, not a single phase ; $\therefore$ (I,2) does not apply ; the total energy equation applies, whence for const. v, $Q = \varDelta H = +\underline{129 \cdot 5}$ B.T.U., $\varDelta\phi = +\underline{0 \cdot 1388}$; (b) (I,2) applies ; $V_1 = 2 \cdot 252$ cu. ft. per lb. ; $w = 22 \cdot 2$ lb. ; $P_2 = 203 \cdot 6$ lb. per sq. in. ; $\underline{\text{dew-point} = 383 \cdot 3° \text{F.}}$; $E_1 = 1,208 \cdot 0$ and $E_2 = 1,114 \cdot 9$ B.T.U. per lb., $\underline{Q = -2,070 \text{ B.T.U.}}$]

7. Steam is expanded in a cylinder from a pressure of 80 lb. per sq. in. to a pressure of 15 lb. per sq. in. according to the law $PV^n = $ constant. The steam at the start of expansion is superheated to a temperature of $392°$ F., and at the end of expansion is $0 \cdot 98$ dry.

Using the steam tables, find :

(a) the heat interchange per lb. of steam between the steam and the cylinder walls during the expansion only ;

(b) the increase of work done per lb. of steam over that by isentropic expansion from the original state to the final pressure.   (*U. Lond.*)

[Per lb. of steam :   (a) $V_1 = 6 \cdot 13$ cu. ft. ; $V_2 = 25 \cdot 8$ cu. ft. ; $n = 1 \cdot 163$; W.D. $= 118 \cdot 0$ B.T.U. by (I,4) ; $E_1 = 1,135 \cdot 4$ B.T.U. and $E_2 = 1,060 \cdot 6$ B.T.U. by (I,1) ; $\underline{Q = +43 \cdot 2 \text{ B.T.U.}}$ by (I,2) ;   (b) $x_3 = 0 \cdot 943$ by (I,26) ; $V_3 = 24 \cdot 8$ cu. ft. ; $E_3 = 1,027 \cdot 3$ B.T.U. ;   W.D. $= 108 \cdot 1$ B.T.U. by (I,2) ; $\underline{\text{increase} = 9 \cdot 9 \text{ B.T.U.}}$]

8. One pound of steam at 100 lb. per sq. in., superheated $20°$ F. expands hyperbolically to 15 lb. per sq. in. Heat is then abstracted at 15 lb. per sq. in. and afterwards the steam is compressed adiabatically to its initial state.

Find :   (i) the net work done per lb. of steam ;

(ii) the heat supplied to the steam, and the efficiency of the cycle.
                    (*U. Lond.*)

[*Per lb. of steam :* after hyperbolic exp. $V = 30 \cdot 44$ cu. ft., $H = 1,199 \cdot 6$ B.T.U. from (I,32) ;   adiabatic phase must be without internal loss, i.e. $\phi = $ constant, $\therefore x = 0 \cdot 905$ at commencement ;   Heat is rejected at const. press. only $= 142 \cdot 4$ B.T.U. ;   Heat is supp. during hyperbolic phase only $= 160 \cdot 3$ from (I,2) and (I,5) (note $\varDelta E = \varDelta H$, if $PV = $ constant) ; Ans. (i) $\underline{17 \cdot 9 \text{ B.T.U.}}$;   Ans. (ii) $\underline{11 \cdot 2\%}$ from (IV,1).]

9. The cylinder of a steam engine, at the beginning of expansion, contains $\frac{1}{2}$ cu. ft. of steam at 140 lb. per sq. in. abs. and at $403°$ F. ($206°$ C.). At the end of expansion the pressure is 30 lb. per sq. in. abs. and the volume is $1 \cdot 80$ cu. ft. Assuming that no steam enters or leaves the cylinder during the process, find the total heat, internal energy, and entropy of the steam in the cylinder, at the beginning and at the end of the expansion. How much heat is received or given out by the steam ?   (*I.Mech.E.*)

[$V_1 = 3 \cdot 47$ cu. ft. per lb. ; $w = 0 \cdot 144$ lb. ; $x_2 = 0 \cdot 910$;   actual H, E and ϕ at 1 are $\underline{176 \cdot 0 \text{ B.T.U.}, 163 \cdot 2 \text{ B.T.U.}, 0 \cdot 232}$ and at 2 are $\underline{155 \cdot 5 \text{ B.T.U.}, 145 \cdot 5 \text{ B.T.U.}}$, $\underline{0 \cdot 228}$ respectively ;   assuming $PV^n = C$ holds, $n = 1 \cdot 202$;   W.D. $= 14 \cdot 55$ B.T.U. ; $\underline{Q = -3 \cdot 1 \text{ B.T.U.}}$ from (I,2).]

10. A pressure vessel of 2·29 cu. ft. capacity contains 1 lb. of water and water vapour initially at 14 p.s.i. and 209·6° F. It is then heated until the temperature of the contents is 381·8° F. For the initial state determine, without using any approximation, the weight of water in the form of vapour.

For the heating process, determine the quantity of heat put in, and compare it with the change in total heat.

Data from steam tables :

Pressure p.s.i.	Saturation Temp. ° F.	Total Heat of—		Specific Vol. (cu. ft./lb.) of—	
		Water	Steam	Water	Steam
200	381·8	355·5	1,199·5	0·0184	2·29
14	209·6	177·7	1,149·9	0·0167	28·03

(U. Melb.)

[Allowing for volume of water, lb. of dry vapour initially = 0·08115 lb.; $H_1 = 256·6$; $E_1 = 250·7$; final dryness must be unity ; $H_2 = 1,199·5$; $E_2 = 1,114·7$; $\underline{Q = + 864 \text{ B.T.U.}}$ by (I,2) ; $\varDelta H = + 942·9$, diff. is due to increase in PV term.]

11. Steam is supplied by a boiler at 140 lb. per sq. in. with a dryness fraction of 0·80. It is throttled to a pressure of 80 lb. per sq. in. and then expanded hyperbolically in an engine cylinder to a pressure of 4 lb. per sq. in. Find the final internal energy and entropy per lb. of steam and the heat passing through the walls per lb. of steam during expansion in the cylinder. *(U. Lond.)*

[$H_1 = H_2 = 1,020$ B.T.U. per lb. ; $x_2 = 0·818$ (at $P_2 = 80$); $x_3 = 0·988$ (at $P_3 = 4$); $E_3 = 1,049$ B.T.U. per lb. ; $\phi_3 = 1·843$ per lb. ; W.D.$_{2-3} = 199$ B.T.U. ; $\underline{Q_{2-3} = 295 \text{ B.T.U. per lb.}}$]

12. In the cylinder of a steam engine, the pressure and volume at cut-off are 100 lb. per sq. in. and 1·7 cu. ft. respectively, and the dryness 0·8. The pressure and volume at release are 36·3 lb. per sq. in. and 5·10 cu. ft. respectively. Assuming the steam expands according to the law $PV^n = $ constant, calculate the heat passing through the cylinder wall during the expansion. *(U. Lond.)*

[$n = 0·921$, $w = 0·48$ lb., $x_2 = 0·924$, $E_1 = 944·5$ and $E_2 = 1,025·9$ B.T.U. per lb. ; $\therefore \varDelta E$ (*not* per lb.) = 39·1 B.T.U. ; W.D. = 35·4 B.T.U. ; by (I,2) $\underline{Q = + 74·5 \text{ B.T.U.}}$]

13. A closed vessel, having a volume of 100 cu. ft., contains 30 lb. of a mixture of water and steam at a pressure of 100 lb. per sq. in. Find how much heat must be supplied to the vessel to make the steam 0·9 dry and determine the resulting steam pressure.

Neglect the volume of the water. *(U. Lond.)*

[$x_1 = 0·752$, $E_1 = 906·8$ B.T.U. per lb., $V_{s2} = 3·70$ cu. ft. per lb., $\therefore P_2 = 121$ lb. per sq. in. (from tables) ; $E_2 = 1,028·8$ B.T.U. per lb. ; $\underline{Q = 3,660 \text{ B.T.U.}}$ (for 30 lb.)]

CHAPTER XIII

STEAM ENGINE HYPOTHETICAL DIAGRAMS

Introduction

The hypothetical indicator diagram for a steam engine is based on the principal assumptions (i) that the expansion takes place according to the law PV = constant, i.e. is hyperbolic, and (ii) that the clearance volume is neglected. The assumption that the expansion is hyperbolic is not unreasonable, the actual index being frequently about unity. The clearance volume is neglected and the cut-off is expressed as a proportion of the stroke as measured on the indicator diagram.

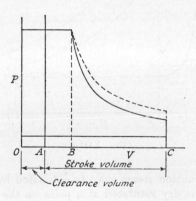

FIG. XIII,1.

In the above diagram, the apparent cut-off neglecting clearance is $\dfrac{AB}{AC}$, i.e. the proportion of the stroke at which cut-off occurs; and the expansion ratio r is $\dfrac{AC}{AB}$. However, if the clearance volume OA be allowed for, the real volumes at cut-off and release are OB and OC, resulting in a real cut-off $\dfrac{OB}{OC}$ and an expansion ratio $\dfrac{OC}{OB}$. The greater volume of steam at cut-off in this case would cause the hyperbolic expansion to follow the dotted line, thus giving a higher value for the mean effective pressure.

1. *A double-acting steam engine runs at 100 r.p.m. From the following data find the missing quantity per hr. at cut-off and at release.*

> *Cut-off : vol., 0·5 cu. ft. ; pressure, 200 lb. per sq. in.*
> *Release : vol., 2·0 cu. ft., pressure, 50 lb. per sq. in.*
> *On compression curve : vol., 0·2 cu. ft. ; pressure, 55 lb. per sq. in.*
> *Engine consumption, 3,450 lb. of steam per hr.*

If the missing quantity at cut-off differs from that at release give an explanation of the circumstances.

(*W.S.S.*)

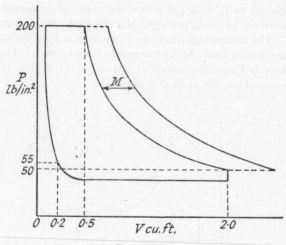

Fig. XIII,2.

The weight of cushion steam may be estimated by making the usual assumption that it is dry saturated at a point on the compression curve, say at 55 lb. per sq. in. (This point is usually taken about $\frac{1}{3}$ along the curve.)

$$\therefore \text{ Weight of cushion steam per stroke} = \frac{0·2}{7·789} = 0·0257 \text{ lb.}$$

The total weight of steam present during the expansion will be equal to the cylinder feed per stroke plus the weight of cushion steam.

$$\text{Weight of cylinder feed per cycle} = \frac{3,450}{60 \times 100 \times 2} = 0·2875 \text{ lb.}$$

$\therefore$ Weight of steam actually present during the expansion

$$= 0·2875 + 0·0257 = 0·3132 \text{ lb.}$$

Indicated dry weight at cut-off $= \dfrac{0\cdot5}{2\cdot290} = 0\cdot218$ lb.

,,   ,,   ,,   ,, release $= \dfrac{2\cdot0}{8\cdot516} = 0\cdot235$ lb.

$\therefore$ Missing quantity at cut-off $= 0\cdot0952$ lb. per cycle $\equiv$ 1,142 lb. per hr.

,,   ,,   ,, release $= 0\cdot0782$,,   ,,   ,, $\equiv$ 938 ,,   ,,   ,,

Ans.

The effects of initial condensation are more pronounced at cut-off than at release, since re-evaporation occurs as the pressure falls and M will generally decrease during expansion.

The student is advised to plot the dry saturated curve for $0\cdot3137$ lb. of steam as shown in the diagram. This will give the missing quantity M in *cu. ft.* at all pressures during the expansion, whence the lb. per hr. may be deduced from the steam tables.

2. *A locomotive has three double-acting cylinders, each 18 in. diameter and 26 in. stroke. The steam supply pressure is 210 lb. per sq. in., exhaust pressure 25 lb. per sq. in., and cut-off takes place at 0·375 of the stroke. Determine the i.h.p. developed by the locomotive when running at 150 r.p.m. Assume a diagram factor of 0·7.*

If the steam consumption is 32,000 lb. per hr. at an initial temperature of 546° F., determine the indicated thermal efficiency of the engine.

(U.L.C.I.)

$$\text{m.e.p.} = \dfrac{210\left(1 + \log_e \dfrac{8}{3}\right)}{\dfrac{8}{3}} - 25 \text{ (cf. I,35)}$$

$$= 131 \text{ lb. per sq. in.}$$

$\therefore$ Actual m.e.p. $= 91\cdot7$ lb. per sq. in.

$$\therefore \text{i.h.p.} = 3 \times 91\cdot7 \times \frac{26}{12} \times \frac{\pi}{4} \times \frac{18 \times 18 \times 300}{33,000}$$

$= \underline{1,380.}$ Ans.

The Total Heat of the steam supplied is obtained from Table II and is equal to 1,292·2 B.T.U.   The liquid heat at 25 lb. per sq. in. $= 208\cdot6$ B.T.U., and

$$\text{thermal efficiency} = \frac{1,380 \times 2,546}{32,000 \times (1,292\cdot2 - 208\cdot6)}$$

$= \underline{10\%, \text{ nearly.}}$ Ans.

3. *Find the gain in thermal efficiency due to the expansive action of steam by considering the work done per lb. of steam in two engines receiving steam at 200 lb. per sq. in. abs. dry saturated and exhausting at 15 lb. per sq. in. abs., one of them taking steam for the whole stroke and the other taking steam for $\frac{1}{3} \times$ stroke. Neglect the effects of clearance and assume hyperbolic expansion.*

(U. Glas.)

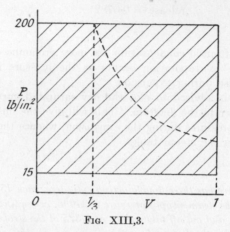

Fᵢ𝓰. XIII,3.

$V_s = 2\cdot29$ cu. ft. per lb. at 200 lb. per sq. in.

(*a*) The W.D. per lb. of steam when used non-expansively equals the rectangular area of the diagram.

This is $\qquad \dfrac{(200 - 15)144 \times 2\cdot29}{778} = 78\cdot4$ B.T.U.

(*b*) When the cut-off is at $\frac{1}{3}$ stroke, the weight of steam admitted will be only $\frac{1}{3}$ lb., and the expansion will follow the dotted line on the diagram. Since the expansion is to be considered hyperbolic, the m.e.p. of this diagram will be

$$\frac{200(1 + \log_e 3)}{3} - 15 = 125 \text{ lb. per sq. in., by (I,35).}$$

$$\therefore \text{ W.D. by } \tfrac{1}{3} \text{ lb. of steam} = \frac{125 \times 144 \times 2\cdot29}{778}$$

$$= 53 \text{ B.T.U.}$$

$$\therefore \text{ W.D. per lb. of steam} = 159 \text{ B.T.U.}$$

$$\text{Thermal efficiency } (a) = \frac{78\cdot4}{1{,}199\cdot5 - 181\cdot2} = 7\cdot7\%.$$

$$(b) = \frac{159}{1{,}199\cdot5 - 181\cdot2} = 15\cdot6\%.$$

Thus the gain in thermal efficiency is 7·9%, representing an increase of more than 100% over that when the steam is used non-expansively.

4. *A steam engine has compression commencing at 60% of the return stroke when the steam remaining in the cylinder may be assumed dry and saturated at 4 lb. per sq. in. abs.   The pressure of the steam near cut-off is 150 lb. per sq. in. abs. when the piston has traversed 31% of the working stroke. If the engine is double acting and runs at 200 r.p.m. ; the cylinder diameter and stroke 12 in. and 18 in. respectively, the clearance volume 25% of the piston displacement and the measured steam consumption 6,720 lb. per hr., estimate the dryness fraction at cut-off.*

(U. Manch.)

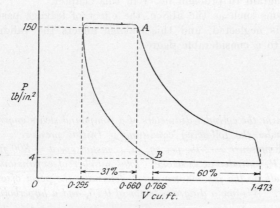

Fig. XIII,4.

The swept volume of the cylinder $= \dfrac{\pi}{4} \times 1 \times 1\cdot5 = 1\cdot178$ cu. ft.

Clearance volume $= 0\cdot25 \times 1\cdot178 = 0\cdot295$ cu. ft.
$\therefore$ Total volume $= 1\cdot473$ cu. ft.

$\therefore$ Volume at point near cut-off when the pressure is 150 lb. per sq. in.
$= 0\cdot31 \times 1\cdot178 + 0\cdot295 = 0\cdot660$ cu. ft.

and the volume at 60% of the return stroke
$= 0\cdot4 \times 1\cdot178 + 0\cdot295 = 0\cdot766$ cu. ft.

These values are shown on the diagram.

The cylinder feed per stroke $= \dfrac{6{,}720}{60 \times 200 \times 2} = 0\cdot280$ lb.

The weight of cushion steam at B is the weight of 0·766 cu. ft. of dry steam at 4 lb. per sq. in.

$$= \frac{0\cdot766}{90\cdot63} = 0\cdot00845 \text{ lb.}$$

∴ The weight of steam present in the cylinder during the expansion

$$= 0.28 + 0.00845 = 0.2885 \text{ lb.}$$

Now the indicated dry weight at $A = \dfrac{0.660}{3.015} = 0.219 \text{ lb.}$

∴ The dryness at $A = \dfrac{0.219}{0.2885} = \underline{0.76, \text{ nearly.}}$ Ans.

The saturation line and the missing quantity could have been shown as in the diagram to problem no. 1 in this chapter.

In problems such as the above, the effect of leakage past the valve and piston is neglected, and this leakage affects the validity of such calculations to a considerable degree.

5. *Determine the cylinder diameters of a compound steam engine to develop 500 i.h.p. under the following conditions : Initial pressure = 180 lb. per sq. in. ; back pressure = 2 lb. per sq. in. ; piston speed = 800 ft. per min. ; cut off in H.P. cylinder at $\frac{1}{3}$ stroke ; total number of expansions = 12. If the initial loads on the pistons are equal, determine the point of cut-off in the L.P. cylinder. Assume a diagram factor of 0·75, and a hyperbolic expansion curve.* (U.L.C.I.)

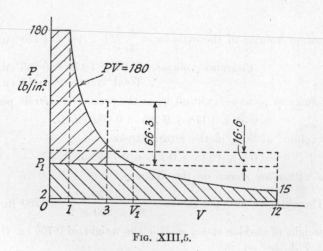

Fig. XIII,5.

To construct the diagram, the cut-off in the H.P. cylinder is assumed to occur at unit volume ; then 3 and 12 units represent the H.P. and L.P.

cylinder volumes respectively, and the equation to the expansion curve is $PV = 180$, in the units adopted.

Let P_1 be the exhaust pressure of the H.P. cylinder, being also the admission pressure to the L.P. cylinder. Since the piston areas are proportional to the volumes and such an engine must be double-acting, we have for equal loads on the pistons [1]:

$$(180 - P_1)3 = (P_1 - 2)12$$
whence $\qquad P_1 = 37 \cdot 6$ lb. per sq. in.

∴ Volume V_1 at the cut-off in the L.P. cylinder will be given by

$$\frac{180}{37 \cdot 6} = 4 \cdot 78.$$

$$\therefore \text{ Cut-off in L.P.} = \frac{4 \cdot 78}{12} = \underline{0 \cdot 398.} \quad \text{Ans.}$$

and $\qquad$ L.P. expansion ratio $= \dfrac{1}{0 \cdot 398} = 2 \cdot 51.$

m.e.p. in H.P. $= 0 \cdot 75 \left[\dfrac{180(1 + \log_e 3)}{3} - 37 \cdot 6 \right] = 66 \cdot 3$ lb. per sq. in.

When referred to the L.P. cylinder, this $= \dfrac{66 \cdot 3 \times 3}{12} = 16 \cdot 6$ lb. per sq. in.

m.e.p. in L.P. $= 0 \cdot 75 \left[\dfrac{37 \cdot 6(1 + \log_e 2 \cdot 51)}{2 \cdot 51} - 2 \right] = 20 \cdot 1$ lb. per sq. in.

∴ Total m.e.p. referred to L.P. cylinder $= 36 \cdot 7$ lb. per sq. in.

Now, if $d =$ diameter of L.P. piston in inches,

$$500 = \frac{36 \cdot 7 \times \frac{\pi}{4} d^2 \times 800}{33 \cdot 000}$$

whence $\qquad d = 26 \cdot 7$ in.

The diameter of the H.P. cylinder will be $\underline{13 \cdot 35 \text{ in.}}$ Ans.

In the diagram, fig. XIII,5, the m.e.p. of the H.P. cylinder, and this m.e.p. referred to the L.P. cylinder, are shown.

[1] The question of piston loads is discussed in more detail in ex. no. 6, p. 216.

6. *What are the main factors to be considered in deciding the sizes of the cylinders in a compound steam engine? Explain briefly the effect on the distribution of the work between the cylinders when governing is carried out (a) by throttling and (b) by cut-off.*

A triple-expansion steam engine has cylinder volume ratios of $1 : 2 \cdot 4 : 7 \cdot 2$. The initial loading on the pistons is equal when the steam supply is 180 lb. per sq. in. and the condenser pressure is 5 lb. per sq. in. The total number of expansions is 15. If the initial steam pressure is reduced by throttling to 160 lb. per sq. in. and the cut-off in each cylinder is allowed to remain constant, find the mean effective pressure of each cylinder referred to the L.P. cylinder.

Neglect the effects of clearances and receiver drops, and assume hyperbolic expansion. (*U. Lond.*)

For thermodynamic reasons it is desirable to have the same temperature range for all cylinders. However, for mechanical reasons it is desirable that the maximum initial loading and the work done should be the same for all cylinders. These three criteria cannot be met simultaneously and a compromise is necessary in practice. Generally, the initial loading is made as nearly equal as possible, and at full load, the work done is reasonably well shared between the cylinders, the temperature range being somewhat variable.

At part load, the throttling of the supply results in a big reduction of work in the L.P. cylinder if the cut-offs remain the same; whereas by making the cut-off proportionately earlier in each cylinder, the least work is done in the H.P. cylinder. In practice, a compromise is made by throttling the steam supply and adjusting the cut-off in each cylinder, the work being shared more or less equally between the cylinders from, say, $\frac{3}{4}$ load to full load.

The diagram is similar to that of the previous question. If the cylinder volumes be scaled off as 1, 2·4 and 7·2 units, the cut-off volume in the H.P. cylinder will be $\dfrac{7 \cdot 2}{15} = 0 \cdot 48$, since the number of expansions is 15. We now have the equation to the expansion curve, using these values, as $PV = 86 \cdot 4$.

Now let P_1 and P_2 be the pressures at admission to the I.P. and the L.P. cylinders respectively. Since the initial loading must be the same for all cylinders we have:

$$(180 - P_1)1 = (P_1 - P_2)2 \cdot 4 = (P_2 - 5)7 \cdot 2.$$

This can be seen by reference to the diagram. In the H.P. cylinder, we have the admission pressure of 180 lb. per sq. in. on one side of the piston whilst the other side is exhausting at a pressure P_1, giving a maximum difference of pressure of $(180 - P_1)$ lb. per sq. in. Similarly, the maximum difference in pressure for the I.P. and the L.P. cylinders is

$P_1 - P_2$) and ($P_2 - 5$) lb. per sq. in. respectively. Also, because each cylinder has the same stroke, the ratios of the areas will be the same as the ratios of the volumes, i.e. $1 : 2 \cdot 4 : 7 \cdot 2$. Therefore the maximum load

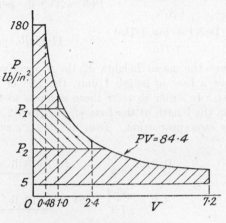

Fig. XIII,6.

per cylinder will be the maximum pressure difference on the two sides of the piston multiplied by the area of the piston, resulting in the above equation. This gives $P_1 = 67 \cdot 5$ lb. per sq. in., and $P_2 = 20 \cdot 6$ lb. per sq. in.

Referring to the I.P. diagram, the volume at the cut-off when the pressure is $67 \cdot 5$ lb. per sq. in. will be $\dfrac{86 \cdot 4}{67 \cdot 5}$, and the total volume at the end of the stroke is $2 \cdot 4$.

∴ The cut-off in the I.P. cylinder is

$$\frac{86 \cdot 4}{67 \cdot 5} \times \frac{1}{2 \cdot 4} = 0 \cdot 533$$

and similarly for the L.P. is

$$\frac{86 \cdot 4}{20 \cdot 6} \times \frac{1}{7 \cdot 2} = 0 \cdot 582.$$

If now the initial pressure be dropped to 160 lb. per sq. in., the equation to the curve will become $PV = 160 \times 0 \cdot 48 = 76 \cdot 8$. The volume at the cut-off in the I.P. cylinder will still be $\dfrac{86 \cdot 4}{67 \cdot 5}$ as before, but the pressure P_1 will now be $76 \cdot 8 \times \dfrac{67 \cdot 5}{86 \cdot 4} = 60$ lb. per sq. in. Similarly, P_2 will drop to $18 \cdot 3$ lb. per sq. in.

Thus we have for the m.e.p.'s :

$$\text{H.P.} = \frac{160(1 + \log_e 2 \cdot 08)}{2 \cdot 08} - 60 = 73 \cdot 3 \text{ lb. per sq. in.}$$

$$\text{I.P.} = \frac{60(1 + \log_e 1 \cdot 875)}{1 \cdot 875} - 18 \cdot 3 = 33 \cdot 9 \text{ lb. per sq. in.}$$

$$\text{L.P.} = \frac{18 \cdot 3(1 + \log_e 1 \cdot 715)}{1 \cdot 715} - 5 = 11 \cdot 45 \text{ lb. per sq. in.}$$

The above are the mean heights of the respective diagrams. The H.P. diagram has a base of length 1 unit, the I.P. of 2·4 units and the L.P. of 7·2 units. In order to refer these m.e.p.'s to the L.P. cylinder we must increase the length of the base of each to 7·2 units; i.e. reduce the height in the same proportion. Thus the m.e.p.'s referred to the L.P cylinder are :

$$\text{H.P.} = \frac{73 \cdot 3}{7 \cdot 2} = \underline{10 \cdot 18 \text{ lb. per sq. in.}}$$

$$\text{I.P.} = \frac{33 \cdot 9}{7 \cdot 2} \times 2 \cdot 4 = \underline{14 \cdot 12 \text{ lb. per sq. in.}}$$

$$\text{L.P.} = 11 \cdot 45 = \underline{11 \cdot 45 \text{ lb. per sq. in.}} \quad \text{Ans.}$$

The work done in the H.P. and L.P. cylinders is almost equal, rather more being done in the I.P.

7. *Discuss the causes of loss of thermal efficiency in compound steam engines.*

A double-acting compound engine is required to give 400 i.h.p. at 150 r.p.m. with a supply at 180 lb. per sq. in. and exhaust at 4 lb. per sq. in. Take the number of expansions at 8·4 ; ratio of cylinder volumes 4·2 to 1·0 ; stroke equal to two-thirds of the L.P. cylinder diameter ; overall diagram factor, assuming hyperbolic expansion and neglecting clearances, 0·66.

Allowing for a loss of 5 lb. per sq. in. in the receiver between the two cylinders, find the piston diameters, common stroke and the L.P. cut-off, if the initial loads on the two piston-rods are to be equal. (U. Lond.)

Initial condensation becomes increasingly serious as the expansion ratio is increased and as the temperature-range across the cylinder becomes greater. The most effective solution adopted in practice is that of compounding, but nevertheless, initial condensation and leakage occur on a reduced scale in each stage of the expansion. The pressure-drop in the receiver, which includes the wire-drawing at the exhaust and inlet ports and valves, is a further loss, resulting in an increase of entropy due to unresisted expansion, and the overall available heat drop is reduced.

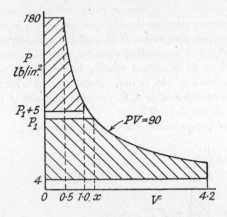

Fig. XIII,7.

The diagram is drawn as previously explained. Since the number of expansions is 8·4, the volume at cut-off in the H.P. cylinder will be 0·5 units. The equation to the curve will be PV = 90.

The overall diagram factor is given as 0·66, so the combined m.e.p. will be :

$$0·66 \left[\frac{180(1 + \log_e 8·4)}{8·4} - 4 \right] = 41·62 \text{ lb. per sq. in.}$$

If d = diameter of L.P. cylinder in feet we have :

$$2 \times 41·62 \times 144 \times \frac{\pi}{4}d^2 \times \frac{2}{3}d \times 150 = 400 \times 33·000$$

whence $d^3 = 14·02$ and $\underline{d = 2·41 \text{ ft.}}$

and the diameter of the H.P. cylinder will be $\dfrac{2·41}{\sqrt{4·2}} = \underline{1·77 \text{ ft.}}$

The stroke is $\underline{1·61 \text{ ft.}}$ Ans.

Now let P_1 be the admission pressure to the L.P. cylinder, then $(P_1 + 5)$ lb. per sq. in. will be the exhaust pressure of the H.P. cylinder, and since the initial loading is to be the same :

$$180 - (P_1 + 5) = (P_1 - 4)4·2$$

whence $P_1 = 36·9$ lb. per sq. in.

∴ x, the volume at cut-off in the L.P. cylinder $= \dfrac{90}{36·9} = 2·44.$

This gives the cut-off in the L.P. cylinder as $\dfrac{2·44}{4·2} = \underline{0·58.}$ Ans.

8. A triple-expansion engine has a steam chest pressure of 180 lb. per sq. in. and the condenser pressure is 3 lb. per sq. in. The overall expansion ratio is 15. If the expansions in the H.P. and I.P. cylinders are carried down to the pressure of the next succeeding cylinder, find the ratio of the cylinder volumes if the work is to be shared equally between them.

If, however, the ratio of the cylinder volumes is 1 : 2·5 : 6, estimate the mean effective pressure referred to L.P. for each cylinder if the cut-off in the I.P. is 0·45, and in the L.P. 0·7.

Assume hyperbolic expansion and neglect clearance.   *(U. Lond.)*

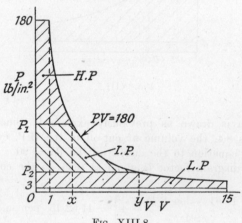

FIG. XIII,8.

Since the expansion is carried down to the pressure of the succeeding cylinder, the expansion line on the combined diagram will be continuous, and the m.e.p. of the whole diagram referred to the L.P. cylinder will be,

$$\frac{180(1 + \log_e 15)}{15} - 3 \text{ lb. per sq. in.}$$

Assuming that the length of the diagram is 15 units, the work done will be proportional to

$$\left[\frac{180(1 + \log_e 15)}{15} - 3\right] \times 15 = 622$$

and the work per cylinder is 207·3, since it is to be equally shared.

Let r_1, r_2 be the expansion ratios in the H.P. and I.P. cylinders respectively ; then

$$\text{H.P., W.D.} = 180 \times 1 + 180 \times 1 \times \log_e r_1 - P_1 x$$
$$= 180 \log_e r_1, \text{ since } 180 \times 1 = P_1 x.$$

Similarly, I.P., W.D. $= 180 \log_e r_2$

$$\therefore \ 207\cdot3 = 180 \log_e r_1 = 180 \log_e r_2$$

whence $r_1 = r_2 = 3\cdot16.$

∴ Volume ratios will be 3·16 : 10 : 15·0   or 1 : 3·16 : 4·75. **Ans.**

These ratios would give equal work per cylinder, but are not according
o the values adopted in practice as shown by the ratios quoted in the
ıext part of the question.

The diagram for the new volume ratios is now drawn, and here the
:ylinder volumes 1, 2·5 and 6 have been marked off. Since the number
ıf expansions is 15, the cut-off in the H.P. cylinder will be 0·4 units, and
he equation to the expansion curve will be PV = 72.

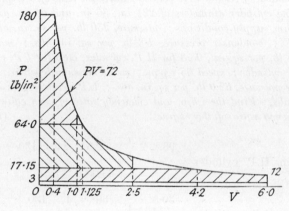

FIG. XIII,9.

The volume at cut-off in the I.P. cylinder will be 2·5 × 0·45 = 1·125 units,
ınd in the L.P. will be 6 × 0·7 = 4·2 units. At these volumes the pressures are 64 and 17·15 lb. per sq. in. respectively, and the diagram can be
completed as shown. The m.e.p.'s for each cylinder referred to the L.P.
cylinder will be :

$$\text{H.P.} = \frac{180(1 + \log_e 2\cdot5)}{2\cdot5} - 64 \quad = 74 \text{ lb. per sq. in.} \equiv 12\cdot3 \text{ lb. per sq. in.}$$

$$\text{I.P.} = \frac{64(1 + \log_e 2\cdot22)}{2\cdot22} - 17\cdot15 = 34\cdot4 \text{ lb. per sq. in.} \equiv 14\cdot8 \text{ lb. per sq. in.}$$

$$\text{L.P.} = \frac{17\cdot15(1 + \log_e 1\cdot57)}{1\cdot57} - 3 \quad = 12\cdot8 \text{ lb. per sq. in.} \equiv 12\cdot8 \text{ lb. per sq. in.}$$

$$\overline{39\cdot9 \text{ lb. per sq. in.}}$$

The m.e.p.'s show that the work done in the H.P. and the L.P. cylinders
is approximately equal, and rather more work is done in the I.P.

It can also be seen that $\dfrac{180(1 + \log_e 15)}{15} - 3 = 41\cdot4$ lb. per sq. in. is

the m.e.p. of the whole engine referred to the L.P. cylinder, when considering the overall diagram. It should be expected that this value is
greater than the sum of the 3 separate m.e.p.'s due to the loss at constant

volume release (or incomplete expansion) in the H.P. and I.P. cylinders. This means that the overall diagram factor K is always smaller than the individual diagram factors k. Here,

$$41 \cdot 4 \times K = 39 \cdot 9k$$

or, $$K = 0 \cdot 964k.$$

9. *The following results were obtained during a trial of a triple-expansion engine having cylinder diameters of $22\frac{1}{2}$ in., 36 in. and 65 in. and stroke of 48 in. Steam supply conditions : pressure, 230 lb. per sq. in. abs. ; super heat, $150°$ F. ; condenser pressure, $1 \cdot 8$ lb. per sq. in. abs. ; mean effective pressures in lb. per sq. in., $98 \cdot 8$ for H.P. cylinder, $30 \cdot 3$ for I.P. cylinder and $9 \cdot 7$ for L.P. cylinder ; speed 65 r.p.m. ; steam consumed per hr., 17,900 lb. I.P. receiver pressure, $62 \cdot 0$ lb. per sq. in. abs. ; L.P. receiver pressure, $20 \cdot 0$ lb. per sq. in. abs. Find the i.h.p. and efficiency ratio of each cylinder and the overall efficiency ratio of the engine.*   (*U. Glas.*)

$$\text{i.h.p. H.P. cylinder} = \frac{98 \cdot 8 \times \dfrac{\pi}{4} \times 22 \cdot 5^2 \times 4 \times 130}{33 \cdot 000} = \underline{619}$$

$$\text{i.h.p. I.P. cylinder} = \frac{30 \cdot 3 \times \dfrac{\pi}{4} \times 36^2 \times 4 \times 130}{33 \cdot 000} = \underline{486}$$

$$\text{i.h.p. L.P. cylinder} = \frac{9 \cdot 7 \times \dfrac{\pi}{4} \times 65^2 \times 4 \times 130}{33 \cdot 000} = \underline{508}. \quad \text{Ans.}$$

The efficiency ratio of each cylinder in the ratio of the actual work done per lb. of steam in that cylinder to the isentropic heat drop across the cylinder :

For the H.P. cylinder,   Actual W.D. per lb. $= \dfrac{619 \times 2{,}546}{17{,}900}$

$$= 88 \text{ B.T.U.}$$

and similarly for the I.P. and the L.P. cylinders,

$$\text{W.D. per lb.} = 69 \cdot 2 \text{ and } 72 \cdot 2 \text{ B.T.U.}$$

Referring to the total heat–entropy diagram, the isentropic heat drop from A to B is 122 B.T.U.

$$\therefore \text{ Efficiency ratio of the H.P. cylinder is } \frac{88}{122} = 72\%.$$

AC = actual W.D., and the total heat at D = total heat at C. DE scales 90 B.T.U. and similarly GH = 150 B.T.U., giving efficiency ratios of $76 \cdot 9\%$ and $48 \cdot 1\%$ respectively for the I.P. and L.P. cylinders.

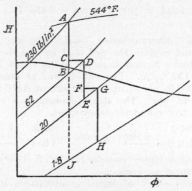

Fig. XIII,10.

The overall isentropic heat drop = AJ = 348 B.T.U.

$$\therefore \text{ The overall efficiency ratio} = \frac{88 + 69 \cdot 2 + 72 \cdot 2}{348}$$

$$= 66 \cdot 0\%. \quad \text{Ans.}$$

Tabulating, we have :

	Actual W.D. per lb.	Isentropic ΔH_T	Effy. ratio
H.P. . .	88	AB = 122	72%
I.P. . .	69·2	DE = 90	76·9%
L.P. . .	72·2	GH = 150	48·1%
Overall .	229·4	AJ = 348	66%

It might be observed that the sum of the cylinder heat drops is 362 B.T.U. thus giving a reheat factor of $\frac{362}{348} = 1 \cdot 04$ (cf. chapter XVI, page 252).

EXAMPLES

1. The L.P. cylinder of a steam engine has a diameter of 65 in., a stroke of 48 in., and a clearance volume of 8 ft.[3] The cylinder is double-acting and consumes 17,900 lb. of steam per hr. when running at 67 revs./min. Compression begins at 0·83 × exhaust stroke, cut-off and release at 0·55 and 0·96 × forward stroke respectively. Find the weight of dry steam present in the cylinder at these three points if the pressures there are 3·2, 12·0 and 6·5 lb./in.[2] abs., respectively. Hence determine the apparent dryness fraction of the steam in the cylinder at cut-off and release. Neglect the effect of the piston rod.

(*U. Glas.*)

[Actual vols. cut-off = 58·7 and release = 96·5 cu. ft. ; weight of dry steam at cut-off, release, comp. = 1·811, 1·678, 0·212 lb. respectively ; feed per diagram $= 2\cdot224$ lb. ;   total w per diagram $= 2\cdot436$ lb. ;   cut-off $x = \underline{0\cdot744}$ release $x = \underline{0\cdot689}$.]

2. Define the terms " diagram factor " and " efficiency-ratio " as applied to reciprocating engines and explain the practical uses of these quantities.

A double-acting cylinder having diameter 16 in., stroke 24 in., gave 308 indi cated horse-power at 150 r.p.m.   The cut-off was at one-third of the stroke Steam was supplied at 200 lb. per sq. in. abs., superheated 60° F. (33° C.).   Exhaus was at 35 lb. per sq. in. abs.   The steam consumption was 8,500 lb. per hr Calculate the diagram factor and efficiency-ratio.   (*I.Mech.E.*)

$$\left[k = \frac{84\cdot2}{104\cdot9} = \underline{0\cdot802} ; \quad \eta \text{ ratio} = \frac{92\cdot3}{140\cdot4} = \underline{0\cdot657}. \right]$$

3. Explain why a much higher vacuum can be effectively used at the exhaust of a steam turbine than of an engine.

State the causes and effect of initial condensation in the cylinder of a reciprocating engine.

A double-acting compound engine is required to give 600 i.h.p. at 200 r.p.m The supply is at 200 lb. per sq. in. dry saturated ; back pressure, 4 lb. per sq. in. ratio of cylinder volumes, 4 ; overall number of expansions, $6\cdot5$; stroke equal to $\frac{2}{3}$ of the low-pressure cylinder diameter ; overall diagram factor, $0\cdot66$.

Assuming hyperbolic expansion with no clearance and allowing for a receiver loss of 3 lb. per sq. in., calculate :

(*a*) the cylinder diameters ;
(*b*) the low-pressure cylinder cut-off to give equal initial piston loads ;
(*c*) the ratio of the work done in the two cylinders ;
(*d*) the difference of temperature between inlet and exhaust of the high-pressure cylinder.   (*U. Lond.*)

[(*a*) Hypothetical m.e.p. of overall diagram ref. to L.P. cylinder $= 84\cdot4$ lb. per sq. in. ; $\underline{\text{diameters } 27\cdot3 \text{ and } 13\cdot65 \text{ in.}}$ (*b*) L.P. admission pressure $= 42\cdot6$ lb per sq. in. ; $\underline{\text{L.P. cut-off} = 0\cdot722.}$ (*c*) ratio, H.P. work : L.P. work $= \underline{0\cdot933}$ (*d*) $\underline{106\cdot8^\circ \text{ F.}}$]

4. The following conditions refer to a compound steam engine.   Steam inlet pressure to H.P. cylinder, 110 lb./in.² abs. ;   L.P. back pressure, $4\cdot3$ lb./in.² abs. ; cylinder ratio, $2\cdot2$;   total number of expansions, 8 ;   L.P. receiver pressure, 30 lb./in.² abs.   Determine the ratio of L.P. to H.P. piston loads and the ratio of the L.P. to H.P. power.   Find the effect on these quantities if the cylinder ratio is increased to $2\cdot9$ and the L.P. cut-off is decreased to $0\cdot45$.   (*U. Glas.*)

[Ratio of loads $= 0\cdot707$; ratio of powers $= 1\cdot13$; new receiver press $= 23\cdot2$ lb. per sq. in. ;   ratio of loads $= 0\cdot632$;   ratio of powers $= 0\cdot910$, assuming cut-off in H.P. cyl. is not affected and that receiver press. and no. of expansions is adjusted accordingly.]

5. A double-acting triple expansion engine has cylinders 27, 45 and 78 in. diameter, with a stroke of 54 in.

The steam enters the H.P. cylinder at 180 lb. per sq. in., the final pressure of the L.P. exhaust being 3 lb. per sq. in., with a drop in pressure of 3 lb. per sq. in. between the cylinders.

The cut-off in the H.P. cylinder is at $0\cdot6$ of the stroke.   Assuming hyperbolic expansion of the steam and neglecting the effects of clearance, find (*a*) the positions of cut-off in the I.P. and L.P. cylinders if the maximum loads on the three pistons are equal, (*b*) the horse-power developed at 100 r.p.m., taking a diagram factor $0\cdot75$ for each cylinder, and (*c*) the overall diagram factor.

(*U. Lond.*)

[(a) Ratio of cylinder volumes 1 : 2·77 : 8·32 ; admission pressures, I.P. = 61·7 nd L.P. = 16·9 lb. per sq. in. ; cut-off I.P. = 0·63 and L.P. = 0·77 ; (b) hypo- hetical m.e.p.'s referred to H.P. cylinder 98·3, 102·7, 108·2 lb. per sq. in. for H.P., .P., L.P. in order ; i.h.p. = 3,620. (c) overall hyp. m.e.p., ref. to H.P. = 369 lb. er sq. in. ; (c) k = 0·63.]

6. A triple expansion marine engine has the following cylinder volume ratios : $\frac{\text{..P.}}{\text{I.P.}} = 7·0$; $\frac{\text{I.P.}}{\text{H.P.}} = 2·8$. Initial steam pressure is 200 lb. per sq. in. abs. and ..P. back pressure is 2 lb. per sq. in. abs. L.P. terminal pressure is 15 lb. per q. in. abs. Receiver pressures are fixed at 66 and 21 lb. per sq. in. abs. Deter- nine the cut-off for each cylinder, the relative values of initial piston loads and owers developed referred to the L.P. cylinder. Determine the theoretical loss f work due to incomplete expansion in H.P. and I.P. cylinders. (U. Witw.)

[Cut-off's H.P., I.P., L.P. in order = 0·525, 0·568, 0·714 ; initial loads I.P. : I.P. : L.P. = 1·01 : 0·947 : 1·0 ; m.e.p.'s H.P. : I.P. : L.P. = 0·843 : 0·834 : 1·0 vhen ref. to L.P. cyl. ; overall m.e.p. ref. to L.P. = 51·8 lb. per sq. in. ; Σ m.e.p. f cyls. ref. to L.P. = 48·4 lb. per sq. in. ; loss = 6·6%.]

7. A double-acting steam engine uses 0·112 lb. steam (corrected for leakage) er stroke. The cylinder diameter is 12 in. and stroke 18 in. The clearance volume is 170 cu. in. Compression begins at 70% of the stroke, the pressure hen being 14 lb. per sq. in., and the steam can be assumed dry at that point. Cut-off takes place at 15% and release at 85% of the working stroke, the corre- ponding pressures being 150 and 42 lb. per sq. in. Estimate the total weight f steam present during expansion and the dryness at cut-off and release. Assuming that the expansion follows the law $PV^n = C$, find the heat passing through the cylinder walls per lb. steam during each expansion. (U. Lond.)

[Weight of cushion steam = 0·0161 lb. ; total steam during expansion = 0·128 lb. per stroke ; x at cut-off = 0·713 ; x at release = 0·855 ; n (in $PV^n = C$) = 0·917 ; W.D. per stroke = 10·92 B.T.U. ; ditto per lb. = 85·3 B.T.U. ; E_1 = 887·4 and E_2 = 969·6 B.T.U. per lb. ; Q = 167·5 B.T.U. per lb.]

8. A compound double-acting steam engine has cylinder diameters 15 and 28 in. and the stroke in each cylinder is 20 in. The cut-off in the H.P. cylinder s at 40% of the stroke and in the L.P. cylinder at 50% of the stroke. Steam s supplied at 150 lb. per sq. in. abs. and the exhaust is at 3 lb. per sq. in. abs. Allowing for a diagram factor of 0·75 in each cylinder, determine the mean effective pressure in each cylinder and the total power developed at 120 r.p.m. Show that the power could be increased by adjusting the point of cut-off in the L.P. cylinder. Estimate the amount of the possible increase and comment on the effect of the adjustment upon the general running of the engine. (I.Mech.E.)

[Receiver P = 34·5 lb. per sq. in. ; total m.e.p., referred to L.P. = (23·1 + 26·2)0·75 = 37·0 ; h.p. = 276 ; earliest cut-off in L.P. = 0·287 of stroke, then total m.e.p. (overall diagram) ref. to L.P. = 51·6 ; increase = 4·7% approx. = 13 h.p. approx.]

CHAPTER XIV

RANKINE CYCLE

1. *Describe the Rankine cycle of operations for a steam engine. Give reasons for the differences between this cycle and the Carnot cycle.*

A steam engine working on the Rankine cycle is supplied with steam at a pressure of 120 lb. per sq. in. and dryness 0·9. It exhausts at a pressure of 2 lb. per sq. in. Determine its efficiency and the magnitude of the feed pump term per lb. of steam used. (*I.C.E.*)

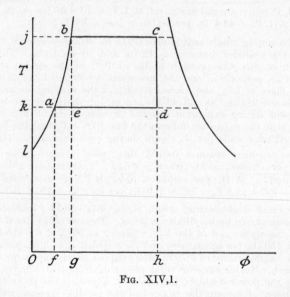

FIG. XIV,1.

The description of the various phases through which the working fluid passes in the Rankine cycle is given in chapter I, pages 20 and 21. In the diagram, the W.D. per lb. of steam is *abcd* and this is equal to $H_c - H_d$ (I,37) ; the heat supplied per lb. of steam is *fabch*, and equals $H_c - h_a$. It is usual to assume that the phase *ab* is coincident with the liquid line.

The Carnot cycle between the same temperature limits is shown by the area *ebcd*, *eb* being an isentropic compression. The W.D. per lb. of fluid is less than before, but the heat supplied is much less, *gbch*. The efficiency is $\dfrac{be}{bg}$, which is equal to $\dfrac{T_1 - T_2}{T_1}$ (I,23).

If the Rankine cycle be analysed it can be seen that the deficiency from the Carnot cycle lies in the triangular piece abe for the work done, and abg for the heat supplied. The difference between the two cycles is not great at ordinary pressures and temperatures because the latent heat of steam is relatively great, i.e. the lengths bc and ad are long compared with ae.

In the Carnot cycle all the heat is supplied at the highest temperature, whereas in the Rankine cycle some is supplied at lower temperatures. It may be shown that this criterion is responsible for the Rankine cycle being irreversible, and that its efficiency must therefore be less than that of the corresponding reversible Carnot cycle.

As may be seen in chapter XVIII, the Rankine cycle may be modified by feed heating which in effect reduces the area abe and so approximates more closely to the Carnot cycle.

In the example,
$$H_c = 312 \cdot 5 + 0 \cdot 9 \times 878 \cdot 9 = 1{,}103 \cdot 5 \text{ B.T.U.}$$
By (I,26) $\phi_c = 0 \cdot 4918 + 0 \cdot 9 \times 1 \cdot 0973 = 1 \cdot 479.$

Since this equals the entropy at d we have :
$$1 \cdot 479 = 0 \cdot 1749 + x_d \times 1 \cdot 7451$$
$$\therefore \ x_d = \frac{1 \cdot 304}{1 \cdot 7451} = 0 \cdot 747 \text{ dry.}$$
$$\therefore \ H_d = 94 \cdot 0 + 0 \cdot 747 \times 1{,}022 \cdot 2 = 858 \text{ B.T.U.}$$

So, by (I,37)   W.D. per lb. $= 1{,}103 \cdot 5 - 858 = 245 \cdot 5$ B.T.U.

and   Rankine efficiency $= \dfrac{245 \cdot 5}{1{,}103 \cdot 5 - 94} = 24 \cdot 3\%.$ Ans.

The feed-pump term is the amount of work required to feed 1 lb. of water at 2 lb. per sq. in. into the boiler. The volume per lb. of water is
$$0 \cdot 01602 + 0 \cdot 000023 \times 8 \cdot 5 = 0 \cdot 0162 \text{ cu. ft. (I,30).}$$
$$\therefore \text{ Feed-pump term} = \frac{0 \cdot 0162(120 - 2) \times 144}{778} = 0 \cdot 353 \text{ B.T.U.}   \text{ Ans.}$$

and is clearly negligible when compared with the W.D. or the heat supplied.

The W.D. could have been found by using (I,33).
$$be = 341 \cdot 3^\circ - 126 \cdot 1^\circ = 215 \cdot 2^\circ$$
$$G_b = \text{area } jlb = 81 \cdot 3$$
$$G_a = \text{area } kla = 8 \cdot 5$$
$$\therefore \ \text{W.D. per lb.} = (T_c \phi_c - G_c) - (T_d \phi_d - G_d)$$
$$= (\phi_h \times be) + G_d - G_c$$
$$= 1 \cdot 479 \times 215 \cdot 2 + 8 \cdot 5 - 81 \cdot 3$$
$$= 245 \cdot 7 \text{ B.T.U.}$$

2. *The steam consumption of an engine is 2,530 kg. per hr. and the indicate* *power developed is 305 metric horse-power. The steam is supplied dr* *saturated at a pressure of 10·55 kg. per sq. cm. and the hot-well temperatur* *is 42° C. The barometer has a height of 75·2 cm. Hg., and the vacuum* *67·7 cm. Hg.*

Find the thermal efficiency and the Rankine efficiency of the engine.

1 metric horse-power (force de cheval) = 75 kg. metres per sec.

1 kg. cal. = 427 kg. metres.

1 in. = 2·54 cm.

453·6 gm. = 1 lb.   (*U. Lond.*)

Since the steam tables provided are in B.T.U.'s it will be necessar to convert the metric units into f.p.s. units. It is worth noting tha C.H.U. per lb. = kg. cals. per kg.

Barometer = 75·2 cm. Hg. = $\dfrac{75\cdot2 \times 13\cdot6}{1,000}$ = 1·022 kg. per sq. cm.

and

Absolute steam pressure = $\dfrac{10\cdot55 \times 1,000}{453\cdot6} \times 2\cdot54^2$ = 150·5 lb. per sq. in

The total heat of dry saturated steam is 1,195·1 B.T.U. = 663·9 C.H.U

$\therefore$ Thermal efficiency = $\dfrac{305 \times 75 \times 3,600}{2,530[663\cdot9 - 42] \times 427}$ = $\underline{12\cdot25\%}$.   Ans

For the Rankine efficiency it is probably better to work entirely in B.T.U.'s as follows :

Condenser pressure = $\dfrac{75\cdot2 - 67\cdot7}{760} \times 14\cdot7$ = 1·45 lb. per sq. in., nearly.

$\therefore$ W.D. per lb. = 1,195·1 − (574·2 × 1·5705) + 6·5
= 300 B.T.U. using (I,33) and (I,37).

Thus, the Rankine efficiency = $\dfrac{300}{1,195\cdot1 - 82\cdot5}$ = $\underline{27\%}$.   Ans.

3. *The steam cylinder of a pump operates on the non-expansive cycle and* *is supplied with dry saturated steam at 100 lb. per sq. in., exhaust taking place* *at 15 lb. per sq. in.*

Give sketches of the theoretical P–V and T–ϕ diagrams and explain why *this cycle is less efficient thermodynamically than the corresponding Rankine* *cycle.*

Find (a) *the theoretical dryness of the steam at the beginning of the constant* *pressure exhaust ;* (b) *the mean effective pressure in the cylinder ;* (c) *the* *heat rejected in the exhaust per lb. of steam ;* (d) *the steam consumption in* *lb. per i.h.p.-hr.*

(*U. Lond.*)

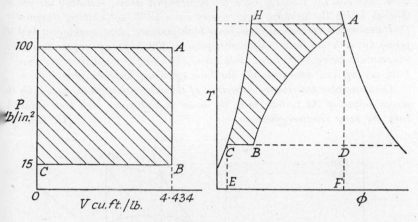

Fig. XIV,2.

The theoretical indicator diagram is shown in fig. XIV,2, which is drawn for 1 lb. of steam. The rejection of heat, i.e. the exhaust, takes place in two phases; AB represents the rejection of heat at constant volume and BC the rejection of heat at constant pressure in the usual manner. On the entropy diagram, the work done represented by the shaded area, is much less than the Rankine work when the expansion would proceed from A to D. The loss of work equals BAD, and since the heat supplied is the same in both cases, the efficiency must be lower than the Rankine efficiency.

The theoretical dryness at $B = \dfrac{4\cdot434}{26\cdot28} = \underline{0\cdot169}$. Ans. (a).

The m.e.p. in the cylinder is clearly

$$100 - 15 = \underline{85 \text{ lb. per sq. in.}} \quad \text{Ans. } (b).$$

The heat rejected (during both phases of the exhaust) = area AFECBA
= heat supplied − W.D. = HAFECH − HABCH

$$= (1,188\cdot2 - 181\cdot2) - \frac{144 \times 85 \times 4\cdot434}{778} = 1,007 - 69\cdot7$$

$$= \underline{937\cdot3 \text{ B.T.U.}} \quad \text{Ans. } (c).$$

The specific steam consumption $= \dfrac{2,546}{69\cdot7} = \underline{36\cdot5 \text{ lb. per h.p.-hr.}}$ Ans. (d).

4. *Describe the Rankine cycle for superheated steam, sketching the phase through which the working fluid passes on a total heat–entropy diagram.*

Compare the theoretical cycle for a high-pressure plant working at 900 lb. per sq. in. with that for a low-pressure plant at 300 lb. per sq. in., the maximum temperature being 750° F. in both cases. Taking a condenser pressure of 1 lb. per sq. in., determine the Rankine efficiency for each plant.

Compare also the relative capacities of the condensing plant, assuming the power output of the turbine to be the same in both cases, and both plants to have the same relative efficiency. (U. Lond.)

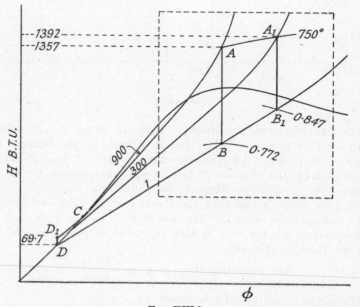

Fig. XIV,3.

It is not usual to show the liquid phase of the Rankine cycle on a total heat-entropy diagram, but the refrigeration cycle is frequently demonstrated on a total heat–entropy diagram as explained in chapter XIX. The limits of the ordinary steam diagram are shown by the dotted lines.

In the skeleton diagram above, the superheated steam at A is expanded isentropically in the cylinder to the state B, when it is passed into the condenser. B to D represents condensation at constant pressure, D being the liquid at the temperature and pressure of condensation in the condenser. The liquid is withdrawn by the extraction pump and then pumped into the boiler at the same temperature. The line DD_1 represents the feed-pump term, which may be seen from the previous example to be of negligible proportions and this has been much exaggerated on the diagram. The feed is heated up to saturation conditions at C and converted into superheated steam at A, ready to proceed round the cycle again.

Taking the values from the chart we have:

High pressure	Low pressure
$\Delta H_{A-B} = 494$ B.T.U.	$\Delta H_{A_1-B_1} = 448$ B.T.U.
$H_A = 1{,}357$ B.T.U.	$H_{A_1} = 1{,}392$ B.T.U.
$h_D = 69.7$ B.T.U.	$h_D = 69.7$ B.T.U.

$$\text{Rankine efficiency} = \frac{494}{1{,}287} \qquad \text{Rankine efficiency} = \frac{448}{1{,}322}$$
$$= 38.4\% \text{ Ans.} \qquad\qquad = 33.9\% \text{ Ans.}$$

For equal power, if w lb. per sec. are used,

$$494w_{\text{H.P.}} = 448w_{\text{L.P.}}$$

H.P. heat abstracted $= (863 - 69.7)w_{\text{H.P.}} = 793w_{\text{H.P.}}$ B.T.U.

L.P. ,, ,, $= (944 - 69.7)w_{\text{L.P.}} = 874w_{\text{L.P.}}$ B.T.U.

$$\therefore \frac{\text{Condensing capacity, H.P.}}{\text{Condensing capacity, L.P.}} = \frac{793}{874} \times \frac{448}{494} = \frac{1}{1.215}. \text{ Ans.}$$

It can be seen that the volume per lb. of steam is greater at B_1 than at B, and so with the lower pressure of 300 lb. per sq. in. we need a larger turbine and a still larger condensing plant for the same power output.

5. *A reciprocating steam engine is supplied with steam at a pressure of 200 lb. per sq. in. and 50° C. of superheat, specific volume 2·64 cu. ft. per lb. The ratio of expansion is 12·9 and the condenser pressure 2 lb. per sq. in. If the expansion of the steam is isentropic, find the pressure in the cylinder at the instant before the exhaust valve opens at the end of the working stroke and determine the work done per lb. of steam and the theoretical efficiency of the engine.*

Neglect clearance and compression and assume the pressure in the cylinder is constant during admission and exhaust.

(*U. Camb.*)

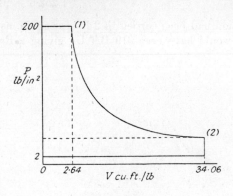

Fig. XIV,4.

$50°$ C. superheat $= 90°$ F.

The initial volume is expanded 12·9 times, so the final volume V_2 will be 34·06 cu. ft. per lb.

The expansion phase is isentropic and the ordinary total heat–entropy diagram does not give lines of constant volume below the saturation line. There are charts which give this information, and the pressure of the steam at (2) could be found directly from them. However, we can get a very close solution in the following manner.

Using Tables II and III, we find $H_1 = 1{,}252·6$ B.T.U. and $\phi_1 = 1·6051$. Since the final volume V_2 is 34·06 cu. ft. we have an idea of the order of the pressure, say 8–10 lb. per sq. in., and can construct the following table. The dryness is read from the chart and V_s from the tables.

p	x	V_s	$xV_s = V_2$
10	0·878	38·42	33·7
8	0·868	47·35	41·25
9	0·873	42·4	37·0

It is near enough for all practical purposes to quote the release pressure as 10 lb. per sq. in., as a more nearly exact figure for this pressure would involve interpolation, and result in an apparent accuracy of the answer out of keeping with a practical problem.

Assuming then that the release pressure is 10 lb. per sq. in., we find from the chart that the heat drop from 1 to 2 is 228 B.T.U. To this must be added the extra W.D. equivalent to the rectangular area of length 34·06 and height $10 - 2 = 8$ lb. per sq. in.

$$\text{This equals} \quad \frac{34·06 \times 8 \times 144}{778} = 50·4 \text{ B.T.U.}$$

$$\therefore \text{ Total W.D. per lb. of steam} = \underline{278·4 \text{ B.T.U.}} \quad \text{Ans.}$$

$$\text{The thermal efficiency will be} \quad \frac{278·4}{1{,}252·6 - 94} = \underline{24\%}. \quad \text{Ans.}$$

If the expansion had been carried to 2 lb. per sq. in. as in the Rankine cycle, the W.D. would have been 319 B.T.U., giving a Rankine efficiency of 27·5%.

6. *Steam at 200 lb. per sq. in. superheated 100° F., is supplied to an engine in which it expands adiabatically to the release pressure of 20 lb. per sq. in. when the pressure falls at constant volume to the exhaust pressure of 4 lb. per sq. in.*

Determine :

    (a) *the steam consumption in lb. per h.p.-hr.*

    (b) *the mean effective pressure ;*

    (c) *the heat to be removed by the condenser per lb. of exhaust steam.*

                                                        (U. Lond.)

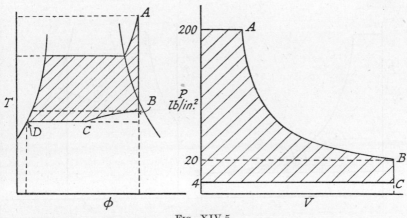

FIG. XIV,5.

H_A (Table II) $= 1,258 \cdot 2$ B.T.U. ; ϕ_A (Table III) $= 1 \cdot 6111$.

Equating the entropy of A to that at B, 20 lb. per sq. in.

$$1 \cdot 6111 = 0 \cdot 3358 + x_B(1 \cdot 7327 - 0 \cdot 3358)$$

whence $\qquad\qquad x_B = 0 \cdot 913.$

$$\therefore \ H_B = 196 \cdot 3 + 0 \cdot 913 \times 960 \cdot 4 = 1,073 \cdot 1 \ \text{B.T.U. per lb.}$$

and $\qquad\qquad V_B = 0 \cdot 913 \times 20 \cdot 09 = 18 \cdot 34$ cu. ft. per lb.

$$\therefore \ \text{W.D. per lb. of steam} = (1,258 \cdot 2 - 1,073 \cdot 1) + \frac{(20 - 4)144 \times 18 \cdot 34}{778}$$

$$= 185 \cdot 1 + 54 \cdot 3 = 239 \cdot 4 \ \text{B.T.U.}$$

The value $185 \cdot 1$ B.T.U. is the W.D. on the Rankine cycle between the pressures of 200 and 20 lb. per sq. in. The rectangular area between 20 and 4 lb. per sq. in. as shown on the PV diagram represents $54 \cdot 3$ B.T.U.

$$\therefore \ \text{Specific consumption} = \frac{2,546}{239 \cdot 4} = \underline{10 \cdot 63 \ \text{lb. per h.p.-hr.}} \quad \text{Ans. } (a).$$

$$\text{The m.e.p.} = \frac{239 \cdot 4 \times 778}{144 \times 18 \cdot 34} = \underline{70 \cdot 55 \ \text{lb. per sq. in.}} \quad \text{Ans. } (b).$$

The heat to the condenser $=$ heat supplied $-$ W.D.

$$= (1,258 \cdot 2 - 121) - 239 \cdot 4 = \underline{897 \cdot 8 \ \text{B.T.U.}} \quad \text{Ans. } (c).$$

7. *Why is a high vacuum desirable in a steam turbine installation whereas a moderate vacuum suffices in the case of an ordinary reciprocating steam engine? The vacuum in the suction pipe of a single-acting air pump is 28·5 in. Hg. (barometer, 30·2 in. Hg.) and the temperature is 85° F. The diameter of the pump is 20 in. and the stroke is 30 in. and it works at 45 double strokes per min. The weight of condensate passing through the pump per hr. is 18,000 lb. Assuming the volumetric efficiency of the pump is 65% (referred to the pressure and temperature in the suction pipe), determine the weight of air dealt with by the pump per hr.*   *(U. Dur.)*

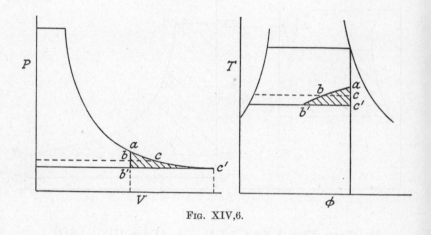

FIG. XIV,6.

When release takes place in an engine a good deal of internal energy in the steam is rejected into the condenser, mainly at constant volume *ab*, and a lower back pressure will only slightly increase the area of the P–V diagram at the expense of extra work required to provide the higher vacuum.

Steam turbines, however, require no such release point and the internal energy is utilized right down to the back pressure, point *c*. It was shown in chapter I, page 2, that the W.D. in the flow-cycle, with adiabatic expansion, is equal to the heat drop, $H_1 - H_2$. Expansions in turbines approach this condition closely (i.e. the adiabatic, though not isentropic expansion) and an inspection of the H–ϕ chart will show that the heat drop per lb. per sq. in. increases considerably at the lowest back pressures. The available heat drop is therefore considerably greater for high vacua than for moderate ones. Also, as the vacuum is increased from *b* to *b'* the *extra* W.D. in the reciprocating engine becomes progressively less, the point *b'* on the entropy diagram moving further to the left.

Absolute Pressure in suction pipe = 30·2 − 28·5 = 1·7 in Hg.

                           = 1·7 × 0·49 = 0·834 lb. per sq. in.

Saturation Pressure of steam at 85° F. = 0·595 lb. per sq. in.

by interpolation of the steam tables.

By Dalton's Law of Partial Pressures,

Partial Pressure of air = 0·834 − 0·595 = 0·239 lb. per sq. in.

By (I,7) Volume of per lb. of air $= \dfrac{53\cdot3 \times 545}{0\cdot239 \times 144} = 844$ cu. ft.,

and this is also the volume of the vapour (i.e. wet steam) present per lb. of air.

Now, swept volume of pump per hr. $= \dfrac{\pi}{4} \times \dfrac{20^2 \times 30}{1,728} \times 90 \times 60$

$$= 29,420 \text{ cu. ft.}$$

and for a volumetric efficiency of 65% referred to suction pipe conditions, we have :

Effective volume of pump per hr. = 0·65 × 29,420 = 19,130 cu. ft.

Volume of condensate (water) per hr. = 18,000 × 0·016 = 288 cu. ft.

(Note, the volume of 1 lb. of water at 85° F. should really be found from (I,30) where G = 2·8 approx. from the table. It will, however, be found that V_w will be 0·016, very nearly, as the temperature is so near to 32° F., the datum.)

∴ Volume of vapour and air per hr. = 19,130 − 288 = 18,842 cu. ft.

But we have already found that 844 cu. ft. are occupied by air and steam per lb. of air.

∴ Weight of air dealt with per hr. $= \dfrac{18,842}{844} = 22\cdot3$ lb. Ans.

EXAMPLES

1. The steam supplied to a heat engine is at 300 lb. per sq. in. abs. pressure superheated to 300° C. and the exhaust pressure is 2 lb. per sq. in. abs. Find the theoretical amount of work available per lb. of steam if the engine works on the Rankine cycle.

If 30% of this work is lost by friction and reconverted back into heat, find the dryness of the steam as it leaves the engine.

What is the steam consumption per effective horse-power hour of an engine working between these given conditions of steam supply and exhaust, and having a relative efficiency of 70%, when compared with a Rankine engine ? (*I.C.E.*)

[$\Delta H_T = 363$ B.T.U. per lb. ; $x = 0\cdot930$; 10·0 lb. per h.p.-hr.]

2. Describe fully, and by means of a sketch of the appropriate temperature–entropy diagram, the various stages in the ideal Rankine cycle using superheated steam. Explain the heat and work quantities involved in each stage and define the efficiency of the cycle, with due attention to the term for feed pump work.

A steam turbine installation takes steam at 1,000 lb. per sq. in. abs., 180° F. (100° C.) superheat, and expands to an exhaust pressure of 0·9 lb. per sq. in. abs.

If the efficiency ratio on the Rankine cycle is 0·75 determine the thermal efficiency of the installation and the consumption rate in pounds per kilowatt-hour.

(I.Mech.E.)

[ΔH_T = 492·3 B.T.U. per lb. ; <u>th. η = 29·0%</u> ; <u>9·25 lb. per kW.-hr.</u>]

3. (a) Determine, by calculation, the efficiency of the Rankine cycle when the initial pressure and temperature are 250 lb. per sq. in. and 305° C. (581° F.) and the exhaust pressure 1 lb. per sq. in.

(b) A steam plant receives steam at 250 lb. per sq. in. and 305° C. (581° F.) and expands it adiabatically to 50 lb. per sq. in. The steam is then throttled until dry saturated and then reheated at constant pressure until the degree of superheat is 60° C. (108° F.). Finally the steam expands adiabatically to 1 lb. per sq. in.

Draw this cycle of operation on the total heat–entropy chart provided, and by measurement from the chart determine : (i) the available work per lb. of steam ; (ii) the final dryness fraction ; (iii) the heat supplied per lb. of steam during the reheating process. *(U.L.C.I.)*

[(a) η = 31·6% ; (b) (i) 358 B.T.U. per lb. ; (ii) x = 0·899 ; (iii) 52 B.T.U. per lb.]

4. Describe the essential *differences* between the Rankine and Carnot cycles and the phases through which the working fluid actually passes, if supplies superheated to an engine.

Compare the Rankine and Carnot engine consumptions in lb./h.p.-hr. if dry saturated steam is generated at 200 lb./in.², exhaust taking place at 1 lb./in.²

What accounts for the difference of efficiency ?

Calculate the equivalent m.e.p. in the Rankine engine and the heat to be removed in the condenser per lb. of exhaust steam. *(U. Lond.)*

[Rankine : ΔH = 336, spec. consumption = <u>7·58</u> ; Carnot : η = 0·333, W.D. = 281, spec. consumption = 9·06 ; x of steam entering condenser = 0·766 ; m.e.p. = $\dfrac{\text{W.D. per lb.}}{\text{Vol. per lb.}}$ = 7·1 lb. per sq. in. ; heat removed = 794 B.T.U.]

5. Explain the sequence of operations in the modified Rankine cycle, in which the expansion of the steam is incomplete, and give reasons for its adoption.

Using the steam tables, calculate the Rankine efficiency of an engine supplied with dry saturated steam at 200 lb. per sq. in., and exhausting at 15 lb. per sq. in., and compare this efficiency with that of the modified Rankine cycle operating between the same supply and exhaust pressures, the steam being released to exhaust at constant volume when the pressure has fallen to 40 lb. per sq. in. *(U. Lond.)*

[Rankine : ΔH = 189, η = 18·5% ; modified : W.D. = 126 + 43·6 = 169·6 B.T.U. per lb., η = 16·6%.]

6. Steam is supplied to an engine at 250 lb./in.² and 630° F. Adiabatic expansion takes place to the release point at 20 lb./in.² after which there is a sudden drop of pressure to the exhaust at 1 lb./in.²

Find : (a) the work done per lb. of steam supplied ;
(b) the internal energy per lb. of steam at release ;
(c) the work done in ft.lb. by the extraction and boiler feed pumps per lb. of water returned to the boiler. *(U. Lond.)*

[(a) Dryness at release = 0·950 ; W.D. = 226 + 67 = <u>293 B.T.U.</u> ; (b) <u>1,037 B.T.U.</u> by (I,1) ; (c) increase of press. = 249 lb. per sq. in. ; <u>W.D. = 575 ft.lb.</u>]

CHAPTER XV

EXPANSION THROUGH NOZZLES

Introduction

The following points have been summarized as a help to the many students who have difficulty in deciding on the correct assumptions in connection with nozzle questions. The treatment is not intended to be comprehensive.

(i) The expansion of a vapour or gas through a nozzle is a " flow " process, consisting of the admission of the vapour into the nozzle at constant pressure, the actual " phase " expansion and the rejection from the nozzle at constant pressure. This description applies to the P–V diagram representing the Rankine cycle if the feed-pump term is neglected, and if the expansion phase is truly adiabatic. In the absence of losses, the expansion phase is fully resisted by the stuff itself acting as a piston. The work done by an element in expanding is spent in accelerating the mass of fluid in front of it, i.e. the W.D. is converted into K.E.

(ii) If the expansion is frictionless and adiabatic, the net work done will equal the isentropic heat drop $H_1 - H_2$, by (I,37). This isentropic, or *total*, heat drop will now be designated by ΔH_T, and is the same as the Rankine heat drop dealt with in the previous chapter. The magnitude of ΔH_T will depend, in the case of vapours, upon whether the expansion has been stable or metastable (cf. below).

(iii) The W.D. which equals ΔH_T may be expressed as

$$\frac{n}{n-1} P_1 V_1 \left[1 - \left(\frac{P_2}{P_1} \right)^{\frac{n-1}{n}} \right] \text{ by (I,39).}$$

The index n must be that for frictionless adiabatic expansion, and this expression must only be used for determining ΔH_T, the isentropic heat drop. For, non-isentropic or polytropic expansions are usually due to unresisted frictional losses, etc. (cf. below), which are irreversible ; in this case the net W.D. is less than ΔH_T and is no longer equal to $\int P \, dV$,

the area of the P–V diagram. An evaluation of (I,39), using an apparent value of n for a friction resisted expansion will therefore lead to an incorrect answer. The correct procedure is to evaluate ΔH_T and to allow for the losses which are usually expressed as a fraction of ΔH_T.

237

(iv) Supersaturation or metastable expansion is discussed in example No. 5 in this chapter.

(v) For superheated steam the adiabatic index is 1·3, giving a critical (or throat) pressure ratio of 0·545. For initially dry saturated steam the index is about 1·135 in accordance with Zeuner's equation (I,34) ; this leads to a critical pressure ratio of 0·577 for stable expansions, and the chart may be used in these cases. If it is assumed, however, that the expansion is so rapid that supersaturated conditions prevail (an assumption which is more nearly correct), then the expansion may be taken to follow the law $PV^{1·3}$ = constant whatever the initial state, and also that $\dfrac{PV}{T}$ = constant. These two statements lead to the important statement

that $\dfrac{P}{T^{1\cdot3}}$ = constant. In such a case the chart must not be used. A

few remarks about the selection of appropriate indices will be found in exercise no. 6, chapter XVI.

(vi) Under the heading of frictional losses we have (a) skin friction of the fluid at the nozzle surface, (b) internal friction of the fluid itself and (c) losses due to shock. The problem of dealing with these complex losses is usually dismissed by the statement that a certain percentage of the isentropic heat drop, ΔH_T, is lost by friction, etc. Almost certainly, the losses near the entrance to the nozzle are much less than those near the exit owing to the small inlet velocity. This is sometimes allowed for by expressing the percentage loss of ΔH_T between throat and exit conditions only. In any case, the throat pressure is assumed to be independent of any losses. The energy dissipated as friction reappears as heat *within* the fluid, thus reducing the velocity and increasing the specific volume.

(vii) Definition :

$$\text{Nozzle Efficiency} = \frac{\text{Useful Heat Drop}}{\text{Isentropic Heat Drop}} = \frac{\Delta H_U}{\Delta H_T},$$

where ΔH_T has been previously defined and ΔH_U is the actual or *useful* heat drop converted into kinetic energy, all the losses mentioned in para. (vi) above being covered by this term. In fig. XV,1 $AB = \Delta H_T$, $AC = \Delta H_U$ and the final state point is at D at the pressure of B and the total heat of C.

1. *Steam flows through a turbine nozzle at the rate of 7 lb. per sec. from a pressure of 120 lb. per sq. in. abs. with 20° F. superheat to 50 lb. per sq. in. abs., 0·98 dry.*

Calculate the nozzle exit area and the change in internal energy of the steam in passing through the nozzle. For superheated steam use—

$$V = 1\cdot25(H - 835\cdot2)/P.$$

(U. Glas.)

It is implied that the expansion is to be considered as stable, and the kinetic energy developed will be equal to the heat drop between the initial and final conditions.

From Table II the total heat at 120 lb. per sq. in., with 20° F. superheat

$$= 1{,}202\cdot8 \text{ B.T.U. per lb.}$$

The total heat of the wet steam at exit

$$= 250\cdot2 + 0\cdot98 \times 924\cdot6 = 1{,}156\cdot3 \text{ B.T.U. per lb.}$$

$$\therefore \text{ W.D. per lb.} = 1{,}202\cdot8 - 1{,}156\cdot3, \text{ by (I,37)}$$

i.e. $\Delta H_U = 46\cdot5$ B.T.U.

This work is wholly converted into kinetic energy in the absence of all losses, so that per lb. of steam $46\cdot5 = \dfrac{v^2}{2gJ}$, neglecting the vel. of approach.

$$\therefore \text{ Velocity at exit} = \sqrt{2gJ \times 46\cdot5}$$
$$= 8\cdot03\sqrt{46\cdot5 \times 778}$$
$$= 1{,}530 \text{ ft. per sec.}$$

Volume per lb. at exit $= 0\cdot98 \times 8\cdot516 = 8\cdot34$ cu. ft. (I,31).

For continuity of flow,

$$\text{Area} \times \text{Velocity} = \text{lb. per sec.} \times \text{cu. ft. per lb.}$$

$$\therefore \text{ Area at exit} = \frac{7 \times 8\cdot34}{1{,}530} \times 144 \text{ sq. in.}$$

$$= \underline{5\cdot5 \text{ sq. in.}} \quad \text{Ans.}$$

$$\text{Initial volume per lb.} = \frac{1\cdot25(1{,}202\cdot8 - 835\cdot2)}{120}$$

$$= 3\cdot83 \text{ cu. ft.}$$

Using (I,1), we find the change in internal energy as follows :

$$E_1 = 1{,}202\cdot8 - \frac{120 \times 144 \times 3\cdot83}{778} = 1{,}202\cdot8 - 85\cdot0$$

$$= 1{,}117\cdot8 \text{ B.T.U.}$$

$$E_2 = 1{,}156\cdot3 - \frac{50 \times 144 \times 8\cdot34}{778} = 1{,}156\cdot3 - 77\cdot2$$

$$= 1{,}079\cdot1 \text{ B.T.U.}$$

$$\therefore E_2 - E_1 = - \underline{38\cdot7} \text{ B.T.U. (i.e. a decrease).} \quad \text{Ans.}$$

2. *Steam at 30 lb. per sq. in. abs., dry saturated, passes through a convergent nozzle of throat area 4 sq. in. to a final pressure of 20 lb. per sq. in. abs. Calculate the weight of steam discharged per hour, (a) assuming that the steam expands in thermal equilibrium, and (b) that the steam is supersaturated during the expansion. Neglect frictional losses and the kinetic energy of the steam approaching the nozzle.* (*I.Mech.E.*)

The nozzle is a convergent one since the pressure drop across the nozzle is smaller than the critical one.

(*a*) *Thermal equilibrium.* The steam increases in wetness as the expansion proceeds, and the temperature at all stages of the expansion is the saturation temperature.

The heat drop may be estimated in three ways : (i) from the chart, (ii) by calculation using the Tables, and (iii) by calculation from the formula (I,39), given the index of expansion. As frictional losses are to be neglected, $\Delta H_T = \Delta H_U = \Delta H$.

(i) The heat drop from the chart is estimated as 29·5 B.T.U. and the resulting dryness as 0·978. However, with such a small pressure drop it is difficult to get an accurate figure and for this problem it would be better to calculate as in (ii).

(ii) Using (I,33),

$$\text{Heat drop} = \phi_1(t_1 - t_2) - G_1 + G_2$$
$$= 1 \cdot 7004(250 \cdot 3 - 228 \cdot 0) - 42 \cdot 4 + 34 \cdot 6$$

i.e. $$\Delta H = 30 \cdot 1 \text{ B.T.U. per lb.} = \frac{v^2}{2gJ}$$

$\therefore$ Velocity at exit $= 8 \cdot 03\sqrt{30 \cdot 1 \times 778} = 1{,}230$ ft. per sec.

The dryness may be obtained by equating the entropy before and after expansion.

$$1 \cdot 7004 = 0 \cdot 3358 + x_2 \times 1 \cdot 3969$$
$$\therefore x_2 = 0 \cdot 976$$

and $\qquad$ Area $\times$ velocity $=$ mass flow $\times$ specific volume,

$$\therefore \text{ Weight per hr.} = \frac{1{,}230 \times 4 \times 3{,}600}{0 \cdot 976 \times 20 \cdot 09 \times 144} = \underline{6{,}265 \text{ lb.}} \quad \text{Ans. } (a).$$

(iii) If the index of expansion under conditions of stability be assumed to have a mean value of 1·135 for *initially* dry saturated steam (see I,34), the W.D. per lb. would be, by (I,39),

$$\frac{1 \cdot 135}{0 \cdot 135} \times \frac{30}{778} \times 144 \times 13 \cdot 73 \left[1 - \left(\frac{20}{30} \right)^{\frac{0 \cdot 135}{1 \cdot 135}} \right] \text{ B.T.U.}$$

$$= 642 \left[1 - \left(\frac{3}{4 \cdot 5} \right)^{\frac{1}{8 \cdot 41}} \right] = 642 \left[1 - \frac{1 \cdot 139}{1 \cdot 196} \right] = 30 \cdot 8 \text{ B.T.U.}$$

This value is not easy to obtain on a slide rule owing to the difficulty of estimating the quantity in the brackets. In any case the figure is not as reliable as that obtained by method (ii), since the index is only an approximation.

(b) *Supersaturated flow.* Here the index of expansion will be 1·3 and the W.D. per lb.

$$= \frac{1\cdot3}{0\cdot3} \times \frac{30}{778} \times 144 \times 13\cdot73 \left[1 - \left(\frac{20}{30}\right)^{\frac{0\cdot3}{1\cdot3}} \right] \text{ B.T.U.}$$

$$= 330\cdot5 \left[1 - \left(\frac{3}{4\cdot5}\right)^{0\cdot2308} \right] = 330\cdot5 \left[1 - \frac{1\cdot289}{1\cdot415} \right] = 29\cdot4 \text{ B.T.U.}$$

This value is less than that for stable adiabatic expansion as explained more fully in example No. 5 in this chapter.

Exit velocity $= \sqrt{2g\text{J} \times \text{W.D.}} = 8\cdot03\sqrt{29\cdot4 \times 778} = 1{,}215$ ft. per sec.

Also,   Volume per lb. $= \left(\frac{30}{20}\right)^{\frac{1}{1\cdot3}} \times 13\cdot73 = 18\cdot75$ cu. ft.

$$\therefore \text{ Weight per hr.} = \frac{1{,}215 \times 4 \times 3{,}600}{18\cdot75 \times 144} = \underline{6{,}480 \text{ lb.}} \quad \text{Ans. (b).}$$

The temperature at the end of expansion will be

$$710 \times \left(\frac{20}{30}\right)^{\frac{0\cdot3}{1\cdot3}} = 647° \text{ F. abs.,}$$

i.e. 40·7° F. below the saturation temperature at 20 lb. per sq. in.

The evaluation of the above has been carried out entirely on the slide rule. In order to be able to use the log–log scale $\frac{20}{30}$ has been re-written

as $\frac{3}{4\cdot5}$ instead of $\frac{1}{1\cdot5}$.

3. *What area in sq. in. would be required at the exit from the nozzles of the first stage of an impulse turbine, if 50,000 lb. of steam are supplied per hr. at 200 lb. per sq. in. abs. 120° F. superheat, and the pressure after the runner blades is 50 lb. per sq. in. abs. The efficiency may be taken as 90% and the reheating of the steam due to losses is to be taken into account.*

(U. Manch.)

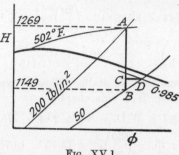

FIG. XV,1.

In this question the wording suggests that the expansion is to be considered as stable. When the nozzle length is sufficient, the supersaturated conditions may become partly stabilized in actual practice. The exit pressure of the nozzles will be 50 lb. per sq. in., since in an impulse machine the wheel chamber is at a constant pressure.

The point A on the total heat–entropy diagram showing the superheated steam at admission gives a total heat of 1,269 B.T.U. The frictionless adiabatic expansion down to 50 lb. per sq. in. is represented by the constant entropy line AB, and the heat drop ΔH_T is 120 B.T.U. Of this heat drop, 90% is developed into kinetic energy, and the remainder is dissipated as heat which reheats the steam. The steam at exit has therefore a total heat H_C, and as the pressure is 50 lb. per sq. in., the state must be at D. The steam is drier, has a greater volume per lb., and the velocity is less than the ideal.

The heat drop AC which is developed as kinetic energy is

$$\Delta H_U = 120 \times 0{\cdot}9 = 108 \text{ B.T.U.}$$
$$\therefore \ H_C = 1{,}161 = H_D.$$

$\therefore$ The dryness at D can be read off from the chart as $x_D = 0{\cdot}985$ and $x_D V_s = 0{\cdot}985 \times 8{\cdot}516.$

The velocity at exit $= \sqrt{2g J \, \Delta H_U}$

$$= 8{\cdot}03\sqrt{108 \times 778}$$

$$= 2{,}330 \text{ ft. per sec.}$$

$\therefore$ Area at exit $= \dfrac{50{,}000 \times 0{\cdot}985 \times 8{\cdot}516}{3{,}600 \times 2{,}330} = 0{\cdot}05$ sq. ft.

$$= \underline{7{\cdot}2 \text{ sq. in.}} \quad \text{Ans.}$$

4. *Steam at a pressure of 120 lb. per sq. in. with a superheat of 160° F. is passed through a convergent-divergent nozzle, being expanded to 25 lb. per sq. in. Frictionless adiabatic expansion takes place according to the law $PV^{1\cdot3} = constant$, until the throat pressure is reached. The subsequent expansion in the divergent portion of the nozzle is affected by frictional losses amounting to 10% of the adiabatic heat drop over this range. If the expansion throughout is under metastable conditions, find by calculation, the exit velocity, and estimate the exit temperature of the steam.*

(The specific heat at 25 lb. per sq. in. may be taken as 0·52.)

(U. Lond.)

Here the flow is under supersaturated conditions [1] and the exit pressure is less than the critical pressure.

The critical pressure at the throat is

$$120 \times 0\cdot545 = 65\cdot4 \text{ lb. per sq. in.}$$

and the initial volume per lb. is

$$\frac{1\cdot253(1,277\cdot5 - 835)}{120} = 4\cdot62 \text{ cu. ft. (cf. I,32).}$$

The W.D. per lb. from entrance to throat

$$= \frac{1\cdot3}{0\cdot3} \times \frac{120 \times 144}{778} \times 4\cdot62\left(1 - 0\cdot545^{\frac{0\cdot3}{1\cdot3}}\right), \text{ by (I,39),}$$

$$= 57\cdot75 \text{ B.T.U.}$$

The W.D. per lb. from entrance to exit, there being no losses,

$$= \frac{1\cdot3}{0\cdot3} \times \frac{120 \times 144}{778} \times 4\cdot62\left[1 - \left(\frac{25}{120}\right)^{\frac{0\cdot3}{1\cdot3}}\right]$$

$$= 134\cdot6 \text{ B.T.U.}$$

∴ Heat drop, throat to exit $= 134\cdot6 - 57\cdot75 = 76\cdot85$ B.T.U.

∴ Kinetic energy lost due to friction $= 7\cdot685$ B.T.U.

leaving 126·9 B.T.U. developed as kinetic energy.

Since the velocity of approach is to be neglected, the exit velocity will be $8\cdot03\sqrt{126\cdot9 \times 778}$

$$= \underline{2,520 \text{ ft. per sec.}} \text{ Ans.}$$

The frictional loss will be spent in reheating the supersaturated steam, the specific heat of which is to be taken as 0·52.

[1] See ex. No. 5, page 244, for general discussion of supersaturation.

Using (I,18), the final temperature at exit, assuming no reheat, would be

$$961 \cdot 3 \times \left(\frac{25}{120}\right)^{\frac{0 \cdot 3}{1 \cdot 3}} = 670° \text{ F. abs.}$$

(Cf. also introduction (v), page 238.)

The rise in temperature due to reheating $= \dfrac{7 \cdot 69}{0 \cdot 52} = 14 \cdot 7°$ F.

$\therefore$ Final temperature $= 684 \cdot 7°$ F. abs. $= \underline{224 \cdot 7°$ F.} Ans.

t_{sat} at 25 lb. per sq. in. $= 240 \cdot 1°$ F.

$\therefore$ Degrees of supersaturation $= 15 \cdot 4°$.

---

5. *Steam is expanded in a suitably shaped nozzle without loss from a pressure of 80 lb. per sq. in. with 60° F. superheat to 20 lb. per sq. in. The expansion follows the law $PV^{1 \cdot 3} = constant$. By calculation, find the temperature and the velocity of the steam at exit from the nozzle. What is the pressure at the throat?*

Estimate also the state of the steam and its velocity at exit, assuming the expansion is in thermal equilibrium throughout.

By means of suitable entropy diagrams, demonstrate the difference between the two expansions. (*U. Lond.*)

The supersaturated frictionless expansion of the steam is shown on the diagram as AC. Since no condensation is taking place, the curved constant pressure lines from the superheated region may be assumed to be extended as shown by the dotted lines, and the expansion would cease at the point C. The stable isentropic expansion would have been represented by AB, and it can be seen that there must always be less work done by the steam when it expands under supersaturated conditions. The steam at C stabilizes itself at D, the partial condensation releasing sufficient latent heat to raise the temperature to the saturation temperature. An increase in entropy takes place from C to D during the "change-over", but the expansion ACD has been adiabatic.

Total heat at A $= 1,216$ B.T.U. (Table II).

$$\therefore \text{ Volume} = \frac{1 \cdot 253(1,216 - 835)}{80} = 5 \cdot 99 \text{ cu. ft. per lb.}$$

From (I,18) we have $\qquad \dfrac{T_A}{T_C} = \left(\dfrac{P_A}{P_C}\right)^{\frac{n-1}{n}}$

or

$$\frac{460 + 372}{T_C} = \left(\frac{80}{20}\right)^{\frac{0\cdot3}{1\cdot3}} = 1\cdot377$$

$$\therefore T_C = 605° \text{ F. abs.;}$$

$$\underline{t_C = 145° \text{ F.}} \quad \text{Ans.}$$

The saturation temperature is 228° F., and the degree of supersaturation or undercooling is $228 - 145 = 83°$ F.

The W.D. per lb. of steam ($= AC$) is, by (I,39),

$$= \frac{1\cdot3}{0\cdot3} \times 80 \times 144 \times 5\cdot99\left(1 - \frac{1}{1\cdot377}\right)$$

$$= 81,800 \text{ ft.lb. (105 B.T.U.).}$$

$$\therefore \text{ Velocity at exit} = 8\cdot03\sqrt{81,800} = \underline{2,300 \text{ ft. per sec.}} \quad \text{Ans.}$$

Since $PV^{1\cdot3} = $ constant, the throat pressure will be

$$0\cdot545 \times 80 = \underline{43\cdot6 \text{ lb. per sq. in.}} \quad \text{Ans.}$$

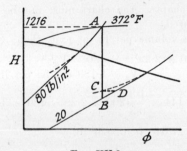

FIG. XV,2.

Calculating the W.D. under stable conditions (equal to the heat drop AB) using (I,33):

$$\text{W.D.} = H_A - \phi_B \times T_B + G_B, \quad \text{and} \quad \phi_B = \phi_A = 1\cdot6615$$
$$= 1,216 - 1\cdot6615 \times 687\cdot7 + 34\cdot6 = 108\cdot6 \text{ B.T.U.}$$

$$v_B = 8\cdot03\sqrt{108\cdot6 \times 778} = \underline{2,335 \text{ ft. per sec.}} \quad \text{Ans.}$$

$$x_B = \frac{1\cdot6615 - 0\cdot3358}{1\cdot7327 - 0\cdot3358} = \underline{0\cdot952 \text{ dry.}} \quad \text{Ans.}$$

It should be noted that the difference CB between the two heat drops is relatively small, being $108\cdot6 - 105 = 3\cdot6$ B.T.U., the diagram being exaggerated for the purposes of explanation.

6. *Prove that the ratio of the pressures at the throat and inlet of a nozzle expanding steam to a pressure below the critical is given by* $\left(\dfrac{2}{n+1}\right)^{\frac{n}{n-1}}$.

Calculate the required cross-sectional area at the outlet of a nozzle to pass 1·2 lb. per sec. of steam expanding without loss from 200 lb. per sq. in., dry saturated, to 130 lb. per sq. in. according to $PV^{1·3} = constant$:

    (a) *if the speed at inlet is small ;*

    (b) *if the speed at inlet is 500 ft. per sec.*

(U. Lond.)

The critical pressure ratio is deduced in the usual manner, and has the value 0·545 when $n = 1·3$ for supersaturated conditions. The exit pressure is 130 lb. per sq. in. which is greater than the critical pressure (109 lb. per sq. in.). Also, it should be observed that although the steam is dry saturated at entrance, the conditions of flow according to the law $PV^{1·3} = constant$ imply that supersaturated conditions prevail and, as explained in the introduction of this chapter, the chart must not be used but the heat drop must be calculated.

(*a*) Let V_2 be the volume per lb. at exit, then

$$200 \times 2·29^{1·3} = 130 \times V_2^{1·3}$$

whence
$$V_2 = 3·189 \text{ cu. ft. per lb.}$$

$$\therefore \text{ Heat drop} = 144 \times \frac{1·3}{0·3}(200 \times 2·29 - 130 \times 3·189), \text{ by (I,39)},$$

$$= 27,040 \text{ ft.lb. per lb.}$$

$$\therefore \text{ Velocity} = 8·03\sqrt{27,040} = 1,320 \text{ ft. per sec.}$$

$$\therefore \text{ Area} = \frac{1·2 \times 3·189}{1,320} = 0·0029 \text{ sq. ft.}$$

$= 0·418$ sq. in.   Ans. (*a*).

(*b*) In this case we have the W.D. = gain in kinetic energy, the initial value of which is $\dfrac{500^2}{2g}$ ft.lb. per lb.

$$\therefore 27,040 = \frac{v_2^2}{2g} - \frac{500^2}{2g}$$

$$\therefore \frac{v_2^2}{2g} = 30,920 \text{ ft.lb., and } v_2 = 1,410 \text{ ft. per sec.}$$

$$\therefore \text{ Area} = \frac{1·2 \times 3·189}{1,410} = 0·0027 \text{ sq. ft.}$$

$= 0·391$ sq. in.   Ans. (*b*).

7. *Steam at 250 lb. per sq. in. with 60° C. superheat enters a set of nozzles which have a total cross-sectional area of 10 sq. in. at exit. The pressure of the steam at exit is 60 lb. per sq. in. and its dryness fraction is 0·97. Find (a) the velocity at exit ; (b) the change in internal energy per lb. ; and (c) the discharge in lb. per sec. The initial specific volume of the steam may be taken as 2·189 cu. ft.* (*U.L.C.I.*)

Since the conditions at exit are given, we can calculate the useful heat drop directly.

$60°$ C. $= 108°$ F. and, using Table II, we find :

$$\text{Total heat required} = 1{,}263 \cdot 4 + 8 \times \frac{11 \cdot 5}{20} = 1{,}268 \text{ B.T.U.}$$

Total heat of the wet steam at exit

$$= 262 \cdot 2 + 0 \cdot 97 \times 916 \cdot 2 = 1{,}151 \text{ B.T.U.}$$

Volume per lb. at exit $= 0 \cdot 97 \times 7 \cdot 175 = 6 \cdot 96$ cu. ft.

Velocity at exit $\quad = 8 \cdot 03 \sqrt{(1{,}268 - 1{,}151)778}$

$$= \underline{2{,}420 \text{ ft. per sec.}} \quad \text{Ans. } (a).$$

The change in Internal Energy per lb., by (I,1)

$$E_2 - E_1 = H_2 - H_1 - \left(\frac{P_2 V_2 - P_1 V_1}{J} \right)$$

$$= 1{,}151 - 1{,}268 - (60 \times 6 \cdot 96 - 250 \times 2 \cdot 189) \frac{144}{778}$$

$$\therefore E_2 - E_1 = \underline{- 93 \text{ B.T.U.}} \text{ (i.e. a decrease).} \quad \text{Ans. } (b).$$

$$\text{The weight per sec.} = \frac{2{,}420 \times 10}{6 \cdot 96 \times 144} = \underline{24 \cdot 1 \text{ lb. per sec.}} \quad \text{Ans. } (c).$$

8. *In a test on a nozzle, steam was supplied to the nozzle at a pressure of 50 lb. per sq. in. and a temperature of 200° C., and allowed to discharge into the atmosphere at a pressure of 15 lb. per sq. in. The jet issuing from the nozzle impinged normally on a fixed plate so arranged that the force on the plate could be measured. When the discharge was 35 lb. of steam per min., the force on the plate was 37 lb. Find the percentage of heat absorbed in friction in the nozzle and the condition of the steam at exit.* (U. Lond.)

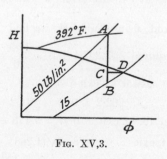

Fig. XV,3.

$$200° \text{ C.} = 392° \text{ F.}$$

The initial temperature of the steam is 392° F., and by reference to the total heat–entropy chart the isentropic heat drop $AB = \Delta H_T$ brings the state of the steam at 15 lb. per sq. in. only just below the saturation line. Since there will be reheating of the steam due to friction and shock, the probability is that the steam will be slightly superheated at exit. The chart will be used for this problem, since the chart heat drop in the superheated region will very nearly equal that calculated by assuming $n = 1.3$.

From the chart, $\Delta H_T = AB = 95.4$ B.T.U.

$$\therefore \text{ Ideal velocity} = 8.03\sqrt{95.4 \times 778} = 2,180 \text{ ft. per sec.}$$

Now the force on the plate will be equal to the momentum destroyed per sec., assuming that the velocity of the steam leaving the plate is parallel to the plate surface.

$$\therefore \text{ Force on plate} = \frac{35}{60} \times \frac{(v_D - 0)}{32.2} = 37 \text{ lb.}$$

whence $v_D = 2,040$ ft. per sec.

$\therefore$ Percentage of heat drop in nozzle lost as friction, i.e. $1 - \text{nozzle } \eta$

$$= \frac{2,180^2 - 2,040^2}{2,180^2} \times 100 = \underline{12.55\%}. \quad \text{Ans.}$$

Actual heat drop utilized $AC = \Delta H_U = 95.4 \times 0.8745 = 83.4$ B.T.U.

By reference to the chart the steam is just <u>dry saturated</u> at the point D. Ans.

EXAMPLES

1. At a certain stage of a pressure compounded impulse turbine steam enters the nozzles at 40 lb./in.^{2} abs. 20° F. superheat and is expanded to 20 lb./in.^{2} abs. The velocity of the steam entering the nozzles is 300 ft./sec. ; determine the exit velocity of the steam and its quality, if the nozzle efficiency is 0·9.

If the steam is to be discharged at 18 lb./sec., calculate the total exit area of the nozzles. (*U. Manch.*)

[$\Delta H_T = 51·6$ B.T.U. ; exit $x = 0·977$; exit $v = 1,555$ ft. per sec. ; exit $V = 19·60$ cu. ft. per lb. ; A = 32·7 sq. in.]

2. A steam nozzle is supplied with dry saturated steam at 150 lb. per sq. in. and exhausts at 1 lb. per sq. in. If the steam flow is to be 1,200 lb. per hr., determine the required throat and exit areas assuming stable frictionless adiabatic flow.

If the actual velocity at exit is found to be 3,800 ft. per sec., estimate the loss in the nozzle expressed as a percentage of the total heat drop. (*U.L.C.I.*)

[Throat P = 86·6 lb. per sq. in. ; ΔH_T to throat = 44·3 B.T.U. ; ΔH_T to exit = 318 B.T.U. ; throat $v = 1,491$ ft. per sec. ; exit $v = 3,990$ ft. per sec. ; throat and exit areas = 0·157 and 0·313 sq. in. respectively ; 9·3%.]

3. A convergent-divergent nozzle supplied with steam at 50 lb. per sq. in. dry and saturated, is to discharge at 0·5 lb. per sec. into a vessel in which the pressure is maintained at 15 lb. per sq. in. Find the throat area of the nozzle, and also the exit area assuming a friction loss amounting to 10% of the total heat drop to occur in the diverging portion. The steam may be assumed to condense normally and to discharge without shock.

If the nozzle is made up of converging and diverging cones, sketch the curve of pressure drop along its length. Explain briefly the effect of increasing gradually the back pressure in the vessel from 15 lb. per sq. in. to 40 lb. per sq. in. (*U. Lond.*)

[Throat pressure, 29 lb. per sq. in. ; dryness at throat, 0·968 ; vel., 1,450 ft./sec. ; area at throat, 0·68 sq. in. ; useful heat drop to exit, 76 B.T.U. per lb. ; vel. exit, 1,950 ft./sec. ; dryness, 0·944 ; area at exit, 0·916 sq. in.]

4. The pressure of a fluid is 120 lb. per sq. in. and its density at this pressure is 0·3 lb. per cu. ft. It is expanded through a convergent-divergent nozzle and the expansion follows the law $PV^{1·2} = $ constant. Find the throat area of the nozzle which will discharge 15 lb. per min. (*U. Lond.*)

[Assume 1·2 is adiab. index for the fluid and there are no losses ; critical pressure ratio (cf. ex. No. 6 above) = 0·564 if $n = 1·2$; W.D. inlet to throat = 31,500 ft.lb. per lb. by (I,39) ; throat $v = 1,425$ ft. per sec. ; throat V = 5·36 cu. ft. per lb. ; throat area = 0·136 sq. in.]

5. A steam turbine is required to generate 4,000 h.p. using 9·5 lb. of steam per h.p.-hr., at 200 lb. per sq. in., dry saturated. The turbine is of the impulse type and in the first stage the steam is expanded through nozzles with an efficiency of 0·88 to a pressure of 120 lb. per sq. in. The nozzles are to extend over approximately one-third of the circumference with a pitch circle diameter of 2 ft. and a pitch of 2 in. The nozzle angle being 15° to the plane of the wheel and the division plates 0·112 in. thick, determine the total length of the nozzle arc and the radial height of the nozzles. (*U. Lond.*)

[$\Delta H_U = 36·4$ B.T.U. ; $v = 1,350$ ft. per sec. ; V = 3·61 cu. ft. per lb. ; A = 4·07 sq. in. ; nearest no. of nozzles = 13 ; requd. length = 26 in. ; height = 0·77 in.]

6. Steam at 300 lb. per sq. in. and 100° F. superheat passes through a nozzl and is expanded to a pressure of 50 lb. per sq. in. The diameter of the nozzle a the throat is 0·5 in.

Calculate the weight of steam flowing per hr., assuming $PV^{1\cdot3} = C$ throughou the expansion and determine the degree of undercooling at exit. (*U. Lond.*)

[By (I,39), W.D. to throat = 44,200 ft.lb. ; throat v = 1,690 ft. per sec. throat V = 2·88 cu. ft. per lb. ; <u>W = 2,880 lb. per hr.</u> T_{exit} = 645° F. abs. degree of undercooling = 96° F.]

7. Dry saturated steam at 250 lb./in.^{2} is metered by means of a well-lagge Venturi or tapered passage fitted in the pipe-line.

The inlet and throat diameters are 8 and 7 in. respectively. The pressure a the reduced section is 245 lb./in.^{2}

Calculate, using the steam tables, the rate of flow in lb./sec., neglecting friction (*U. Lond.*)

[Due to the small pressure drop, great accuracy is required in the Arithmetic at throat : x = 0·9982, H_2 = 1,200·4 ; ΔH = 1·7 ; $v_2{}^2 - v_1{}^2$ = 85,200 ft.lb. per lb $\dfrac{v_1}{v_2}$ = 0·7524 ; v_1 = 333·5 ft. per sec. ; v_2 = 443 ft. per sec. ; <u>W = 63 lb. per sec.</u>]

8. A nozzle is to discharge 20 lb. of steam per min., with a supply pressur of 200 lb. per sq. in., and temperature 270° C., the back pressure being 40 lb per sq. in. Using a Total Heat–Entropy chart, calculate the throat and exi diameters of the nozzle, assuming that the flow is adiabatic, and that 10% o the heat drop is wasted in friction in the diverging part of the nozzle.

(*U. Lond.*)

[ΔH up to throat = 59 B.T.U., throat v = 1,720 ft. per sec., throat V = 4·42 cu. ft., throat d = 0·396 in. ; ΔH_U entrance to exit = 59 + 73·8 = 132·8 B.T.U. final x = 0·972, exit v = 2,580 ft. per sec., <u>exit d = 0·491 in.</u>]

9. Show that the pressure at the throat of a nozzle is given by $P_1\left(\dfrac{2}{n+1}\right)^{\frac{n}{n-1}}$ where P_1 is the pressure at entrance. State clearly the assumptions which are made.

In a nozzle expanding steam without loss from a pressure of 100 lb. per sq. in. and 400° F., to 25 lb. per sq. in., calculate the weight flowing per sec. per sq. in. of throat area, and find the velocity at exit. Find the temperature at exit and explain why this differs from the saturation temperature at this pressure. Use $PV^{1\cdot3}$ = constant. (*U. Lond.*)

[W.D. up to throat = 39,900 ft.lb. per lb., throat v = 1,600 ft. per sec., throat V = 7·85 cu. ft. per lb., <u>W = 1·42 lb. per sec. per sq. in.</u> ; W.D. entrance to exit = 84,200 ft.lb. per lb., <u>exit v = 2,330 ft. per sec.</u> ; exit t = 164° F., i.e. 76° F. undercooled.]

CHAPTER XVI

STEAM TURBINE PERFORMANCE

Introduction

Most problems on this subject require, above all, a thorough understanding of the total heat–entropy chart. Difficulty is sometimes experienced, however, in interpreting correctly a number of terms and efficiencies which arise in general turbine work.

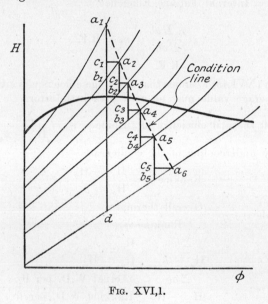

FIG. XVI,1.

In the above diagram the expansion of steam through a number of turbine stages has been shown. a_1b_1 is the isentropic heat drop for the first stage; of this the amount c_1b_1 is not available for useful work due to friction, etc., and it is assumed that this heat drop reappears as heat entirely, so that the point a_2 is obtained at the pressure of b_1 and the total heat of c_1. Similarly, a_3, a_4, etc., can be plotted. Also, a_1d is the Rankine heat drop for the initial state and the final pressure.

Definitions.

The locus of all the points " a " is called the condition or state line of the expansion; the steam probably expands along some such path.

The heat drops ac which are actually converted into *useful* work in each stage will be abbreviated ΔH_U.

251

The *total* stage heat drops ab will be referred to as ΔH_T.

$$\eta_s = \text{Stage Efficiency} = \frac{ac}{ab} = \frac{\Delta H_U}{\Delta H_T} \qquad . \qquad . \qquad \text{(XVI,1)}$$

$$\text{Cumulative Heat Drop} = \Sigma ab \qquad . \qquad . \qquad \text{(XVI,2)}$$

and due to the diverging constant pressure lines the cumulative heat drop is always greater than the Rankine or direct heat drop, a_1d in our case giving

$$\text{R.F.} = \text{Reheat Factor} = \frac{\Sigma ab}{a_1 d} = \frac{\Sigma \Delta H_T}{a_1 d} > 1 \qquad . \qquad \text{(XVI,3)}$$

$$\eta_i = \text{Internal Turbine Efficiency} = \frac{\Sigma \Delta H_U}{a_1 d} = \frac{\Sigma ac}{a_1 d} \qquad \text{(XVI,4a)}$$

$$= \frac{\eta_s \Sigma ab}{\dfrac{\Sigma ab}{\text{R.F.}}} = \eta_s \times \text{R.F.} \qquad . \qquad . \qquad . \qquad \text{(XVI,4b)}$$

Expression (XVI,4b) assumes that the stage efficiency is either constant or that an average value may be used with little error.

$$\text{Overall thermal efficiency of turbine} = \eta_0 = \frac{\Sigma ac}{H_{a_1} - h_{a_6}} \qquad \text{(XVI,5)}$$

neglecting any undercooling of the condensate.

$$\text{Rankine } \eta = \frac{H_{a_1} - H_d}{H_{a_1} - h_{a_6}}$$

$$\text{Relative } \eta = \frac{\text{Overall thermal } \eta}{\text{Rankine } \eta} \qquad . \qquad . \qquad . \qquad . \qquad \text{(XVI,6a)}$$

$$= \frac{\Sigma ac}{H_{a_1} - h_{a_6}} \times \frac{H_{a_1} - h_{a_6}}{H_{a_1} - H_d}$$

$$= \frac{\Sigma ac}{H_{a_1} - H_d} = \frac{\text{Actual W.D. per lb.}}{\text{Rankine W.D. per lb.}} \qquad . \qquad \text{(XVI,6b)}$$

This last efficiency is sometimes referred to as the adiabatic efficiency or simply efficiency of the turbine, and is also the same as (XVI,4a).

The stage efficiency is also referred to as the efficiency ratio for the stage and is the same as the efficiency of expansion for the stage.

A rather misleading practice is to refer to the internal efficiency as the overall (though not overall *thermal*) efficiency. It is helpful in this respect to know that η_i usually lies between 60 and 80%, whereas η_0 as defined by (XVI,5) lies between 20 and 35% for turbines.

1. *A pass-out turbine is supplied with 12,000 lb. of steam per hr. at 225 lb. per sq. in. abs., 200° F. (93·3° C.) superheat. In the high-pressure section of the turbine the steam expands to 30 lb. per sq. in. abs., and at this pressure 6,000 lb. of process steam leave the turbine per hr. The remaining steam passes through the low-pressure section, expanding to the final pressure of 1 lb. per sq. in. abs. The efficiency ratio for the high-pressure section is 72%, and for the low-pressure section 78%.*

Find the amount of superheat in the process steam, also the power generated in the turbine. (I.Mech.E.)

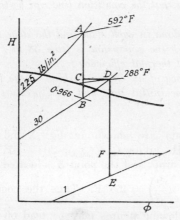

FIG. XVI,2.

$$t_s \text{ at 225 lb. per sq. in.} = 391 \cdot 8° \text{ F.}$$
$$\therefore t_{sup} \text{ at } A = 592° \text{ F.}$$

Between 225 and 30 lb. per sq. in.,

$$\Delta H_T = 182 \text{ B.T.U.} = AB, \text{ from the chart.}$$

For an efficiency ratio of 0·72,

$$AC = \Delta H_U = 131 \text{ B.T.U. per lb.}$$

This gives a total heat of 1,184 for the point D, the amount of superheat being __38° F.__   Ans.

For the next stage, also from the chart,

$$DE = \Delta H_T = 220 \text{ B.T.U. per lb.}$$
$$DF = \Delta H_U = 0 \cdot 78 \times 220 = 172 \text{ B.T.U. per lb.}$$

$$\text{Power developed by turbine} = \frac{12,000 \times 131 + (12,000 - 6,000)172}{2,546}$$

$$= \underline{1,023 \text{ h.p.}} \quad \text{Ans.}$$

2. *A pressure compounded impulse turbine has four stages, the state of the steam at the salient points being as follows :*

	Pressure lb. per sq. in. (approx.)	Degrees of superheat ° C. or dryness
Supply	525	114
1st intermediate	155	58
2nd ,,	38	0·998
3rd ,,	7	0·942
Exhaust	1	0·890

On the assumption that the condition line can be traced on the Iϕ chart determine :

(i) *the work done in each stage and the stage efficiency for the stage in which the expansion is from 38 to 7 lb. per sq. in. ;*

(ii) *the overall thermal efficiency ;*

(iii) *the efficiency of an engine working on the Rankine cycle between the same initial state and final pressure.*

(U. Camb.)

The salient points are shown in fig. XVI,3. Note, 114° C. of S.H. = 205° F. of S.H., giving $t_1 = t_{\text{sat}_1} + 205 = 677°$ F. $H_1 - H_2$ is the stage isentropic heat drop, and the point 3 is located at 155 lb. per sq. in. and $t_3 = 361 + \left(58 \times \dfrac{9}{5}\right) = 465°$ F. Thus the condition line 13579 is obtained and the following figures may be read off :

		W.D. per stage, ΔH_U	ΔH_T
H_1	1,342 B.T.U.	} 87 B.T.U.	
H_3	1,255 ,,	} 86	
H_5	1,169 ,,	} 89	120 B.T.U.
H_7	1,080 ,,	} 90	
H_9	990 ,,		

$$\Sigma \, \Delta H_U = 352 \text{ B.T.U.}$$

By (XVI,1)   Required $\eta_s = \dfrac{89}{120} = \underline{74\%}$.   Ans.

By (XVI,5) $\eta_0 = \dfrac{352}{1,342 - 69\cdot7} = \underline{27\cdot6\%}$.   Ans.

By (I,38)   Rankine $\eta = \dfrac{H_1 - H_{10}}{H_1 - h_{10}} = \dfrac{453}{1,342 - 69\cdot7} = \underline{35\cdot6\%}$.   Ans.

(Note, the turbine η or η_{rel} as defined by (XVI,6a and b) would be $\dfrac{27\cdot6}{35\cdot6} = 77\cdot6\%$.)

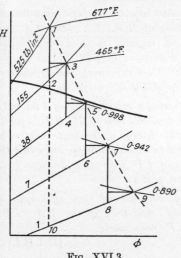

Fig. XVI,3. Fig. XVI,4.

3. *A turbo-alternator has an output of 12,000 kW., the efficiency of the alternator being 0·95. The high-pressure section of the turbine expands steam from 600 lb. per sq. in. and 700° F. to 30 lb. per sq. in. with an efficiency ratio of 0·8. Before entering the low-pressure section the steam is re-superheated at 30 lb. per sq. in. to 600° F. In the low-pressure section expansion takes place to 1 lb. per sq. in. with an efficiency ratio of 0·8.*

If the efficiency of boiler and re-superheater are each 0·85, find :

    (a) *the overall efficiency of the plant ;*

    (b) *how much coal of calorific value 12,000 B.T.U. per lb. will be used per hr.*   (U. Lond.)

Plotting the available information on the chart, we have (fig. XVI,4)

$$H_A = 1,350 ; \quad H_C = 1,083 ; \quad H_E = 1,334 ; \quad H_F = 1,057.$$

High-pressure section   Low-pressure section

$\Delta H_T = AC = 267$ $\Delta H_T = EF = 277$

$\Delta H_U = AB = 0.8 \times 267 - 214$ $\Delta H_U = EK = 0.8 \times 277 = 221.6$

$\therefore H_B = H_D = 1,136$ $\therefore H_K = H_G = 1,112.4$

Total turbine W.D. $= 214 + 221.6 = 435.6$ B.T.U. per lb.

Heat supplied to the steam $= (1,350 - 69.7) + (1,334 - 1,136)$
$$= 1,478.3 \text{ B.T.U. per lb.}$$

for which $\dfrac{1,478.3}{0.85} = 1,739$ B.T.U. must be supplied in the fuel.

$$\text{Overall } \eta = \frac{435.6 \times 0.95}{1,739} = \underline{23.7\%}. \quad \text{Ans. } (a).$$

$$\text{Steam consumption} = \frac{12,000 \times 3,413}{435.6 \times 0.95} = 99,070 \text{ lb. per hr.}$$

$$\text{Coal consumption} = \frac{99,070 \times 1,739}{12,000} = \underline{14,350 \text{ lb. per hr.}} \quad \text{Ans. } (b).$$

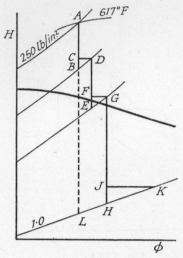

FIG. XVI,5.

4. *An impulse turbine installation consisting of H.P., I.P., and L.P. tur bines, is required to work with initia steam conditions of 250 lb. per sq. in with 120° C. of superheat, and a condense pressure of 1·0 lb. per sq. in.*

Allowing a reheat factor of 1·05 and ι loss of available heat of 6 C.H.U.'s per lb of steam, determine the heat units to bε allocated to each turbine in order that thε H.P. and I.P. may each develop ¼ oj the total power.

You may assume stage efficiencies of 0·77, 0·75 and 0·72 in the H.P., I.P., and L.P. respectively.

(*U.L.C.I.*)

$$120° \text{ C. of S.H.} = 216° \text{ F.,} \quad \therefore \; t_A = 617° \text{ F.}$$
$$6 \text{ C.H.U.} = 10·8 \text{ B.T.U.}$$

From the chart, Rankine heat drop = AL = 402 B.T.U. per lb. The diagram may be sketched, as above, and

$$\text{Reheat factor} = 1·05 = \frac{\text{AB} + \text{DE} + \text{GH} + 10·8}{402}$$

$$\therefore \; \text{AB} + \text{DE} + \text{GH} = 411 \text{ B.T.U. per lb.,}$$

the 10·8 B.T.U. representing the loss of available heat.

The W.D. in each turbine (ΔH_U) is AC, DF and GJ, and we know that

$$\text{AC} = \text{DF} = \frac{\text{GJ}}{2}. \quad \text{Also, allowing for } \eta_s, \; \text{AB} = \frac{\text{AC}}{0·77}, \text{ etc.}$$

$$\therefore \; \frac{\text{AC}}{0·77} + \frac{\text{AC}}{0·75} + \frac{2\text{AC}}{0·72} = 411$$

$$5·407\text{AC} = 411 ; \quad \text{AC} = 76.$$

Hence, in B.T.U. per lb. :

	ΔH_U	η_s	ΔH_T	
H.P.	AC = 76	0·77	AB = 99	}Ans.
I.P.	DF = 76	0·75	DE = 101	
L.P.	GJ = 152	0·72	GH = 211	
Total	304		411	

5. *In a four-stage pressure-compounded turbine the steam is supplied at a pressure of 350 lb. per sq. in. and superheated to a temperature of 650° F. The exhaust pressure is 1 lb. per sq. in., and the overall turbine efficiency is 0·72. Assuming that the work is shared equally between the stages, and that the condition line is straight, estimate the stage pressures, the efficiency of each stage and the reheat factor.* (U. Lond.)

The term "overall turbine efficiency" is here used in the sense of "internal efficiency" or simply "efficiency" of the turbine (p. 252).

The superheated steam supplied at 350 lb. per sq. in. and a temperature of 650° F. is plotted on the total heat–entropy chart at A. The isentropic heat drop to 1 lb. per sq. in. is $AK = 427$ B.T.U.

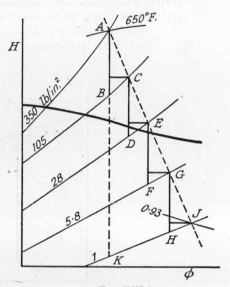

$\therefore$ The total useful W.D. is $0·72 \times 427 = 307·4$ B.T.U. $= \Sigma \Delta H_U$. This gives the point J, where the dryness is 0·93. The condition line can now be drawn from A to J, it being assumed straight in this problem.

Since the work is shared equally between the stages, the

Fig. XVI,6.

work per stage is $307·4 \div 4 = 76·9$ B.T.U. $= \Delta H_U$.

The diagram can now be completed by drawing.

$$H_C = H_A - 76·9 = 1,261·1, \quad H_E = 1,184·2, \quad H_G = 1,107·3.$$

The stage pressures are <u>105, 28, 5·8 lb. per sq. in.</u> and the isentropic heat drop per stage can be estimated. Ans. (a).

$AB = 122$, $CD = 113$, $EF = 109·2$, $GH = 105·3$ B.T.U.
$\therefore$ The efficiencies of the stages are :

$$\frac{76·9}{122'} \qquad \frac{76·9}{113'} \qquad \frac{76·9}{109·2'} \qquad \frac{76·9}{105·3}$$

i.e. <u>63%</u>   <u>68·2%</u>   <u>70·5%</u>   <u>73·0%</u>.   Ans. (b).

Cumulative heat drop $= \Sigma \Delta H_T = AB + CD + EF + GH$
$$= 447·5 \text{ B.T.U.}$$

$\therefore$ Reheat factor $= \dfrac{447·5}{427}$.   <u>R.F. = 1·05.</u>   Ans. (c).

6. *A 300 h.p. impulse turbine is supplied with steam at 120 lb. per sq. in. and 400° F. At the throttle the pressure is reduced to 100 lb. per sq. in. The exhaust pressure is 1 lb. per sq. in. and there are three stages each of 0·75 relative efficiency and each giving the same amount of work.*

Estimate, using the Hφ diagram :

    (a) *the two intermediate stage pressures ;*

    (b) *the reheat factor on conditions after the throttle ;*

    (c) *the total area of the throats of the nozzles of the first stage, assuming stable frictionless expansion.*

Give a sketch of the Hφ diagram, indicating the various steps.

(U. Lond.)

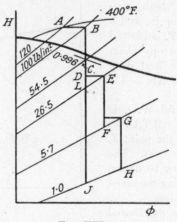

Fig. XVI,7.

The throttling process is shown by the line AB. The Rankine heat drop BJ scales 304 B.T.U. per lb. The given condition is that ΔH_U is to be the same for the three stages ; and since η_s is 0·75 for each stage, therefore ΔH_T is also equal for the stages. Due to the reheat factor (cf. XVI,3) $\Sigma \Delta H_T > 304$, and the actual solution must be done by trial and error.

Assume R.F. = 1·05, then

Cumulative heat drop $= \Sigma \Delta H_T = 1·05 \times 304 = 320$ B.T.U., giving $\Delta H_T = 107$ B.T.U. per stage. This is found to be rather too much on plotting it on the chart, but $\Delta H_T = 105$ B.T.U. per stage satisfies the conditions very nearly.

This gives stage pressures (at E and G) of 26·5 and 5·7 lb. per sq. in.   Ans.

Cumulative heat drop $= \Sigma \Delta H_T = 315$ B.T.U. per lb.

$$\text{R.F.} = \frac{315}{304} = 1·037. \quad \text{Ans.}$$

When steam is assumed to expand under stable conditions in a nozzle, t is customarily assumed that the index of expansion (and hence the throat pressure) is determined by the *initial* state of the steam, n being chosen as $1 \cdot 3$ for initially superheated steam, or as $(1 \cdot 035 + 0 \cdot 1x)$ where x is the *initial* dryness according to Zeuner's equation (cf. I,34). Both these assumptions may be nearly correct if the pressure ratio for the expansion s fairly small. In addition, there are cases in which neither assumption can be expected to hold, e.g. if the initial state is only very slightly superheated. Such discrepancies arise, because (a) the expansions are usually not stable, but metastable (cf. chapter XV) and, (b) if the expansion can reasonably be considered as stable, there is no physical law which makes it necessary for the steam to expand according to $PV^n = $ constant, with a constant value of n. In most cases, however, a reasonably close answer can be obtained by making the latter assumption.

Here, the critical pressure ratio will be either $0 \cdot 545$ $(n = 1 \cdot 3)$ or $0 \cdot 577$ $(n = 1 \cdot 135)$, and since the expansion up to the throat is almost wholly in the superheat region, we may say that the throat pressure will be $54 \cdot 5$ lb. per sq. in. nearly, giving a dryness of $x_C = 0 \cdot 996$ at the throat, for stable frictionless expansion.

$H_B - H_C = 50$ B.T.U. per lb., which is converted into K.E.

i.e.
$$50 \times 778 = \frac{v^2}{2g}.$$

Vel. at throat $= 8 \cdot 03 \sqrt{50 \times 778} = 1,580$ ft. per sec.

Specific vol. at throat $= 0 \cdot 996 \times 7 \cdot 855 = 7 \cdot 82$ cu. ft. per lb.

We now require the steam consumption of the turbine :

$\Delta H_U = 0 \cdot 75 \times 315$ B.T.U. per lb., as above.

$$\therefore \text{ Consumption} = \frac{300 \times 2,546}{3,600 \times (0 \cdot 75 \times 315)} = 0 \cdot 898 \text{ lb. per sec.}$$

$$\therefore \text{ Throat area} = \frac{0 \cdot 898 \times 7 \cdot 82}{1,580} = 0 \cdot 00444 \text{ sq. ft.}$$

$$= \underline{0 \cdot 640 \text{ sq. in.}} \quad \text{Ans.}$$

7. *In some types of impulse turbine governing is effected by controlling the number of nozzles in operation at the first stage. Explain, with diagrams :*

    (a) *the advantage claimed for the method ;*

    (b) *the effect on the Willans Line.*

The high-pressure (H.P.) supply to a mixed-pressure turbine of 1,500 h.p. output is 200 lb. per sq. in. superheated 100° F., the low-pressure (L.P.) supply being dry saturated at 20 lb. per sq. in. and the condenser pressure 1 lb. per sq. in.

The Willans Lines, for both H.P. and L.P. supplies, are straight and in each case the total steam used per hr. at zero load is 0·12 of that required at full load. Assuming that the relative efficiency at full load is 0·8, whether H.P. or L.P. steam alone is supplied, find how much H.P. steam will be required for a load of 1,200 h.p., if 14,000 lb. per hour of L.P. steam are available.

(U. Lond.)

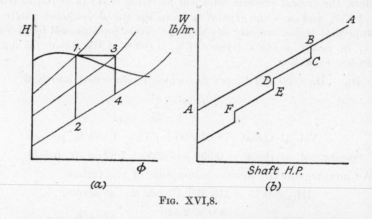

Fig. XVI,8.

(a) The principal advantage claimed is illustrated in fig. XVI,8a, where 1–2 represents ΔH_T for a turbine under full load conditions. At part load, if throttle governing is employed, the state of the steam entering the first stage would be at 3, i.e. at a lower pressure, and the available ΔH_T would be reduced. With nozzle governing this reduction in the available heat drop is avoided as the steam can always be supplied at a pressure approximately equal to that at point 1.

(b) Since ΔH_T is greater with nozzle governing at part load, therefore the steam consumption will be reduced at a given part load providing the stage efficiencies remain unaffected. Let AA be the Willans Line for throttle governing, fig. XVI,8b. At a load corresponding to point B a group of nozzles may be taken out of operation, resulting in a drop of consumption given by BC. Further load reduction from C to D will normally be throttle governed, as the portion AB. At D the load is low enough for an additional group of nozzles to be cut out resulting in a further

reduction of steam flow DE, etc. The portions DC, EF, etc., are parallel to AA.

It is only fair to add, however, that in large turbines the effect of cutting out some of the first stage nozzles may result in bad distribution of heat drop and the resulting lower stage efficiencies may counteract the saving in heat consumption.

	H.P. turbine alone	L.P. turbine alone
Pressure Drop . . .	200—1	20—1
ΔH_T	358·5	189
η_{rel}	0·8	0·8
ΔH_U	287	151
Full load, lb. per hr. .	$\dfrac{1,500 \times 2,545}{287} = 13,320$	$\dfrac{1,500 \times 2,545}{151} = 25,280$
No load, ,, ,, ,, .	$0\cdot12 \times 13,320 = 1,599$	$0\cdot12 \times 25,280 = 3,030$

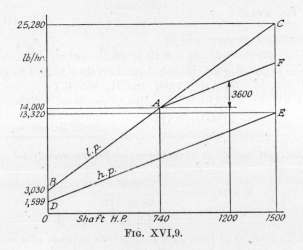

Fig. XVI,9.

The two Willans Lines may now be drawn as above. By calculation, or from the graphs, 14,000 lb. per hr. of L.P. steam will give 740 h.p.; the difference to 1,200 h.p. must be supplied by the H.P. turbine and if AF is drawn parallel to DE, the required intercept is

3,600 lb. per hr. Ans.

(Note, the required figure is 3,600, *not* 3,600 + 1,599; the two turbines are in the same cylinder and on the same shaft, so that the rotor frictional and windage losses are fully covered by 3,030 lb. of L.P. steam and the corresponding quantity of 1,599 lb. H.P. steam must not be allowed for again.)

8. *A turbo-generator of 10,000 kW. output is supplied with steam at 600 lb. per sq. in. and 700° F. and exhausts to a vacuum of 28·59 in. mercury when*

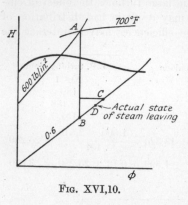

the barometer reads 29·80 in. The steam expands with an efficiency ratio of 0·84, while the efficiency of the generator is 0·96.

Determine (a) *the mass of steam used per second ;* (b) *the dryness of the steam at exit from the turbine if it is moving at 600 ft. per sec. ;* (c) *the consumption expressed in kg. per metric h.p.-hr. at the generator coupling, given that 1 kg. = 2·204 lb. ; 1 metre = 3·281 ft. and 1 metric h.p. = 4,500 kg. metres per min.*

Fig. XVI,10.

(*U. Lond.*)

The condenser pressure will be

$$(29\cdot80 - 28\cdot59) \times 0\cdot49 = 0\cdot6 \text{ lb. per sq. in.}$$

Referring to the diagram, the adiabatic heat drop from A to B measures 496 B.T.U. per lb., H_A being 1,351 and H_B 855 B.T.U.

Since 1 kW.-hr. = 3,413 B.T.U., the consumption will be :

$$\frac{10,000 \times 3,413}{3,600 \times 496 \times 0\cdot84 \times 0\cdot96} = 23\cdot69 \text{ lb. per sec. } \underline{\text{Ans. } (a).}$$

Now the total energy at C includes the kinetic energy (cf. chapter I, pages 1–2) and

$$\text{Kinetic energy} = \frac{600^2}{2g \times 778}$$

$$= 7\cdot2 \text{ B.T.U. per lb.}$$

This K.E. must have been produced at the expense of a reduction of total heat, the velocity of approach being neglected.

∴ Total heat at D will equal the total heat at C − 7·2 B.T.U.

Now $H_C = 1,351 - 0\cdot84 \times 496$ B.T.U.

∴ $H_D = 1,351 - 0\cdot84 \times 496 - 7\cdot2 = 926\cdot8$ B.T.U.

$$\therefore x_D = \frac{926\cdot8 - 53\cdot2}{1,045\cdot4} = \underline{0\cdot835.} \qquad \text{Ans. } (b).$$

1 metric h.p. = $4,500 \times 2\cdot204 \times 3\cdot281$ ft.lb. per min.

= 32,580 ft.lb. per min.

(N.B. This value is very close to the horse-power in the f.p.s. system.)

and Specific consumption = $\dfrac{2,546}{496 \times 0\cdot84}$

= 6·11 lb. per h.p.-hr. at the generator coupling,

or in metric units

$$\frac{6\cdot 11}{2\cdot 204} \times \frac{32,580}{33,000}$$

$$= 2\cdot 736 \text{ kg. per metric h.p.-hr.} \quad \text{Ans. } (c).$$

9. *Show that, for a tapered blade where the stress is limited to f_1,*

$$\frac{f_1}{f_a} = \frac{1}{1 + \log_e \frac{a_2}{a_1}}$$

where $\frac{a_2}{a_1}$, is the area ration and f_a is the stress with an equivalent parallel blade.

What is the effect of the use of tapered blades in the design of large power plant?   (U. Dur.)

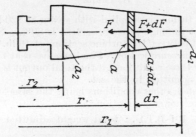

FIG. XVI,11.

Let w = specific weight of blade material, lb. per cu. in.

$\quad F$ = internal force at radius r.

$F + dF = \quad$,, $\quad$,, $\quad$,, $\quad$,, $\quad r + dr$.

$\quad f_1$ = allowable uniform centrifugal stress.

Then, $\qquad\qquad dF = f_1\, da$

But, $\qquad\qquad dF = -\dfrac{wa\, dr}{g}\omega^2 r \text{ lb.}$

since dF decreases with increasing values of r.

$$\therefore \int_{a_1}^{a_2} \frac{da}{a} = -\frac{w\omega^2}{gf_1}\int_{r_1}^{r_2} r\, dr$$

$$\log_e \frac{a_2}{a_1} = \frac{w\omega^2}{2gf_1}(r_1^{\,2} - r_2^{\,2}). \qquad . \qquad . \qquad . \quad \text{(i)}$$

If, however, the blade is parallel, i.e. a — constant,

$$\int_{F_1}^{F_2} dF = -\frac{wa}{g}\omega^2 \int_{r_1}^{r_2} r\, dr$$

$$f_a = \frac{F_2 - F_1}{a} = \frac{w\omega^2}{2g}(r_1^{\,2} - r_2^{\,2}) \qquad . \qquad . \qquad . \quad \text{(ii)}$$

Upon expressing f_1 from (i) and taking the ratio with (ii),

$$\frac{f_1}{f_a} = \frac{1}{\log_e \dfrac{a_2}{a_1}}. \quad \text{Q.E.D.}$$

The use of tapered blades avoids excessive stresses near the root of the blade and makes a uniform centrifugal stress possible. Tapering may interfere with the required area for clear steam passage and blades are frequently twisted to compensate for this and to allow for the correct inlet angles along the blade length if the latter is large. The very considerable cost of production must be borne in mind when such improvements are contemplated.

EXAMPLES

1. A pass-out steam turbine is supplied with steam at 220 lb./in.^{2} and 580° F. The relative efficiency of the high-pressure section is 80%. Steam amounting to 1,200 lb./hr. is extracted between the turbine sections at 16 lb./in.^{2}, the remainder passing direct to the low-pressure section. Final exhaust is at 1·0 lb./in.^{2} 93% dry.

When working under these conditions, if the total output is 350 h.p., determine the rate of steam flow admitted to the set.

If no steam is extracted, other conditions being the same, what would be the thermal efficiency of the power generation ? (*U. Sheff.*)

[Total $\Delta H_U = 177 + 101$ B.T.U. ; total weight admitted to set = 3,650 lb. thermal $\eta = 22\cdot5\%$.]

2. Develop the relation between stage efficiency, internal efficiency and reheat factor for a multi-stage turbine.

A four-stage impulse turbine has terminal conditions of 250 lb./in.^{2} (abs.), 650° F. and 0·5 lb./in.^{2} (abs.). Assuming a stage efficiency of 0·7 throughout the turbine and that the heat drop is divided approximately equally between the stages determine, from the H–ϕ chart, the pressure and condition of the steam leaving each stage. Show the results in tabular form. (*U. Manch.*)

[Rankine $\Delta H^T = 446$ B.T.U. ; assume a likely reheat factor and deduce cumulative ΔH, hence ΔH_T and ΔH_U per stage ; plot condition line on chart ; the final point should be at 0·5 lb. per sq. in. A second trial should be sufficient to obtain the correct answer, viz.

P lb. per sq. in. . .	83	21	3·8	0·5
t° F.	460	270	—	—
x	—	—	0·968	0·922

3. Steam is supplied to a four-stage pressure compounded turbine at 400 lb. per sq. in. at 600° F. and exhausts into a condenser at 1 lb. per sq. in. There is a drop in pressure of 40 lb. per sq. in. in the control valves and the inter-mediate pressures are 100, 30 and 5 lb. per sq. in. If the stage efficiency is 0·8, determine the cumulative heat and the reheat factor. What is the percentage oss due to throttling at the inlet valves ? (*U. Dur.*)

[Stage ΔH_T's $= 121, 93, 120, 90$; ditto, ΔH_U's $= 97, 74, 96, 72$ B.T.U.; cum. $\Delta H = 424$ B.T.U.; R.F. $= 1\cdot025$; throttling loss $\backsimeq 7$ B.T.U., approx. $1\frac{1}{2}\%$.]

4. Steam enters a four-stage impulse turbine at 300 lb./in.^{2} abs. 600° F., and exhausts at 20 lb./in.^{2} abs. dry saturated. Assuming the useful heat drop in each stage to be approximately the same, estimate the average stage efficiency and reheat factor. Assume the condition line to be straight. (*U. Manch.*)

[Rankine $\Delta H_T = 230$ B.T.U.; by trial from chart: ΔH_T's $= 62, 61, 61, 60$ B.T.U.; ΔH_U's $\backsimeq 39\cdot5$ B.T.U. per stage; average stage $\eta = 65\%$; R.F. $= 1\cdot06$.]

5. A five-stage section of a turbine receives steam at 200 lb./in.^{2} and 500° F. and exhausts at $1\cdot0$ lb./in.^{2}. Each stage has an efficiency ratio of 75% and all do equal work. Find the reheat factor and determine the conditions (pressure and quality) at exit from each stage. (*U. Sheff.*)

[By trial, from chart, R.F. $= 1\cdot044$;

P lb. per sq. in. . .	89	34	12 $\bullet$	3·7	1·0
$t°$ F.	363	—	—	—	—
x	—	0·985	0·948	0·914	0·882

6. Steam at 230 lb. per sq. in. abs. and 196° F. superheat is supplied to a triple-expansion engine. The condenser pressure is $1\cdot5$ lb. per sq. in. abs., the efficiency ratio is $0\cdot67$ and the mechanical efficiency is $0\cdot89$. Calculate the actual work done on the shaft per lb. of steam.

If this engine is now fitted with an exhaust turbine geared to the propeller shaft, estimate the percentage increase in S.H.P. of the combination over that of the reciprocating engine alone.

Data for combined engine and turbine :

Back pressure on engine and admission pressure to turbine = 6 lb. per sq. in.; Dryness fraction of steam entering turbine = $0\cdot94$; Efficiency ratio of engine = $0\cdot76$; Mechanical Effy. of engine = $0\cdot875$; Effy. ratio of turbine on shaft = $0\cdot68$; Temperature at condenser top = 100° F. (*U. Dur.*)

[$\Delta H_T = 370$ B.T.U.; shaft W.D. $= 221$ B.T.U. per lb.; engine : $\Delta H_T = 292$ B.T.U.; actual W.D. $= 194$ B.T.U.; turbine : back press. $= 0\cdot95$ lb. per sq. in. ; $\Delta H_T = 109$ B.T.U., shaft W.D. $= 74\cdot2$; increase $= 21\cdot5\%$.]

7. In the H.P. section of a steam turbine the supply pressure and temperature are 400 lb./in.^{2} abs. and 640° F., and the steam leaves this section at a pressure of 52 lb./in.^{2} abs., the efficiency ratio being $0\cdot73$. The steam is then reheated to a temperature of 460° F. before entering the L.P. section at a pressure of 50 lb./in.^{2} abs. The exhaust pressure for the L.P. section is $1\cdot2$ lb./in.^{2} abs., and the efficiency ratio for this section is $0\cdot70$. Find the overall thermal efficiency, the rate of heat consumption in B.T.U./h.p.-hr. and the power developed when the rate of steam flow is 10 lb./sec. (*U. Glas.*)

[Total $\Delta H_U = 137 + 188$ B.T.U.; amount of reheat $= 71$ B.T.U.; thermal $\eta = 24\cdot5\%$; 10,400 B.T.U. supplied per h.p.-hr.; h.p. $= 4,600$.]

CHAPTER XVII

STEAM TURBINE VELOCITY DIAGRAMS

Introduction

1. The subject-matter of this chapter is mainly Dynamics, rather than Thermodynamics, and it is worth recalling that force is equal to the rate of change of momentum,

i.e.
$$F(\text{lb.}) = \frac{W(\text{lb.})}{g} \times \left(\frac{v_1 - v_2}{t} \right)$$

or, as is more useful here,

$$F(\text{lb.}) = \frac{W(\text{lb. per sec.})}{g} \times (v_1 - v_2).$$

Most questions involving velocity diagrams are intended to be solved graphically, though it will be seen that certain types of " reaction " diagrams are easily solved by calculation, and this is appropriate when the solution is likely to involve small differences between relatively large numbers.

2. Steam Turbines divide themselves into two main groups, viz.

    (i) Impulse Turbines, comprising

        (a) velocity compounded machines ;

        (b) pressure compounded machines ;

        (c) a mixture of (a) and (b).

    (ii) Reaction Turbines, comprising

        (a) axial flow machines ;

        (b) radial flow machines.

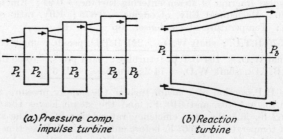

(a) Pressure comp.   (b) Reaction
impulse turbine   turbine

Fig. XVII,1.

Plain impulse turbines are distinguished by the fact that the expansion of the steam takes place only in *fixed* nozzles and that it does not expand further in passing over the blades. The wheel chambers are therefore at constant pressure, or very nearly so (cf. fig. XVII,1a).

The so-called reaction turbines are really mixed impulse-reaction turbines; the steam expands over both fixed blades, acting as nozzles, and also over the moving blades. Thus, there is a continuous generation of kinetic energy and the pressure falls throughout the turbine. The rate of steam flow depends on the annular area available between the rotor and stator, and as the specific volume of steam increases at lower pressures, the diameters of reaction turbines increases considerably towards the exhaust end (cf. fig. XVII,1b).

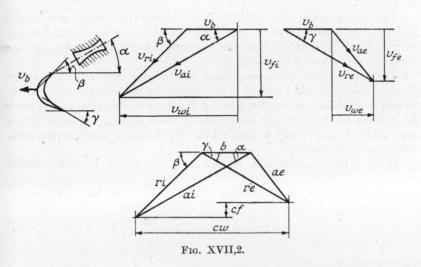

Fig. XVII,2.

3. The above diagram shows the construction of the velocity diagrams; these diagrams are straightforward, providing an appropriate nomenclature is used consistently.

Let α = nozzle angle measured to the direction of blade motion
β = blade inlet angle measured to same direction
γ = ,, outlet ,, ,, ,, ,, ,,
Let v = velocity
b = blade, so that v_b = blade velocity
r = relative
a = absolute
i = inlet
e = exit
f = flow; cf = change in flow
w = whirl; cw = ,, ,, whirl.

Suffices 1 and 2 may be used to indicate first and second moving blades in velocity compounded machines.

In fig. XVII,2, v_b or simply b shows the mean blade velocity, v_{ai} or simply ai denotes the absolute steam velocity at inlet to a moving blade, i.e. the absolute steam velocity issuing from the nozzle or stationary blade at the angle α; then v_{ri} or simply ri is the relative steam velocity at inlet and if the steam is to enter the blade without shock, then ri must be inclined at an angle β, the blade inlet angle, to b. The component of ai in the direction of blade motion is called velocity of whirl at inlet, wi, and the component normal to the blade motion is called velocity of flow at inlet, fi.

The corresponding outlet triangle is also shown; γ is blade outlet angle and the steam *must* leave the blade with a relative velocity, re, inclined at γ to b. Hence, we have ae, the absolute velocity at exit, having two components we and fe respectively.

The two triangles are shown drawn together, so that cw is the change in the velocity of whirl and cf is the change in the velocity of flow. It should be especially noted that α and γ are MUST angles, as ai and re must be inclined according to the magnitude of these angles. However, β is a MAY angle because ri may be inclined to b by the angle β only, if the steam enters without shock.

If W is the steam flow in lb. per sec., then for an impulse machine

$$\text{Force in direction of motion} = \frac{W}{g} \times cw, \text{ lb.}$$

$$\text{Power developed} = \frac{W}{g} \times cw \times b \text{ ft.lb. per sec.}$$

or,
$$\text{W.D.} = \frac{1}{g} \times cw \times b \text{ ft.lb. per lb.}$$

$$\text{K.E. supplied} = \frac{1}{2g} \times ai^2 \text{ ft.lb. per lb.}$$

$\therefore$ The diagram or blading efficiency is given by

$$\eta_{\text{dia}} = \frac{\text{W.D.}}{\text{K.E. supp.}} = \frac{2 \times b \times cw}{ai^2}$$

and gross stage efficiency, $\eta_s =$ Nozzle $\eta \times$ Diagram η.

The net stage efficiency must also allow for friction and windage losses of the rotor.

Force in direction at right angles to blade motion

i.e.
$$\text{axial thrust} = \frac{W}{g} \times cf, \text{ lb.}$$

If there is more than one ring of moving blades, the terms cw and cf must be summed for the correct number of moving blades.

For reaction machines (i.e. impulse-reaction), the W.D. per sec. is as above ; but K.E. is now also supplied due to a heat drop over the moving blades, so that $re > ri$. Then,

$$\text{K.E. supp.} = \frac{1}{2g}[ai^2 + (re^2 - ri^2)] \text{ ft.lb. per lb.}$$

Heat Drop through the fixed blades, acting as nozzles,

$$= \frac{1}{2g\text{J}}(ai^2 - ae^2) \text{ B.T.U. per lb.}$$

Heat Drop through moving blades

$$= \frac{1}{2g\text{J}}(re^2 - ri^2) \text{ B.T.U. per lb.}$$

End Thrust on Rotor

= Pressure Drop per *moving* ring of blades × Blade Area of the ring in addition to the thrust due to *cf*, if the diagram is asymmetrical.

Corresponding expressions for diagram efficiency may be written down.

4. The steam which passes over the blades, moving or fixed, will usually be subject to a friction loss. This results in a re-heating of the steam and a correspondingly reduced velocity. This loss is usually expressed as a percentage of the velocity (usually 10–15%) of the steam entering a blade ;

e.g. velocity coefficient $= \dfrac{re}{ri}$ for a moving blade or $= \dfrac{ai_2}{ae_1}$ for a fixed blade,

cf. fig. XVII,7.

1. *A steam turbine of the de Laval type receives steam at a pressure of 150 lb. per sq. in. and exhausts it at atmospheric pressure. There are four nozzles, each of which is inclined at 20° to the plane of the wheel. The average peripheral speed of the blades is 1,350 ft. per sec.*

Obtain the best angle for the blade, assuming that the inlet and outlet angles are the same. What is the approximate h.p. developed if the area at the throat of each nozzle is 0·03 sq. in. ?   (*W.S.S.*)

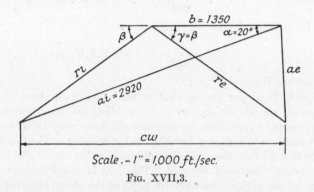

Scale. - 1″ = 1,000 ft./sec.

FIG. XVII,3.

A de Laval turbine is a single-wheel type of impulse turbine.

In the absence of other information, it must be assumed that the steam supply is dry saturated at 150 lb. per sq. in., that the efficiency of the nozzles is 100% (i.e. $\Delta H_T = \Delta H_U$) and that frictional effects in the blading may be neglected.

From the chart, $\Delta H_T = 170$ B.T.U. from 150 to 14·7 lb. per sq. in.

$$\therefore \ 170 \times 778 = \frac{v^2}{2g}, \quad \text{and} \quad v = 2,920 \text{ ft. per sec.}$$

This is the absolute velocity of the steam issuing from the nozzles and is shown as ai in fig. XVII,3, where $\alpha = 20°$, and $b = 1,350$. This enables us to complete the inlet triangle, giving the relative velocity at inlet $ri = 1,710$ ft. per sec. ; also the angle β is the " best " inlet angle since it allows the steam to enter the blades without shock.

$$\beta = 35\tfrac{3}{4}°. \quad \text{Ans.}$$

Since β is to be equal to γ here, and $re = ri$ in an impulse machine if friction is neglected, the outlet triangle may be completed.

∴ Change in steam velocity in the direction of motion

$$= cw = 2,770 \text{ ft. per sec.}$$

$$\text{W.D. per lb.} = \frac{2,770 \times 1,350}{g} = 116,100 \text{ ft.lb.}$$

The weight of steam flowing in an impulse machine is determined by the throat conditions of the nozzles.

Throat Pressure $= 0\cdot577 \times 150 = 86\cdot6$ lb. per sq. in. (cf. introduction to chapter XV).

ΔH_T to throat $= 45$ B.T.U. and $x = 0\cdot962$.

$\therefore$ Velocity at throat $= \sqrt{2gJ \times 45} = 1,500$ ft. per sec.

$$V = 0\cdot962 \times 5\cdot077 = 4\cdot88 \text{ cu. ft. per lb.}$$

$\therefore$ Mass flow $= \dfrac{\text{area} \times v}{V} = \dfrac{4 \times 0\cdot03}{144} \times \dfrac{1,500}{4\cdot88} = 0\cdot256$ lb. per sec.

$$\text{h.p.} = \frac{116,100 \times 0\cdot256}{550} = \underline{54\cdot1}. \quad \text{Ans.}$$

2. *The steam reaches the nozzles of one stage of an impulse turbine at a pressure of 35 lb. per sq. in., with a velocity of 200 ft. per sec., and a dryness fraction of 0·96. The pressure drops along the nozzle to 10 lb. per sq. in. and 5% of the available isentropic heat drop is absorbed in overcoming friction. The nozzles are inclined at an angle of 15° to the plane of the one-row wheel, and the ratio of the blade speed to the tangential component of the steam speed is 0·4. If the velocity coefficient for the blades is 0·85, find the blade angles so that the steam may enter them without shock and leave them in an axial direction. Draw up an energy balance sheet for the stage per lb. of steam.*

(*U. Camb.*)

The isentropic nozzle heat drop, ΔH_T, from the chart is 87 B.T.U. per lb. Of this, 5% is used to reheat the steam due to friction, giving $\Delta H_U = 0\cdot95 \times 87 = 82\cdot6$ B.T.U., which is converted into K.E. If v is the steam velocity issuing from the nozzle,

$$82\cdot6 \times 778 = \frac{v^2 - 200^2}{2g}, \quad \therefore v = 2,044 \text{ ft. per sec.}$$

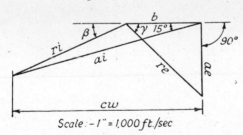

Scale: $-1'' = 1,000$ ft./sec

FIG. XVII,4.

In the diagram, $ai = 2,044$ ft. per sec. at $15° = \alpha$ to the direction of blade motion, b. The component of ai in the direction of b scales 1,975 ft. per sec., $\therefore b = 0\cdot4 \times 1,975 = 790$ ft. per sec. The inlet triangle can now be completed, giving the required inlet angle,

$$\beta = 24°. \quad \text{Ans.}$$

The steam is to leave the blades in an axial direction; this mean‹ that ae may be drawn at 90° to b, since this clearly refers to the absolut‹ velocity leaving the blades. We also have a velocity coefficient of 0·85 for the blade, so that

$$re = 0·85ri = 0·85 \times 1,300 = 1,105 \text{ ft. per sec.}$$

This fixes the outlet triangle and we have an exit angle

$$\gamma = 44°. \quad \text{Ans}$$

Also, $cw = 1,975$ ft. per sec. and $ae = 770$ ft. per sec.

$$\text{Diagram W.D. per lb.} = \frac{1,975 \times 790}{gJ} = 62·2 \text{ B.T.U.}$$

$$\text{Friction loss over blades per lb.} = \frac{1,300^2 - 1,105^2}{2gJ} = 9·3 \text{ B.T.U.}$$

$$\text{K.E. lost at exit per lb.} = \frac{770^2}{2gJ} = 11·9 \text{ B.T.U.}$$

$$\text{K.E. supplied at inlet per lb.} = \frac{200^2}{2gJ} = 0·8 \text{ B.T.U.}$$

The above information leads to this energy balance in B.T.U. per lb

Available to stage		Allocated in stage	
Isentropic ΔH . . .	87·0	Useful work . . .	62·2
K.E. entering . . .	0·8	Nozzle friction . .	4·4
		Blade friction . . .	9·3
		K.E. leaving . . .	11·9
	87·8		87·8

3. *A simple impulse turbine has one ring of moving blades running at 720 ft. per sec. The nozzle angle is 20° ; nozzle efficiency, 0·85 ; available heat drop, 251 B.T.U. per lb. ; blade exit angle, 30°. The rate of flow of steam is 660 lb. per hr., developing 30·2 h.p. at the blading.*

Find (a) *the heat equivalent of the blade friction in B.T.U. per lb. of steam ;* (b) *the total axial thrust on the blading.*   (U. Lond.)

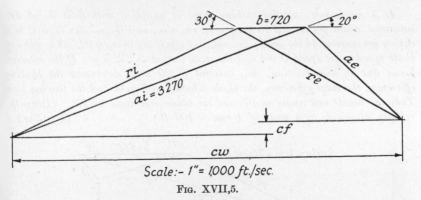

Scale:- 1"= 1,000 ft./sec.

FIG. XVII,5.

In this problem it will be necessary to find the change of whirl in order o find the exit velocity of the steam from the blade.

The exit velocity of the steam from the nozzle

$$= 8{\cdot}03\sqrt{0{\cdot}85 \times 251 \times 778} = 3{,}270 \text{ ft. per sec.}$$

The diagram work per lb. of steam $= \dfrac{60 \times 30{\cdot}2 \times 33{,}000}{660}$ ft.lb.

$$= \dfrac{cw \times 720}{g}, \quad \therefore cw = 4{,}054 \text{ ft. per sec.}$$

By completing the diagram with the above information, re scales 1,968 ft. per sec. and ri scales 2,586 ft. per sec.

Thus, Heat equivalent of blade friction $= \dfrac{ri^2 - re^2}{2g\text{J}}$

$$\therefore \text{Heat lost in blade friction} = \dfrac{2{,}586^2 - 1{,}968^2}{2g{.}778}$$

$$= 56{\cdot}2 \text{ B.T.U. per lb.} \quad \text{Ans. } (a).$$

The change of velocity of flow, $cf = 107$ ft. per sec.

$$\therefore \text{Axial thrust} = \dfrac{107}{g} \times \dfrac{660}{3{,}600}$$

$$= 0{\cdot}609 \text{ lb.} \quad \text{Ans. } (b).$$

$\left(\text{Note, blade velocity coefficient} = \dfrac{1{,}968}{2{,}580} = 0{\cdot}762.\right)$

4. *A single-row impulse turbine stage is supplied with 6·55 lb. of dr*
saturated steam per sec. at 75 lb. per sq. in. abs., and the nozzles expand to
casing pressure of 44 lb. per sq. in. abs., the efficiency being 0·92. The ratio o
blade speed to jet speed is 0·4 and the stage output is 232 h.p. If the interna
losses due to disc friction, etc., amount to 20 h.p., determine the bladin
efficiency, the stage efficiency, the blade velocity coefficient and the leaving loss
Take the nozzle exit angle as 16° and the blade exit angle as 17°. (Draw th
velocity diagrams to a scale of 1 cm. = 100 ft.)   (*U. Glas.*)

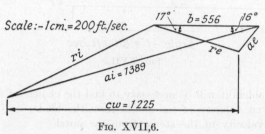

FIG. XVII,6.

The nozzle heat drop may be read off from the chart, but the pressure
range is so small, as to make accuracy difficult. It is easy to calculate
ΔH, for

$$H_1 = 1{,}182{\cdot}8, \quad \phi_1 = \phi_2 = 1{\cdot}6271.$$

By (I,33) $H_2 = 732{\cdot}8 \times 1{\cdot}6271 - 51{\cdot}1 = 1{,}141$ B.T.U. per lb.
after isentropic expansion,

$$\therefore \text{ nozzle } \Delta H_T = 41{\cdot}75 \text{ B.T.U.}$$

$$\frac{ai^2}{2gJ} = 41{\cdot}75 \times 0{\cdot}92$$

$$ai = 8{\cdot}03\sqrt{41{\cdot}75 \times 0{\cdot}92 \times 778} = 1{,}389 \text{ ft. per sec.}$$

$$\therefore b = 0{\cdot}4 \times 1{,}389 = 556 \text{ ft. per sec.}$$

We are told that the stage output, i.e. the *shaft* h.p., is 232; if disc
friction and windage amounts to 20 h.p., the blade or diagram h.p. must
be 252.

$$\therefore 252 = 6{\cdot}55\frac{cw \times 556}{g \times 550}, \quad cw = 1{,}225 \text{ ft. per sec.}$$

The diagram may now be drawn, as above, and it yields the following
information:

$$ri = 868; \quad re = 470; \quad ae = 170 \text{ ft. per sec.}$$

Blading (or diagram) $\eta = \dfrac{\dfrac{cw \times b}{g}}{\dfrac{ai^2}{2g}} = \dfrac{2 \times 556 \times 1{,}225}{1{,}389^2} = \underline{70{\cdot}7\%}$. Ans.

Gross Stage $\eta = 0.92 \times 0.707 = 65.0\%$.

Net Stage $\eta = 0.92 \times 0.707 \times \dfrac{232}{252} = \underline{59.8\%}$.   Ans.

Alternatively,   Net Stage $\eta = \dfrac{\text{shaft h.p.}}{\text{available } \Delta H_T}$

$$= \dfrac{232 \times 550}{41.75 \times 6.55 \times 778} = 60.0\%,$$

the difference being the cumulative error due to graphical solution.

Blade velocity coefficient $= \dfrac{470}{868} = \underline{0.542}$.   Ans.

Leaving loss $= 6.55 \times \dfrac{170^2}{2g} \times \dfrac{1}{550} = \underline{5.34 \text{ h.p.}}$ Ans.

5. *In a two-row velocity-compound stage for an impulse turbine the initial speed of the steam is 1,800 ft. per sec. The speed of the blades is 350 ft. per sec. The nozzles have discharge angle 18° and the discharge angles of the three rows of blades, in order, are $21\frac{1}{2}°$, 28° and 45°. Assuming a frictional loss of speed of 15% in each row of blades, find the work done by the steam per lb. and the efficiency of the blading.*

Neglecting any increase of volume of the steam, find the height required for each row of blades, taking the height of the nozzles as 0.70 in.   (*I. Mech.E.*)

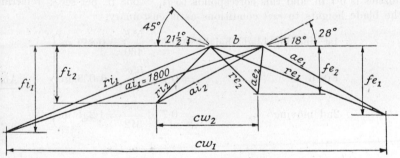

Scale:– 1 cm. = 250 ft./sec.

FIG. XVII,7.

The diagram is shown above to a rather small scale. The student should carefully re-draw this to as large a scale as possible.

The construction is as follows :

$b = 350$ ft. per sec.   and $ai_1 = 1,800$ ft. per sec. at 18° to b
$\therefore ri_1 = 1,470$ and $re_1 = 0.85 \times 1,470 = 1,250$ at 21.5° to b
$\therefore ae_1 = 936$ and $ai_2 = 0.85 \times 936 = 796$ at 28° to b
$\therefore ri_2 = 520$ and $re_2 = 0.85 \times 520 = 442$ at 45° to b

It should be noted that the velocity coefficient of 0·85 applies to th moving blades *and* the fixed blade which merely serves to re-direct th steam on the second moving blade. Also, the exit angle of the fixed blad (28°) is a " must " angle (cf. introduction to this chapter) and gives th direction of the steam entering the second moving blade, viz. ai_2, i the same way as the nozzle angle fixes ai_1. Suffices 1 and 2 refer to th first and second moving blade. From the diagram,

$$cw_1 = 2,520 ; \quad cw_2 = 667 ;$$

$$fi_1 = 558 ; \quad fe_1 = 460 ; \quad fi_2 = 378 ; \quad fe_2 = 312 \text{ ft. per sec.}$$

$$\therefore \text{ W.D. per lb.} = \frac{2,520 + 667}{g} \times 350 = \underline{346,000 \text{ ft.lb.}} \quad \text{Ans}$$

$$\text{K.E. supp. per lb.} = \frac{1,800^2}{2g} = 503,000 \text{ ft.lb.}$$

$$\text{Diagram (or blading) } \eta = \frac{346,000}{503,000} = \underline{68\cdot9\%.} \quad \text{Ans}$$

For continuity of flow, the ratio $\dfrac{\text{area} \times \text{velocity of flow}}{\text{specific volume}}$ which equals the lb. per sec. must be constant. Neglecting the increase of volume o the steam which would result from the re-heating due to friction over the blades, and also assuming that the blades are parallel (i.e. not tapered), the product blade height × velocity of flow = const. The height of the nozzles is 0·7 in. and this corresponds to $fi_1 = 558$ ft. per sec. ; referring the blade heights to *exit* conditions as is customary,

$$\text{1st moving blade height} = 0\cdot7 \times \frac{558}{460} = 0\cdot849 \text{ in.} \left.\begin{array}{l} \\ \\ \\ \\ \\ \end{array}\right\}$$

$$\text{Fixed} \quad ,, \quad ,, \quad = 0\cdot7 \times \frac{558}{378} = 1\cdot033 \text{ in.} \qquad \underline{\text{Ans.}}$$

$$\text{2nd moving} \quad ,, \quad ,, \quad = 0\cdot7 \times \frac{558}{312} = 1\cdot251 \text{ in.}$$

6. *A reaction turbine uses 20,000 lb. of steam per hr. At one point in the turbine, the blades are $\frac{3}{4}$ in. high and the discharge angle of both fixed and moving blades is 20°. The steam leaves the fixed blades at a pressure of 46 lb. per sq. in. with a dryness fraction of 0·95, and a velocity of 400 ft. per sec. Assuming that the ratio of axial velocity of flow to blade velocity is 0·70 at entry to and 0·76 at exit from the moving blades, find the speed of the turbine in r.p.m. and the h.p. developed in this particular blade ring. Neglect the effect of blade thickness but assume a tip leakage of 6% of the total steam.*

(U. Lond.)

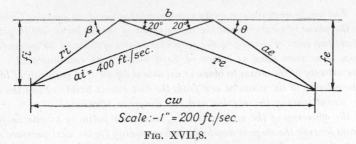

Scale :−1″ = 200 ft./sec.

FIG. XVII,8.

The diagram may be drawn to scale, as above, or the necessary dimensions may be calculated. The diagram should always be sketched in the first place. We have $ai = 400$ ft. per sec. since this is the speed with which the steam leaves the fixed blades, acting as nozzles.

$$fi = 400 \sin 20° = 136\cdot8 \; ; \qquad b = \frac{136\cdot8}{0\cdot7} = 195\cdot4 \; ;$$

$$fe = 0\cdot76 \times 195\cdot4 = 148\cdot5 \; ; \qquad re = \frac{148\cdot5}{\sin 20°} = 434 \; ;$$

$$cw = 400 \cos 20° + 434 \cos 20° - b = 588\cdot6.$$

This is an example of a reaction turbine where the degree of reaction is not 50%, i.e. the diagram is not symmetrical. This is probably due not to different blade inlet angles, but due to shock entry at one or both blades; hence $\beta \neq \theta$ here. The student is again asked to distinguish between the " must " angles (both 20° here) and the " may " angles (inlet angles, not given here).

Neglecting the change of volume in passage over the moving blade
$$V = 0\cdot95 \times 9\cdot209 = 8\cdot75 \text{ cu. ft. per lb. ;}$$

also $W = \dfrac{20,000}{3,600} \times 0\cdot94 = 5\cdot22$ lb. per sec. flowing through the blading,

since 6% of the total flow leaks past the tips of the blades and therefore does no useful work. When a blade height is mentioned, it is customarily quoted with reference to the conditions at *exit* from the blade.

Since, area × velocity of flow = W × V

$$\pi \times D \times \frac{0\cdot75}{12} \times 148\cdot5 = 5\cdot22 \times 8\cdot75,$$

whence $\qquad\qquad\qquad\qquad D = 1\cdot566$ ft.

where D is the mean diameter of the blade annulus,

and $\qquad\qquad \pi D \dfrac{N}{60} = b, \quad \therefore \; N = \dfrac{60 \times 195\cdot4}{\pi \times 1\cdot566} = \underline{2,380 \text{ r.p.m.}}$ Ans.

$$\text{h.p.} = 5\cdot22 \times \frac{588\cdot6 \times 195\cdot4}{g \times 550} = \underline{33\cdot9.} \quad \text{Ans.}$$

7. *The nozzle angle in a velocity compounded stage of an impulse turbine i.*
16° to the plane of rotation, and the mean speed of the blades is 300 ft. per sec
There are two rows of moving blades with exit angles of 22° and 30° respectively
Between these rows there is a row of fixed blades with exit angle 24°. The
relative velocity of the steam to blade is decreased by 10% at each row of blades
and the velocity of the steam at exit from the last row is axial. Find the speec
of the steam leaving the nozzles and the diagram efficiency.

If the efficiency of the nozzles is 95% and the remaining kinetic energy o.
the steam leaving the stage is available as heat energy for the next pressure stage,
estimate the state of the steam entering the next stage. The steam supplied tc
the nozzles is at 120 lb. per sq. in. dry saturated. (U. Lond.)

In this type of problem the velocity diagram must be drawn " backwards ", i.e. starting with the outlet triangle for the second moving blade.
Before attempting any drawing, the student should sketch the complete
diagram in order to be sure of his symbols and avoid confusion.

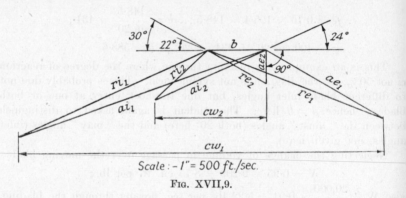

Scale : - 1" = 500 ft./sec.

FIG. XVII,9.

For an axial exit velocity, ae_2 is at right angles to b.

∴ $b = 300$, ae_2 at 90° to b, re_2 at 30° to b

gives the final outlet triangle and $re_2 = 350$. Now, ri_2 will be greater than
this, such that $re_2 = 0.9 ri_2$ for a 10% decrease in relative velocity over
the blade. Hence,

$$ri_2 = \frac{10}{9} \times 350 = 389 \, ; \quad ai_2 \text{ (at 24° to } b\text{)} = 639$$

$$\therefore ae_1 = \frac{10}{9} \times 639 = 710 \, ; \quad re_1 \text{ (at 22° to } b\text{)} = 982$$

$$\therefore ri_1 = \frac{10}{9} \times 982 = 1{,}090.$$

$$\therefore ai_1 = 1{,}375 \text{ ft. per sec.} \quad \text{Ans.}$$

Also, $cw_1 = 1,925$ and $cw_2 = 585$ ft. per sec.

$$\text{W.D. per lb..} = \frac{1,925 + 585}{g} \times 300 = 23,400 \text{ ft.lb.}$$

$$= 30 \cdot 1 \text{ B.T.U.}$$

$$\text{K.E. supp. per lb.} = \frac{1,375^2}{2g} = 29,380 \text{ ft.lb.}$$

$$\text{Diagram } \eta = \frac{23,400}{29,380} = \underline{79 \cdot 6\%}. \quad \text{Ans.}$$

For the nozzle, $\Delta H_T = \dfrac{1,375^2}{2gJ} \times \dfrac{100}{95} = 39 \cdot 7$ B.T.U. per lb.

Setting off $AB = 39 \cdot 7$ B.T.U., as shown in fig. XVII,10, and $AC = 30 \cdot 1$

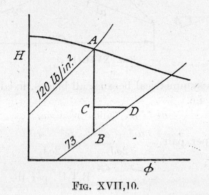

FIG. XVII,10.

as the useful W.D., we have the state of the steam entering the next stage with the assumption given in the text of the question as

$$\underline{73 \text{ lb. per sq. in.,}} \quad x = 0 \cdot 977. \quad \text{Ans.}$$

8. *Explain the essential differences between the reaction and the impuls* *turbines in so far as the functions of the blading are concerned. If the entranc* *and exit angles of the blades of a reaction turbine are* α *and* β *respectively, an* *the blade velocity is u ft. per sec., what is the theoretical heat drop per pair*

In a radial reaction turbine with double motion, each rotor has the sam *speed in opposite directions. Find angles suitable for the blading at a poir* *where the radial steam velocity is twice that of either blade, the exit velocity c* *the steam relative to the blade being 1·6 times that at entrance.* (*U. Lond.*)

The first part of the question is answered in the introduction to thi chapter.

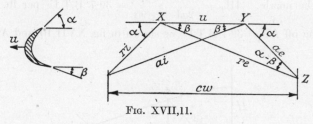

FIG. XVII,11.

The diagram is symmetrical because all blades, fixed and moving, have the same angles; i.e.

$$ai = re, \quad \text{and} \quad ri = ae.$$

$$\Delta\text{H per pair} = \frac{ai^2 - ae^2}{2g\text{J}} + \frac{re^2 - ri^2}{2g\text{J}}$$

$$= \frac{re^2 - ri^2}{g\text{J}} \text{ B.T.U. per lb.}$$

From the diagram, applying the sine-rule to the triangle XYZ,

$$\frac{u}{\sin(\alpha - \beta)} = \frac{re}{\sin(180 - \alpha)} = \frac{ae}{\sin\beta}, \quad \text{and} \quad ae = ri,$$

$$\therefore \quad re = u\frac{\sin\alpha}{\sin(\alpha - \beta)}, \quad \text{and} \quad ri = u\frac{\sin\beta}{\sin(\alpha - \beta)},$$

hence, $$\Delta\text{H per pair} = \frac{u^2}{g\text{J}} \cdot \frac{\sin^2\alpha - \sin^2\beta}{\sin^2(\alpha - \beta)},$$

which may be quoted as the answer. However,

$$\sin^2\alpha - \sin^2\beta = (\sin\alpha + \sin\beta)(\sin\alpha - \sin\beta)$$

$$= 2\sin\frac{\alpha + \beta}{2}\cos\frac{\alpha - \beta}{2} \times 2\cos\frac{\alpha + \beta}{2}\sin\frac{\alpha - \beta}{2}$$

$$= \sin(\alpha + \beta)\sin(\alpha - \beta).$$

$$\therefore \quad \Delta\text{H per pair} = \frac{u^2}{g\text{J}} \cdot \frac{\sin(\alpha + \beta)}{\sin(\alpha - \beta)}. \quad \text{Ans.}$$

(By expanding the compound angle sines and dividing through by $\cos \alpha \cos \beta$, yet another form is $\dfrac{u^2}{2g\mathbf{J}} \cdot \dfrac{\tan \alpha + \tan \beta}{\tan \alpha - \tan \beta}$)

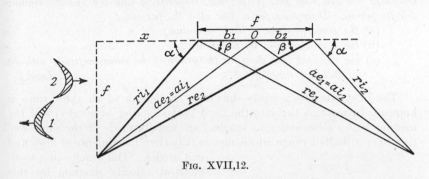

FIG. XVII,12.

The radial flow reaction turbine with double motion is commonly known as the Brush-Ljungström turbine. The steam flow is radial from the centre outwards and there are no fixed blades at all. Alternate blades are attached to rotors revolving in opposite directions and the pressure falls continuously, the heat drop being theoretically equal, if the blades are alike. The velocity diagram is shown in fig. XVII,12, with the usual notation. It should be particularly noted that $ue_1 = ai_2$ and $ae_2 = ai_1$.

The triangle shown in heavy lines is required to solve this question.

Given, $f = 2b_1 = 2b_2$,   and $\dfrac{re_1}{ri_1} = \dfrac{re_2}{ri_2} = 1 \cdot 6$,

we have, $f^2 + (f + x)^2 = re_2{}^2 = (1 \cdot 6 ri_2)^2 = (1 \cdot 6 ri_1)^2$

and $ri_1{}^2 = f^2 + x^2$.

$$\therefore \ 2 \cdot 56(f^2 + x^2) = f^2 + (f + x)^2$$
$$1 \cdot 56 x^2 - 2fx + 0 \cdot 56 f^2 = 0$$

$$x = \frac{2f \pm \sqrt{4f^2 - 4 \times 1 \cdot 56 \times 0 \cdot 56 f^2}}{2 \times 1 \cdot 56} = 0 \cdot 869 f \quad \text{or} \quad 0 \cdot 413 f.$$

$$\left. \begin{array}{l} \cot \alpha = \dfrac{x}{f} = 0 \cdot 869 \text{ or } 0 \cdot 413 \ ; \quad \underline{\alpha = 49° \quad \text{or } 67 \cdot 5°} \\[3mm] \cot \beta = \dfrac{x + f}{f} = \dfrac{1 \cdot 869}{1} \text{ or } \dfrac{1 \cdot 413}{1} \ ; \quad \underline{\beta = 28 \cdot 15° \text{ or } 35 \cdot 3°} \end{array} \right\} \quad \text{Ans.}$$

There are two possible solutions here ; the set 49° and 28·15° is the more likely one.

9. *A group of reaction blading consists of three fixed and three moving rings all of the same height, and the mean blade speed of the moving rings is 220 ft. per sec. For the mean moving ring the inlet absolute and relative velocities are 275 and 102 ft. per sec. respectively and the specific volume 2·5 ft. per lb. Determine for a flow of 5 lb. per sec.:*

(a) *the required area of blade annulus;*

(b) *the h.p. developed by the group;*

(c) *the required heat drop for the group if the steam expands with an efficiency ratio of 0·8.*   (*U. Lond.*)

The inlet triangle is easily drawn as the length of all three sides is known. In reaction turbines the fixed blades (acting as nozzles) and the moving blades (also acting as nozzles) are usually made of the same section over a limited range which means that they have identical inlet and

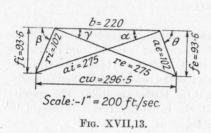

Scale:-1" = 200 ft./sec.

Fɪɢ. XVII,13.

exit angles. This results in a symmetrical velocity diagram for this range of blading, *provided* the steam enters the blades without shock. In fig. XVII,13 β is the blade angle for shockless entry and this is accordingly a " may " angle (cf. introduction to this chapter); α gives the direction of the steam issuing from the fixed blade and is therefore a " must " angle. If both fixed and moving blades are of the same section, an assumption which must now be made, then the moving blade exit angle γ will be equal to α; also *ae* must be so inclined as to enter the fixed blade without shock, i.e. $\theta = \beta$, the common inlet angle.

The construction results in constant velocity of flow,

$$fi = fe = 93 \cdot 6 \text{ ft. per sec.;} \quad \text{also} \quad cw = 296 \cdot 5.$$

For continuity of flow, area × velocity = lb. per sec. × cu. ft. per lb.

$$\therefore \text{ Area of blade annulus} = \frac{5 \times 2 \cdot 5}{93 \cdot 6} = \underline{0 \cdot 1335} \text{ sq. ft.} \quad \text{Ans.}$$

Since there are three pairs in the group or expansion and the diagram is that for the *mean* pair,

$$\therefore \text{ h.p.} = 3 \times \frac{5 \times 296 \cdot 5 \times 220}{550g} = \underline{55 \cdot 3}. \quad \text{Ans.}$$

The heat drop in the fixed blades will be $\dfrac{ai^2 - ae^2}{2gJ}$ B.T.U. per lb., and

the heat drop in the moving blades will be $\dfrac{re^2 - ri^2}{2gJ}$ B.T.U. per lb. It is

clear from the construction of the diagram that these heat drops will be equal, i.e.   Useful heat drop per pair $= 2 \times \dfrac{ai^2 - ae^2}{2gJ}$

$$\therefore \Delta H_T \text{ per pair} = \frac{275^2 - 102^2}{gJ} \times \frac{1}{0 \cdot 8}.$$

$$\therefore \Delta H_T \text{ for the group} = \frac{3}{0 \cdot 8} \frac{377 \times 173}{gJ} = 9 \cdot 78 \text{ B.T.U. per lb.} \quad \text{Ans.}$$

Reaction Turbines with equal fixed and moving blade sections, and thus symmetrical diagrams for shockless entry, are known as Parsons Turbines, or half degree reaction machines, or machines having a 50% reaction. The degree of reaction is defined as

$$\frac{\text{Heat Drop in moving blade}}{\text{Heat Drop in moving blade} + \text{Heat Drop in fixed blade}}$$

and is clearly 50% for the type of turbine discussed here.

10. *In a certain stage in an axial-flow turbine with 50% reaction, the blade angles at inlet and outlet are 80° and 20° respectively. The mean blade ring diameter is 4 ft. and the rotor speed is 1,500 r.p.m.*

If the steam enters the stage at 100 lb. per sq. in., dry and saturated, and 10% is lost in leakage, calculate the blade height for 200 h.p. to be developed in the stage. Assuming a stage efficiency of 0·75, estimate the pressure drop in the stage. (U. Dur.)

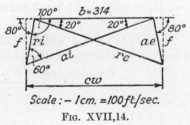

Scale :— 1 cm. = 100 ft./sec.

Fig. XVII,14.

The diagram must be symmetrical for 50% reaction.

$$b = \frac{1,500}{60} \times 2\pi \times 2 = 314 \text{ ft. per sec.,}$$

and the diagram may either be drawn or calculated. As the required pressure drop in one stage is likely to be very small, it is advisable to sketch the diagram and then calculate :

$$\frac{ai}{\sin 100°} = \frac{314}{\sin 60°}; \quad ai = 314 \times \frac{0 \cdot 985}{0 \cdot 866} = 357 = re$$

$$ri = 314 \times \frac{\sin 20°}{\sin 60°} = 124 = ae$$

$$cw = 2 \times 124 \cos 80° + 314 = 357$$
$$f = 124 \sin 80° = 122.$$

(It is clear from the diagram that ai and cw make angles of 80° with ae, $\therefore$ $ai = cw$.)

$$\text{h.p.} = 200 = W \text{ lb. per sec.} \times \frac{357 \times 314}{550g}, \quad \therefore W = 31 \cdot 6.$$

This is the rate of steam flow over the blading.

$$\text{Total steam flow} = 31 \cdot 6 \times \frac{10}{9} = 35 \cdot 1 \text{ lb. per sec.}$$

For continuity of flow, assuming the specific volume of the steam (4·434 cu. ft. per lb.) to remain approximately consistent in the stage

$$\pi \times 4 \times h \times 122 = 31 \cdot 6 \times 4 \cdot 434.$$

$$\therefore h = 0 \cdot 915 \text{ ft.} = \underline{11 \text{ in.}}, \text{ nearly.} \quad \text{Ans.}$$

Per lb. of steam entering the turbine, the gross useful work is

$$\varDelta\mathrm{H_U} = \frac{200 \times 550}{778 \times 35 \cdot 1} = 4 \cdot 03 \text{ B.T.U.}$$

$$\varDelta\mathrm{H_T} = \frac{4 \cdot 03}{0 \cdot 75} = 5 \cdot 38 \text{ B.T.U., say } 5 \cdot 4 \text{ B.T.U.}$$

Now, $\mathrm{H_1} = 1{,}188 \cdot 2$ B.T.U. per lb. and $\phi_1 = 1 \cdot 6038$ at 100 lb. per sq. in. dry saturated. It is clearly very difficult to estimate the pressure drop accurately from the chart, but inspection shows that it might be about 7 lb. per sq. in. Now, $\mathrm{H_2} = 1{,}188 \cdot 2 - 5 \cdot 4 = 1{,}182 \cdot 8$ B.T.U. per lb.

By (I,33) $\quad 1{,}182 \cdot 8 = \mathrm{T} \times 1 \cdot 6038 - \mathrm{G}$
at 92 lb. per sq. in., $\mathrm{T}\phi - \mathrm{G} = 781 \cdot 6 \times 1 \cdot 6038 - 72 \cdot 2 = 1{,}181 \cdot 3.$
at 94 lb. per sq. in., $\quad = 783 \cdot 0 \times 1 \cdot 6038 - 72 \cdot 9 = 1{,}182 \cdot 9.$

$$\therefore \text{ Pressure drop} \eqsim \underline{6 \text{ lb. per sq. in.}} \quad \text{Ans.}$$

EXAMPLES

1. The blade speed of a single ring of impulse blading is 800 ft./sec. and the nozzle angle 20°. The heat drop is 311 B.T.U./lb. and the nozzle efficiency 0·85. The blade discharge angle is 30° and the machine develops 39·6 h.p. when passing 700 lb. of steam per hr.

Draw the vector triangles and determine :
(a) the axial thrust on the blading ;
(b) the heat equivalent, per lb. of steam, of the friction of the blading.
(*U. Lond.*)
[$ai = 3{,}636$ ft. per sec. ; $cw = 4{,}504$ ft. per sec. ; hence vector triangle may be completed ; $fi = 1{,}242$ and $fe = 1{,}088$ ft. per sec. ; $\underline{\text{axial thrust} = 0 \cdot 93 \text{ lb.}}$; $ri = 2{,}894$ and $re = 2{,}186$ ft. per sec. ; $\underline{\text{friction} = 72 \cdot 0 \text{ B.T.U. per lb.}}$]

2. In a Parsons turbine running at 1,800 r.p.m. the available heat for an expansion = 24·3 B.T.U. per lb. If the mean diameter of the rotor in the expansion is 34 in., calculate the number of rows of moving blades necessary in the expansion, given that the stage efficiency $= 0.8$, blade outlet angle $= 20°$ and speed ratio $= 0.7$. (*U. Manch.*)

$$\left[\text{Speed ratio} = \frac{b}{ai}; \; ai = 381 \text{ ft. per sec.}; \; cw = 449 \text{ ft. per sec.}; \; \text{diagram} \right.$$

W.D. per lb. $= 4.79$ B.T.U. per stage or pair; $\varDelta H_T$ per pair $= 6.0$ B.T.U.; 4 rows of moving blades (i.e. 4 pairs).

$$\left. \text{Check, also}: \; \varDelta H_T = \frac{1}{0.8} \times 2 \times \frac{ai^2 - ae^2}{2gJ}. \right]$$

3. What are the essential differences, apart from the method of attachment, between the blading of impulse and reaction turbines ?

All the blades in a reaction machine have inlet and discharge angles of $35°$ and $20°$ respectively. At a particular ring the mean blade speed is 220 ft. per sec. Draw the vector figure and determine :

   (*a*) the height of blade, if this is one-eighth of the mean ring diameter, required to pass 10 lb. per sec. of steam at 20 lb. per sq. in. and 0.9 dry ;

   (*b*) the heat drop required by the pair of rings, if the steam expands with an efficiency of 0.80 ;

   (*c*) the horse-power developed by the pair of rings, according to the vector figure. (*U. Lond.*)

[$fi = fe = 167$ ft. per sec. ; $d = 1.66$ ft. ; $h = 2.49$ in. ; $ai = 487$; $re = 291$ ft. per sec. ; $\varDelta H_U = 6.08$ B.T.U. per lb. ; $\varDelta H_T = 7.60$ B.T.U. per lb. ; $cw = 696$ ft. per sec. ; h.p. $= 86.4$.]

4. Deduce an expression for work done per stage (1 ring of fixed blades plus 1 ring of moving blades) of a reaction machine and determine the conditions for maximum efficiency.

At a stage of a reaction machine the mean ring diameter is 54 in. The speed ratio is 0.7. The speed of rotation is 3,000 r.p.m. Determine the required entrance angle for the blading if the exit angle is $20°$. Determine the work done per lb. of steam flowing per sec.

Calculate the percentage increase in diagram efficiency if the blades are designed for and run at the best theoretical speed, the exit angle being kept at $20°$.

(*U. Witw.*)

$$\left[\text{W.D. per stage} = \frac{b}{Jg}(2ai \cos \alpha - b) \text{ B.T.U. per lb.}; \; \cos \alpha = \frac{b}{ai} = \text{speed} \right.$$

ratio for max. η ; $ai = 1{,}016$ ft. per sec. ; $\beta = 55°$; W.D. $= 34.1$ B.T.U. per lb. ; diagr. $\eta = 90.6\%$; new $b = 956$ and new $cw = 956$ ft. per sec. ; new diagr.

$$\eta = 94.1\% ; \; \text{increase} = 3.9\%. \Big]$$

5. A single-row impulse turbine stage receives 10 lb. of dry saturated steam per sec. at 120 lb./in.^{2} abs. The steam is expanded in the nozzles to a pressure of 80 lb./in.^{2} abs., with an efficiency of 0.94, and discharged at an angle of $20°$ to the plane of rotation of the blades. Find a suitable exit angle for the blades in order that there shall be no axial thrust on the blades, allowing a blade velocity coefficient of 0.85 and a blade speed of 550 ft./sec. If the internal losses, due to disc friction and windage, amount to 1.8 B.T.U./lb. of steam, find the efficiency and horse-power of the stage. Also draw up a heat balance for the stage.

(*U. Glas.*)

[$\varDelta H_T = 33.4$ B.T.U. ; $ai = 1{,}255$ ft. per sec. ; $\gamma = 41\frac{1}{2}°$; diagram W.D.

per lb. = 24·5 B.T.U.; net stage $\eta = 68\cdot0\%$; h.p. = 321; R.H.S. of heat balance: shaft work, 22·7; windage, 1·8; nozzle friction, 2·0; blade friction, 3·2; leaving loss, 3·7 B.T.U. per lb.; $\Sigma = 33\cdot4$.]

6. An impulse stage of a turbine has two rows of moving blades separated by fixed blades. The steam leaves the nozzles at an angle of 20° with the direction of motion of the blades. The blade exit angles are: 1st moving, 30°; fixed, 22°; 2nd moving, 30°.

If the adiabatic heat drop for the nozzle is 80 B.T.U. per lb. and the nozzle efficiency 90%, find the blade speed necessary if the final velocity of the steam is to be axial. Assume a loss of 15% in relative velocity for all blade passages. Find also the blade efficiency and the stage efficiency.   (U. Lond.)

[Draw the velocity diagram " backwards ", i.e. start with ae_2 which is 90° to b; any scale may be chosen; from nozzle details, $ai_1 = 1,900$ ft. per sec. which settles the correct scale, and $\therefore\ b = 384$ ft. per sec.; $cw = 1,348 + 252 = 1,600$ ft. per sec.; diagram or blade $\eta = 71\cdot0\%$; gross stage $\eta = 64\cdot0\%$.]

7. Each of two impulse turbines of the Curtis type has a set of nozzles, three rotating and two stationary sets of blades. Steam at a pressure of 200 lb. per sq. in. and temperature of 300° C. is expanded in the nozzles to atmospheric pressure. The nozzles are inclined at an angle of 20° to the plane of rotation of the blades which have a mean speed of 500 ft. per sec.

Find the magnitude and directions of the absolute velocities of the steam as it leaves the turbines, also the blade angles in every case, given that in turbine (a) the inlet angle is equal to the outlet angle for each blade (each ring of blades is different) and in turbine (b) the inlet angles and the outlet angles of all moving blades have the same value and are identical.   (W.S.S.)

[Assumptions: (i) Expansion in nozzles is stable and isentropic. (ii) All velocity coefficients (fixed and moving blades) are unity; $\Delta H_T = 221\cdot3$ B.T.U. per lb., by (I,33); $ai_1 = 3,330$ ft. per sec. From graphical solution, (a) $\beta_1 = \gamma_1 = 23\frac{1}{2}°$; $\beta_2 = \gamma_2 = 28°$; $\beta_3 = \gamma_3 = 35°$; $\beta_4 = \gamma_4 = 46°$; $\beta_5 = \gamma_5 = 62°$; $ae_3 = 1,150$ ft. per sec. at 85° to b; (b) all β = all $\gamma = 23\frac{1}{2}°$; $ae_3 = 620$ ft. per sec. at 42° to b.]

8. In a certain stage in an axial flow impulse-reaction turbine running at 3,000 r.p.m., the fixed and moving blades are of identical shape and have an outlet angle of 20°. The blade length is 2·5 in., the mean blade ring diameter is 28 in., and the steam is dry and saturated at 80 lb. per sq. in. (abs.). If the mean blade speed is twice the axial velocity of flow of the steam, calculate the correct inlet blade tip angle, the horse-power developed in the stage, and the efficiency of the blading. What would be the rotational speed for maximum blading efficiency, other conditions being unaltered, and the maximum efficiency at that speed?   (U. Birm.)

[$f = 183$ ft. per sec., $\beta = 53\cdot4°$; $cw = 639$ ft. per sec., area for flow = 1·527 sq. ft., W = 51·1 lb. per sec., h.p. = 676; K.E. supp. = 8,090 ft.lb. per lb., diagram $\eta = 90\cdot0\%$; ideal speed $N^1 = 4,130$ r.p.m., when $\cos \alpha = \dfrac{b}{ai}$, whence max. $\eta = 93\cdot8\%$.]

CHAPTER XVIII

IMPROVEMENTS IN TURBINE PLANT

Introduction

The Rankine cycle is less efficient than the Carnot cycle between the same temperature limits (cf. example no. 1, chapter XIV). The reason lies in the fact that in the Carnot cycle 1 2 3 4 1 all the heat absorbed by the working fluid is supplied at the highest temperature T_a, 1 to 2, fig. XVIII,1, and all the heat rejected, 3 to 4, is at the lowest temperature T_b.

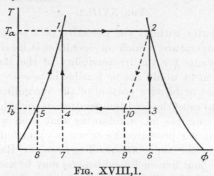

FIG. XVIII,1.

The corresponding Rankine cycle is 1 2 3 5 1. Here, some of the heat is supplied, from 5 to 1, representing the heating of the feed water, at temperatures lower than T_a. If the feed-pump term be neglected, this heat supplied is 5 1 7 8 5, and any modification which would reduce this area, without a corresponding decrease in the net W.D., would result in an improvement in efficiency.

Consider the ideal arrangement in fig. XVIII,2, in which steam is expanded in the turbine from a temperature T_a to T_b. The feed water at T_b is passed through an annular space surrounding the turbine casing; this results in the temperature of the feed water being raised to that of the steam at any section, finally being raised to T_a. The heat thus gained by the feed water is 1 7 8 5 1 (fig. XVIII,1) and the heat given up by the steam must be equal to this, and may be represented by 2 6 9 10 2.

Since area 1 4 5 1 = area 2 3 10 2,

Heat supplied *externally* = area under 1–2 = 1 2 6 7 1
Heat rejected *externally* = area under 10–5
    = area under 3–4 = 3 6 7 4 3.

This is the same as the Carnot cycle; and the Rankine cycle so modified would have an efficiency equal to the Carnot efficiency. The reason for this lies in the fact that, at any section along the turbine, heat is sup-

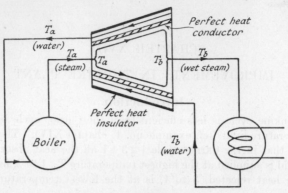

FIG. XVIII,2.

plied to the feed water without the necessity of a temperature gradient, i.e. at constant temperature. Such an operation is ideally reversible and thus removes the cause for the irreversibility of the Rankine cycle.

Such an arrangement would not be feasible in practice, and the method adopted is to extract or bleed a portion of the expanding steam from the turbine and use it to raise the feed temperature in suitable heat exchanges. It will be seen in example no. 5 following that even with a single such heater, and at whatever pressure the steam is extracted the efficiency is always greater than for the corresponding straight Rankine cycle. In large plants, up to about five such feed heaters may be used, the ultimately smaller additional gain in efficiency having to be off-set against the cost and complication of the extra plant, high-pressure heaters being much more expensive than the low-pressure ones.

Fig. XVIII,3 shows two different methods of disposal of the bled steam after condensation in the heaters. (a) shows a method known as " Separate

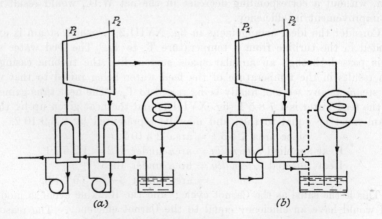

FIG. XVIII,3.

)rain Pumps " where the condensed steam is returned to the feed line at
, point immediately downstream of the relevant heater. (*b*) shows a
" Cascade " arrangement where the condensed steam is cascaded from
igh-pressure heaters to heaters operating at lower pressures, so that a por-
ion of the cascaded condensate will flash into steam at the lower saturation
emperature. The condensate from the last heater is led to the hot-well or
he condenser for simplicity, though this somewhat reduces the efficiency.
juitable steam traps and/or non-return valves must be included. The
liagrams do not include any feed pumps, in order to avoid confusion.
[n the absence of precise information as to the actual temperatures of the
'eed water entering and leaving the heaters and of the condensate temperatures, the following assumptions should always be made in problems :

1. The bled steam just condenses, i.e. gives up its superheat (if any)
und all its latent heat only. The condensed steam therefore leaves the
heater at the saturation temperature corresponding to the bleeding pressure.

2. The feed water is heated to the saturation temperature at the pressure
of the bled steam.

And either, 3*a*. The bled steam is returned to the system by separate
pumps at a point downstream from the heater ;

or, 3*b*. The bled steam discharges into the hot-well, thereby raising the
hot-well temperature ;

or, 3*c*. The bled steam is cascaded down and discharges finally into the
hot-well or condenser.

Some incidental results of feed heating are demonstrated in example
no. 6 below.

A cycle using feed heating is usually referred to as a regenerative cycle.

Another modification of the Rankine cycle may be made by re-superheating the expanding steam at one or more points, or by injecting highly
superheated steam into the expanding steam. This usually produces a
slightly increased efficiency (due to the chart reheat factor), but is done
principally to reduce blade erosion and frictional losses, serious matters
with wet steam. The increased final dryness requires increased condenser
capacity.

The binary vapour turbine is another attempt to improve the thermal
efficiency and example no. 7 in this chapter deals with its thermodynamic
aspect.

1. *Determine the improvement of efficiency which would result if a single stage of regenerative feed heating were added to a steam cycle having terminal conditions of 200 lb. per sq. in. (abs.), 200° F. superheat, and 1 lb. per sq. in. (abs.). The steam for feed heating is to be extracted at 25 lb. per sq. in. (abs.).*

(U. Manch.)

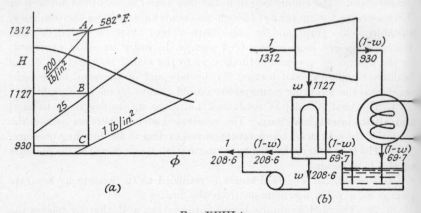

(a)

(b)

Fig. XVIII,4.

Referring to fig. XVIII,4(*a*), it may here be assumed that the steam expands isentropically in the turbine, since no information to the contrary is available.

From the steam tables, $H_A = 1,312 \cdot 1$ and $\phi_A = 1 \cdot 6655$.

H_B and H_C may be found from the chart; but a glance at the chart suggests that the steam will be wet at B and C, so that we can use (I,33) to calculate H_B and H_C; thus

$$H_B = 699 \cdot 7 \times 1 \cdot 6655 - 38 \cdot 8 = 1,127 \text{ B.T.U.}$$
$$H_C = 561 \cdot 4 \times 1 \cdot 6655 - 4 \cdot 7 = 930 \text{ B.T.U.}$$

Referring to fig. XVIII,4(*b*), let 1 lb. of steam enter the turbine, as shown; let *w* lb. be bled at 25 lb. per sq. in. having a total heat of 1,127 B.T.U. per lb.; then $(1 - w)$ lb. will enter the condenser ($H_C = 930$) and, assuming this to be an ideal cycle, $(1 - w)$ lb. will appear in the hot-well and the feed line entering the heater with a total heat equal to the saturation conditions at the condenser pressure of 1 lb. per sq. in. We now make the usual assumptions, given as (1), (2) and (3*a*) in the introduction to this chapter, and write down the corresponding heat balance for the heater :

$$\text{Heat entering} = \text{Heat leaving}$$
$$1,127w + 69 \cdot 7(1 - w) = 208 \cdot 6w + 208 \cdot 6(1 - w)$$

whence,
$$w = \frac{138 \cdot 9}{1,057 \cdot 3} = 0 \cdot 131 \text{ lb.}$$

W.D. $= 1 \times (H_A - H_B) + (1 - w)(H_B - H_C)$
$= (1,312 - 1,127) + 0.869(1,127 - 930) = 356$ B.T.U. per lb.

Heat supplied externally $= 1,312 - 208.6 = 1,103.4$ B.T.U. per lb.

$$\text{Thermal } \eta = \frac{356}{1,103.4} = 32.3\%.$$

Without feed heating the cycle is simply a Rankine cycle working between the same terminal conditions.

W.D. $= H_A - H_C = 382$ B.T.U. per lb.

Heat supplied $= H_A - h_C = 1,312 - 69.7 = 1,242.3$ B.T.U. per lb.

$$\eta = \frac{382}{1,242.3} = 30.7\%.$$

The per cent. improvement is therefore

$$\frac{32.3 - 30.7}{30.7} = 5.2\%. \quad \text{Ans.}$$

2. *A steam engine exhausts into a steam turbine at a pressure of 15 lb. per sq. in., the steam being supplied to the engine at a pressure of 200 lb. per sq. in., dry saturated. The condenser pressure is 1 lb. per sq. in. A feed heater takes steam from the engine exhaust and raises the temperature of the feed water to that of the bled steam. The condensate from the heater is discharged into the hot-well at a temperature of 150° F.*

Estimate the weight of steam taken by the heater per lb. of feed and also find the thermal efficiency of the combined engine and turbine if the efficiency-ratio of each is 75%. (U. Lond.)

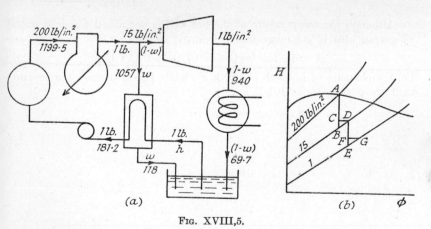

Fig. XVIII,5.

This question should be solved with the aid of the chart. In fig XVIII,5(b) $H_A = 1{,}199{\cdot}5$ at 200 lb. per sq. in., dry saturated. AB i the isentropic heat drop for the engine, so that for an efficiency ratio o 75%, $AC = 0{\cdot}75AB$, and the state of the steam leaving the engine is a' D. Similarly, the state of the steam leaving the turbine is at G. Fron the chart,

$$H_C = H_D = 1{,}057 ; \quad H_F = H_G = 940.$$

All the available information should be written on the diagram (a) above. The bled steam leaves the heater at a temperature of 150° F. ($h = 118$ B.T.U. per lb.) and discharges into the hot-well, thereby raising the sensible heat to h B.T.U. per lb. The feed enters the heater having this sensible heat h and leaves the heater at the temperature of the bled steam, which is 213° F. at 15 lb. per sq. in. (sensible heat, 181·2).

The mixing equation for the hot-well is:

$$69{\cdot}7(1 - w) + 118w = h \times 1$$

i.e. $$h = 48{\cdot}3w - 69{\cdot}7 \qquad . \qquad . \qquad . \qquad . \quad \text{(i)}$$

The heat balance for the heater is:

$$1{,}057w + h \times 1 = 118w + 181{\cdot}2 \times 1 \quad . \qquad . \quad \text{(ii)}$$

(i) in (ii), $\quad 1{,}057w + 48{\cdot}3w - 69{\cdot}7 = 118w + 181{\cdot}2$

$$w = \frac{111{\cdot}5}{987{\cdot}3} = 0{\cdot}113 \text{ lb.} \quad \text{Ans.}$$

$\text{W.D.} = 1 \text{ lb.} \times (H_A - H_D) + (1 - w)\text{lb.} \times (H_D - H_G)$
$= (1{,}199{\cdot}5 - 1{,}057) + 0{\cdot}887(1{,}057 - 940)$
$= 246{\cdot}3$ B.T.U. per lb. of steam.

Heat supplied $= 1{,}199{\cdot}5 - 181{\cdot}2 = 1{,}018{\cdot}3$ B.T.U. per lb.

$$\eta = \frac{246{\cdot}3}{1{,}018{\cdot}3} = 24{\cdot}2\%. \quad \text{Ans.}$$

Although the temperature of the hot-well is not asked for, it is useful to get an idea of its magnitude ; from (i) above

$$h = 48{\cdot}3 \times 0{\cdot}113 - 69{\cdot}7 = 75{\cdot}2 \text{ B.T.U.},$$

i.e. temperature of hot-well is 107·2° F., while the saturation temperature at 1 lb. per sq. in. is 101·7° F.

3. *A steam turbine is fitted with a regenerative feed-water heating system n which the heating is performed by steam extracted from the turbine at two different pressures. The heating steam, condensed to water in the high-pressure heater, is drained into the steam space of the low-pressure heater and, together with the water condensed in the low-pressure heater, is then drained to the condenser. The following table gives particulars of the process.*

			Total heat in B.T.U. per lb.
Steam entering turbine	. . . . .	.	1,388
,, ,, high-pressure heater	. . .	.	1,217
,, ,, low-pressure heater	. . .	.	1,117
,, ,, condenser	. . . .	.	997

			Temperatures
Feed-water entering low-pressure heater	. . .	.	82° F.
,, ,, ,, high-pressure heater	. .	.	167° F.
,, ,, leaving high-pressure heater	. .	.	253° F.
Drain-water ,, low-pressure heater	. .	.	173° F.
,, ,, ,, high-pressure heater	. .	.	260° F.

Assuming that the weight of feed-water passing through the heaters is equal to the weight of steam entering the turbine, each being 30,000 lb. per hr., find the weight of steam passing per hr. into each heater, the power developed by the steam in the turbine, and the thermal efficiency of the process.

(I.Mech.E.)

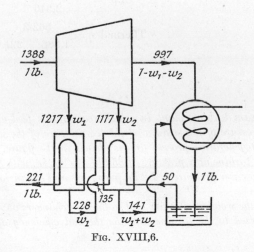

FIG. XVIII,6.

The diagram should be drawn, as above, and all available information should be written down. The student should recall that the total heats are always reckoned from 32° F. for steam, so that the various sensible heats of the water are given very nearly by $(t - 32)$. In this question it is unnecessary to make any assumptions about the temperature of the heater condensates, etc., as the actual temperatures are all given. It should be noted that a certain amount of heat is being wasted when the low-pressure heater discharges into the condenser. In some plants an after-cooler may be employed to utilize some of the 142 B.T.U. per lb. to raise the feed heat above 50 B.T.U. (cf. example no. 6 in this chapter).

Heat Balance for high-pressure heater :

$$1{,}217w_1 + 135 = 228w_1 + 221$$

whence, $$w_1 = \frac{86}{989} = 0.0870 \text{ lb. per lb. of feed.}$$

For low-pressure heater :

$$1{,}117w_2 + 228w_1 + 50 = 141(w_1 + w_2) + 135$$

$$\therefore w_2 = \frac{77.4}{976} = 0.0793 \text{ lb. per lb. of feed,}$$

i.e. $$W_1 = 0.0870 \times 30{,}000 = \underline{2{,}610 \text{ lb. per hr.}} \quad \text{Ans.}$$

and $$W_2 = \underline{2{,}380 \text{ lb. per hr.}} \quad \text{Ans.}$$

$$\begin{aligned}
\text{W.D. in turbine} &= 1 \times (1{,}388 - 1{,}217) + (1 - 0.087)(1{,}217 - 1{,}117) \\
&\quad + (1 - 0.087 - 0.0793)(1{,}117 - 997) \\
&= 171 + 91.3 + 100 = 362.3 \text{ B.T.U. per lb.}
\end{aligned}$$

$$\text{h.p.} = \frac{362.3 \times 30{,}000}{2{,}546} = \underline{4{,}270.} \quad \text{Ans.}$$

$$\text{Thermal } \eta = \frac{362.3}{1{,}388 - 221} = \underline{31\%}. \quad \text{Ans.}$$

---

4. *In a steam turbine plant in which regenerative feed-water heating is applied, the pressure of the steam and the temperature of the water at various points in the regenerative process are as shown in the figure. The steam is supplied to the turbine at a pressure of 350 lb. per sq. in. with 80° C. of superheat. The condenser pressure is 1·2 lb. per sq. in. and expansion in the turbine is isentropic.*

Determine the weights of steam bled to the interchangers at A and B per lb. of steam supplied to the turbine and the thermal efficiency of the plant.

(U. Camb.)

$$80° \text{ C. of S.H.} = 144° \text{ F. of S.H.}$$

At 300 lb. per sq. in. $\quad H = 1{,}292.6$, with 144° F. of superheat,

and at 400 lb. per sq. in. $\quad H = 1{,}299.5$, ,, ,, ,, ,,

$\therefore$ at 350 lb. per sq. in. $\quad H_1 = 1{,}296$ B.T.U. per lb.

Similarly, $\quad \phi_1 = 1.5935$.

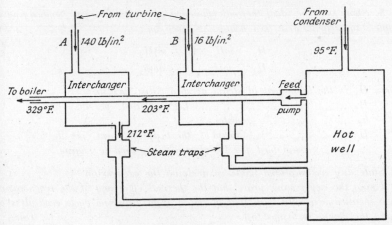

Fig. XVIII,7.

Since the expansion is to be taken as isentropic, by (I,33) at 140 lb. per sq. in.

$$H_A = 812 \cdot 7 \times 1 \cdot 5935 - 87 \cdot 0 = 1{,}208 \text{ B.T.U. per lb.}$$

At 16 lb. per sq. in.,

$$H_B = 676 \quad \times 1 \cdot 5935 - 30 \cdot 8 = 1{,}045 \text{ B.T.U. per lb.}$$

At 1·2 lb. per sq. in.,

$$H_2 = 567 \cdot 6 \times 1 \cdot 5935 - 5 \cdot 5 = 898 \cdot 5 \text{ B.T.U. per lb.}$$

for Heater A,

$$1{,}208 w_A + (203 - 32) = (329 - 32) + (212 - 32) w_A.$$

$$w_A = \frac{126}{1{,}028} = 0 \cdot 1225 \text{ lb.} \quad \text{Ans.}$$

Assuming that the condensate from heater B also leaves at 212° F.,

for Heater B, $1{,}045 w_B + h = 171 + 180 w_B$.   .   . (i)

where h is the sensible heat of the hot-well.

For the hot-well, the following mixing equation holds :

$$63(1 - 0 \cdot 1225 - w_B) + 180(0 \cdot 1225 + w_B) = 1 \times h \qquad \text{(ii)}$$

Equations (i) and (ii) can be solved to give

$$h = 88 \cdot 5 \text{ B.T.U. per lb. and } \underline{w_B = 0 \cdot 0954 \text{ lb.}} \quad \text{Ans.}$$

(Note, hot-well temperature = 120·5° F.)

$$\text{W.D.} = 1 \times (1{,}296 - 1{,}208) + (1 - 0 \cdot 1225)(1{,}208 - 1{,}045)$$
$$+ (1 - 0 \cdot 1225 - 0 \cdot 0954)(1{,}045 - 898 \cdot 5)$$

$$= 88 + 143 + 114 \cdot 5 = 345 \cdot 5 \text{ B.T.U. per lb.}$$

$$\text{Thermal } \eta = \frac{345 \cdot 5}{1{,}296 - 297} = \underline{34 \cdot 6\%}. \quad \text{Ans.}$$

5. *Show that the ideal thermal efficiency of a steam engine, embodying a single-stage regenerative feed heater, is given by :*

$$\frac{H_1 - wH - (1 - w)H_2}{H_1 - wH - (1 - w)h_2},$$

where H_1 is the total heat of steam at stop valve, per lb.

H_2 ,, ,, ,, ,, ,, ,, ,, *L.P. exhaust, per lb.*

h_2 ,, ,, ,, ,, ,, *water* ,, ,, ,, ,, ,,

H ,, ,, ,, ,, ,, *steam* ,, *the tapping point, per lb.*

w ,, ,, *steam bled per lb. of steam supplied to engine.*

State any assumptions made in deriving the expression.

Using the expression, prove that the thermal efficiency of the regenerative cycle is always greater than that of the straight Rankine cycle regardless of where the steam is tapped off. (*U. Dur.*)

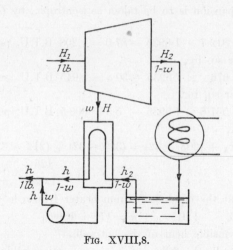

FIG. XVIII,8.

Fig. XVIII,8 illustrates this example ; h represents the sensible heat at the pressure of the bled steam. The following assumptions are made :

1. the bled steam gives up its superheat (if any) and latent heat only ;
2. the heater condensate is returned to the feed ;
3. the feed is heated to the condensation temperature of the bled steam, at which temperature it mixes with the heater condensate ;
4. the condenser does not undercool the exhaust steam.

The heat balance for the heater is

$$w\mathrm{H} + (1 - w)h_2 = wh + (1 - w)h = h.$$

$$\text{Thermal } \eta = \frac{\text{W.D.}}{\text{Heat supplied externally}}$$

$$= \frac{1 \times (\mathrm{H}_1 - \mathrm{H}) + (1 - w)(\mathrm{H} - \mathrm{H}_2)}{\mathrm{H}_1 - h}.$$

Multiplying out and substituting for h,

$$\eta = \frac{\mathrm{H}_1 - \mathrm{H} + \mathrm{H} - \mathrm{H}_2 - w\mathrm{H} + w\mathrm{H}_2}{\mathrm{H}_1 - w\mathrm{H} - (1 - w)h_2}$$

$$= \frac{\mathrm{H}_1 - w\mathrm{H} - (1 - w)\mathrm{H}_2}{\mathrm{H}_1 - w\mathrm{H} - (1 - w)h_2}. \quad \text{Q.E.D.}$$

This may be rewritten,

$$\eta = \frac{(\mathrm{H}_1 - \mathrm{H}_2) - w(\mathrm{H} - \mathrm{H}_2)}{(\mathrm{H}_1 - h_2) - w(\mathrm{H} - h_2)}.$$

The corresponding Rankine Efficiency is

$$\eta_{\mathrm{R}} = \frac{\mathrm{H}_1 - \mathrm{H}_2}{\mathrm{H}_1 - h_2}, \text{ using the same notation,}$$

$$\therefore \eta - \eta_{\mathrm{R}} = \frac{(\mathrm{H}_1 - \mathrm{H}_2) - w(\mathrm{H} - \mathrm{H}_2)}{(\mathrm{H}_1 - h_2) - w(\mathrm{H} - h_2)} - \frac{\mathrm{H}_1 - \mathrm{H}_2}{\mathrm{H}_1 - h_2}$$

$$= \frac{a - b}{c - d} - \frac{a}{c} = \frac{ad - cb}{c(c - d)}.$$

Now,
$$a \times d = w(\mathrm{H}_1 - \mathrm{H}_2)(\mathrm{H} - h_2)$$
$$= w(\mathrm{H}_1\mathrm{H} - \mathrm{H}_1 h_2 - \mathrm{H}_2\mathrm{H} + \mathrm{H}_2 h_2)$$
and
$$c \times b = w(\mathrm{H}_1\mathrm{H} - \mathrm{H}_1\mathrm{H}_2 - h_2\mathrm{H} + h_2\mathrm{H}_2)$$
$$\therefore ad - cb = w(\mathrm{H}_2 - h_2)(\mathrm{H}_1 - \mathrm{H}),$$

and since H must be less than H_1 in all cases, $ad - cb$ is positive.

In any case, $\mathrm{H}_1 - h_2 > w(\mathrm{H} - h_2)$, since $w < 1$

i.e. $c > d$

$$\therefore \frac{ad - cb}{c(c - d)} = \text{positive}$$

$$\therefore \eta > \eta_{\mathrm{R}}. \quad \text{Q.E.D.}$$

The result is independent of the bleeding pressure.

6. *A steam turbine is supplied with steam at 300 lb. per sq. in. and 200° F. of superheat and exhausts at 0·5 lb. per sq. in. Steam is bled off at 70, 20 and 4 lb. per sq. in., the bled steam being cascaded from heater to heater until it discharges through a drain cooler to the condenser. Assuming that the turbine expansion is isentropic and that the drain cooler raises the combined heater condensate to condenser temperature, find :*

(a) *the total weight of bled steam per lb. of feed ;*
(b) *the gain in efficiency over the corresponding Rankine cycle ;*
(c) *the steam consumption per h.p.-hr. with and without feed heating ;*
(d) *the amount of heat carried away by the condenser cooling water per h.p.-hr. with and without feed heating.*

(Batt. Poly.)

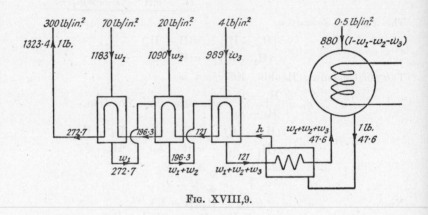

Fig. XVIII,9.

Fig. XVIII,9 is drawn, showing all the relevant information and making the usual assumptions (1) and (2) as explained in the introduction to this chapter.

The total heats of the steam may be calculated from (I,33) or read off from the chart. The student is advised to check the values given in the diagram.

(a) For heater 1, $1{,}183w_1 + 196{\cdot}3 = 272{\cdot}7w_1 + 272{\cdot}7$

$$w_1 = \frac{76{\cdot}4}{910{\cdot}3} = 0{\cdot}0839 \text{ lb.}$$

For heater 2,
$$1{,}090w_2 + 272{\cdot}7 \times 0{\cdot}0839 + 121 = 196{\cdot}3(w_1 + 0{\cdot}0839) + 196{\cdot}3$$

$$\therefore w_2 = \frac{68{\cdot}9}{893{\cdot}7} = 0{\cdot}0772 \text{ lb.}$$

For heater 3,

$$989w_3 + 196 \cdot 3(w_1 + w_2) + 1 \times h = 121(w_1 + w_2 + w_3) + 121$$

whence
$$868w_3 + h = 108 \cdot 9 \qquad . \qquad . \qquad . \qquad . \qquad \text{(i)}$$

For the drain cooler,

$$47 \cdot 6 + 121(w_1 + w_2 + w_3) = h + (w_1 + w_2 + w_3)47 \cdot 6$$

whence
$$h = 59 \cdot 4 + 73 \cdot 4w_3 \qquad . \qquad . \qquad . \qquad . \qquad \text{(ii)}$$

Equations (i) and (ii) solve for $w_3 = 0 \cdot 0526$ lb.

Total weight bled = 0·2137 lb.   Ans.

(b) Heat Drops, $1{,}323 - 1{,}183 = 140$; $1{,}183 - 1{,}090 = 93$
$1{,}090 - \quad 989 = 101$; $989 - \quad 880 = 109$

W.D. $= 140 + (0 \cdot 9161 \times 93) + (0 \cdot 8389 \times 101) + (0 \cdot 7863 \times 109)$
$= 395 \cdot 7$ B.T.U. per lb. of feed.

$$\text{Thermal } \eta = \frac{395 \cdot 7}{1{,}323 \cdot 4 - 272 \cdot 7} = 37 \cdot 6\%.$$

$$\text{Rankine } \eta = \frac{1{,}323 \cdot 4 - 880}{1{,}323 \cdot 4 - 47 \cdot 6} = \frac{443 \cdot 4}{1{,}275 \cdot 8} = 34 \cdot 7\%.$$

$$\text{Gain in } \eta = \frac{37 \cdot 6 - 34 \cdot 7}{34 \cdot 7} = 8 \cdot 4\%. \qquad \text{Ans.}$$

(c) With heaters, $\dfrac{2{,}546}{395 \cdot 7} = 6 \cdot 44$ lb. per h.p.-hr.

Without heaters, $\dfrac{2{,}546}{443 \cdot 4} = 5 \cdot 74$ lb. per h.p.-hr.   } Ans.

(d) With heaters,
Heat to condenser $= (1 - \Sigma w)(880 - 47 \cdot 6) \times 6 \cdot 44$
$= 0 \cdot 7863 \times 832 \cdot 4 \times 6 \cdot 44$
$= 4{,}220$ B.T.U. per h.p.-hr.   Ans.

Without heaters,
Heat to condenser $= 832 \cdot 4 \times 5 \cdot 74$
$= 4{,}780$ B.T.U. per h.p.-hr.   Ans.

This example shows clearly that feed heating (i) increases the thermal efficiency, (ii) requires a larger boiler capacity for a given output, and (iii) requires a reduced condenser capacity.

7. *In a binary turbine plant using mercury and steam, the mercury turbine works between limits of 160 and 3 p.s.i.a., and the steam turbine between 600 and 1 p.s.i.a. The mercury vapour is supplied to its turbine in the dry saturated condition, but the steam is superheated 200° F., its total heat and entropy being 1,342·1 and 1·5785 respectively. Steam is tapped at 60 p.s.i.a. and used for feed heating in an open type heater.*

Taking the efficiency ratio of each turbine as 80% find the quantity of mercury circulated per lb. of steam, and the thermal efficiency of the system.

Data from tables :

Fluid	Pressure, p.s.i.a.	Saturation temperature °F.	Total heat of		Entropy of	
			Liquid	Vapour	Liquid	Vapour
Mercury .	160	980	31·7	156·5	0·0358	0·1225
	3	535	17·0	145·0	0·0233	0·1521
Steam . .	600	486	471·8	1,204·2	0·6722	1·4466
	60	292	262·2	1,178·4	0·4272	1·6450
	1	102	69·7	1,105·8	0·1326	1·9783

(U. Melb.)

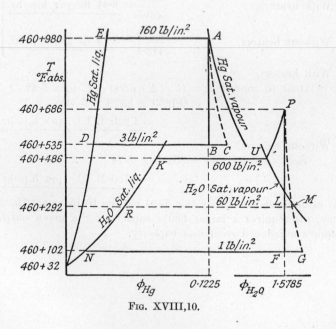

Fig. XVIII,10.

A few plants working on this cycle are in existence, but it presents many difficulties and is very expensive. It does, however, give thermal efficiency considerably higher than any yet realized in pure steam plants. The object of the cycle is to raise the evaporation temperature to the highest value allowable by the properties of the materials available, without having to raise the steam pressure to difficult values (e.g. at 695° F., $P_{sat} = 3,000$ lb. per sq. in. for steam).

In the cycle shown in fig. XVIII,10, a mercury boiler heats the liquid Hg from D to E and evaporates it to A. The vapour expands in a turbine from A to C and is condensed from C to D. The condenser coolant is the H_2O of the cycle which enters the condenser as liquid at R and leaves it as dry saturated steam at U, is superheated in the boiler from U to P, expands in a steam turbine to G and is condensed in the usual way. A single H_2O feed heater is employed, so that the liquid H_2O enters the mercury condenser at R instead of N.

Hg Cycle : $\qquad \phi_A = \phi_B = 0.1225 = 0.0233 + x_B(0.1521 - 0.0233)$

$\qquad\qquad x_B = 0.770 ; \qquad H_B = 17.0 + 0.770(145 - 17) = 115.6$

$\qquad \Delta H_T = 156.5 - 115.6 = 40.9, \quad \therefore \Delta H_U = 32.7 \text{ per lb. of Hg}$

$\qquad \therefore H_C = 123.8.$

$\qquad$ Heat rejected $= H_C - h_D = 106.8$ B.T.U. per lb. of Hg.
$\qquad$ Heat supplied $= H_A - h_D = 139.5$ B.T.U. per lb. of Hg.

H_2O Cycle :

The question requires solution by calculation, not from the chart, so that by following the above procedure, we have

$\qquad x_F = 0.783 ; \quad H_F = 881 ; \quad \Delta H_T = 461 ; \quad \Delta H_U = 369 ; \quad H_G = 973,$

and also, $\quad x_L = 0.946 ; \quad H_L = 1,129 ; \quad \Delta H_T \text{ (to 60 lb. per sq. in.)} = 213$

$\qquad \Delta H_U = 170 ; \quad H_M = 1,172.$

Assuming that w lb. of H_2O are bled for feed heating and that all the heat in the bled steam is returned to the feed via the hot-well, we have
for the hot-well, $\qquad (1 - w)69.7 + 262.2w = h$
and for the heater, $\quad 1,172w + h = 262.2 + 262.2w$
whence $\qquad\qquad w = 0.1745$ lb. per lb. of $H_2O.$

$\qquad$ W.D. $= (H_P - H_M) + (1 - w)(H_M - H_G)$
$\qquad\qquad = 170 + 0.8255(1,172 - 973) = 334.5$ B.T.U. per lb. of $H_2O.$
Heat supp. $= H_P - H_U = 1,342.1 - 1,204.2 = 137.9$ B.T.U. per lb. of $H_2O.$

(a) For thermal balance, neglecting losses,
$\qquad$ Heat given up by Hg = Heat gained by H_2O

$$(H_C - h_D)W = H_U - h_R.$$

$$\therefore W = \frac{1,204.2 - 262.2}{106.8} = 8.82 \text{ lb. of Hg per lb. of } H_2O. \quad \text{Ans.}$$

(b) Net heat supp. per lb. of H_2O

$$= (139.5 \times 8.82) + 137.9 = 1,368 \text{ B.T.U.}$$

Net W.D. per lb. of $H_2O = (32.7 \times 8.82) + 334.5 = 623 \text{ B.T.U.}$

$$\text{Thermal } \eta = \frac{623}{1,368} = \underline{45.5\%}. \text{ Ans.}$$

(Note, Carnot $\eta = \dfrac{980 - 102}{980 + 460} = 60.9\%$.)

The superheating of the steam from U to P cannot be done in the Hg condenser, as a temperature gradient is required for heat flow. The heating of the H_2O from R to K may be done in a separate heater; this reduces the lb. of Hg per lb. of H_2O and the thermal efficiency.

8. *Describe the Rankine cycle using superheated steam and show in what respects this cycle differs from the Carnot cycle between the same temperatures. Compare the values of the two efficiencies if the maximum and minimum temperatures are 750° F. and 100° F., the steam in the case of the Rankine cycle being supplied at 300 lb. per sq. in.*

Estimate the weight of steam required per h.p.-hr. and the thermal efficiency, if the Rankine cycle were modified by re-superheating the steam to 600° F. after it had been expanded to 60 lb. per sq. in. The efficiency of each expansion may be taken as 75%.   (U. Lond.)

The first part of the question is adequately answered in chapter XIV, example no. 1. Fig. XIV,1 shows the Rankine cycle using wet steam together with the corresponding Carnot cycle, while fig. XIV,3 shows two Rankine cycles using superheated steam.

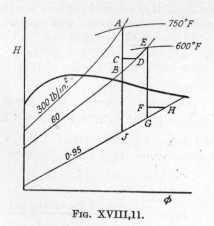

FIG. XVIII,11.

For the Carnot efficiency we have the value $\dfrac{T_1 - T_2}{T_1}$ (I,23).

$$\therefore \text{ Carnot efficiency} = \frac{750 - 100}{750 + 460}$$

$$= \underline{53 \cdot 6\%}. \quad \text{Ans.}$$

Now the saturation pressure for 100° F. is 0·95 lb. per sq. in. approx., and the work done per lb. of steam may be estimated from the total heat–entropy chart, $H_A - H_J$. $H_A = 1{,}395$, $H_J = 943$ B.T.U.

$$\therefore \text{ Rankine efficiency} = \frac{1{,}395 - 943}{1{,}395 - (100 - 32)}$$

$$= \underline{34 \cdot 0\%}. \quad \text{Ans.}$$

When the cycle is modified by re-superheating, the isentropic heat drop AB is measured and $AC = 0 \cdot 75 AB$, thus obtaining the point D representing the state of the steam entering the re-superheater. From the point E after re-superheating the steam is expanded to the condenser pressure of 0·95 lb. per sq. in., the state at entry to the condenser being shown by the point H, when allowance is made for the efficiency of expansion as before.

The values of the total heats read from the chart are :

H_A,   1,395 ; H_B, 1,221 ; H_C, H_D, 1,265 ;
H_E,   1,333 ; H_G, 1,010 ; H_F, H_H, 1,090.

$$\therefore \text{ W.D. per lb. of steam} = (H_A - H_C) + (H_E - H_F)$$
$$= (1{,}395 - 1{,}265) + (1{,}333 - 1{,}090)$$
$$= 373 \text{ B.T.U.}$$

The heat supplied per lb. of steam

$$= (H_A - h) + (H_E - H_D)$$
$$= [1{,}395 - (100 - 32)] + (1{,}333 - 1{,}265)$$
$$= 1{,}395 \text{ B.T.U.}$$

$$\therefore \text{ Thermal efficiency} = \frac{373}{1{,}395}$$

$$= \underline{26 \cdot 6\%}. \quad \text{Ans.}$$

Without re-superheating, the thermal efficiency would be
$$0 \cdot 75 \times 34 \cdot 0 = 25 \cdot 5\%,$$
allowing for the same efficiency of expansion.

$$\text{The specific consumption} = \frac{2{,}546}{373}$$

$$= \underline{6 \cdot 83} \text{ lb. per h.p.-hr.} \quad \text{Ans.}$$

9. *Steam is admitted to a plant at 400 lb. per sq. in. and 600° F. and expands adiabatically without friction to 80 lb. per sq. in. The steam is then reheated at constant pressure to 500° F. and then throttled to 40 lb. per sq. in. before admission to a low-pressure steam turbine, where it expands to 1 lb. per sq. in. with an overall efficiency of 78%.*

Draw out the complete cycle on the Hϕ chart provided, and determine (a) *the heat supplied in the reheater per lb. of steam ;* (b) *the Rankine cycle efficiency of the low-pressure turbine ;* (c) *the final dryness fraction of the steam ;* (d) *the h.p. of the low-pressure turbine for a steam flow of 2,400 lb. per hr.*

(U.L.C.I.)

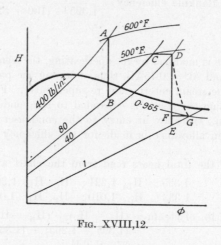

Fig. XVIII,12.

The above diagram shows the stages of the cycle. AB is the high-pressure expansion which takes place adiabatically and without loss, i.e. isentropically. Reheating takes place at constant pressure from B to C, CD represents the throttling operation, and DE is the isentropic heat drop for the low-pressure turbine. The term " overall efficiency " is here used in the sense of " efficiency of expansion " or " internal efficiency " (cf. introduction to chapter XVI). Hence, the useful heat drop is DF = 0·78DE, and the state of the steam leaving the low-pressure turbine is at G, where FG is horizontal. The condition line will be approximately DG.

The following values can be read off the chart (B.T.U. per lb.) :

$$H_A = 1,306 \; ; \quad H_B = 1,158 \; ; \quad H_C = 1,281 = H_D \; ;$$
$$H_E = 1,010 \; ; \quad H_F = H_G = 1,070.$$

(a)　　　　　Heat supplied in reheater $= H_C - H_B$

　　　　　　　　　　　　　　$= $ <u>123 B.T.U. per lb.</u>　Ans.

(b) Rankine η for low-pressure turbine, based upon conditions after the reducing valve

$$= \frac{H_D - H_E}{H_D - h_E}$$

$$= \frac{1,281 - 1,010}{1,281 - 69 \cdot 7} = \underline{22 \cdot 4\%}. \quad \text{Ans.}$$

(c) $\qquad\qquad\qquad\qquad\qquad\qquad x_G = 0 \cdot 965. \quad \text{Ans.}$

(d) $\qquad\qquad\qquad\qquad \text{h.p.} = \frac{2,400}{2,546} \times (H_D - H_G).$

$$\text{h.p.} = \frac{2,400 \times 211}{2,546} = \underline{199}. \quad \text{Ans.}$$

EXAMPLES

1. Explain how the regenerative cycle efficiency may approach the Carnot cycle efficiency.

A compound steam engine uses dry saturated steam at 160 lb. per sq. in. abs. and exhausts at 3 lb. per sq. in. abs. Receiver pressure is 60 lb. per sq. in. abs. Steam is taken from the receiver to heat the feed up to a temperature equal to the saturation temperature at receiver pressure. Determine the thermal efficiency of the cycle and the percentage of steam entering the receiver which must be used for feed heating. *Deduce any formulæ used.* (*U. Witw.*)

[H of bled steam = 1,119 B.T.U. per lb., assuming frictionless adiabatic expansion; % of steam bled = 15·1; th. η = 25·5%.]

2. In a steam plant a single bleed is taken from between the high-pressure and low-pressure sections of the turbine for regenerative feed heating.

The H.P. section is supplied with steam at 500 lb./in.² and 607° F. and exhausts at 20 lb./in.² direct to the L.P. section which in turn exhausts at 1·2 lb./in.². The efficiency ratio of both sections is 80%. There is a difference of 23° F. between the bleed temperature and that of the outlet feed water.

Determine, *using steam tables only*:

(a) the amount of bleed per lb. of main flow through the boiler;
(b) the work output per lb. of main flow. (*U. Sheff.*)

[ΔH_U = 210 and 133·7 B.T.U. per lb.; w = 0·0956 lb.; W.D. = 331 B.T.U. per lb. main flow.]

3. A steam plant, operating between pressures of 600 lb. per sq. in. with 150° F. superheat and 0·6 lb. per sq. in., employs regenerative feed heating. The feed water leaving the hot-well passes through two heaters in succession. The steam for the heaters is bled from the turbine at 100 and 20 lb. per sq. in., and the condensed steam leaving the heaters is pumped into the feed-pipe at points immediately after each heater. Draw a diagram of the arrangement, and add the pressures and total heats at the various parts of the cycle. Assuming that the feed-water leaves each heater at the temperature of the condensing steam,

A.T.E. $\qquad\qquad\qquad\qquad\qquad\qquad\qquad\qquad\qquad\qquad\qquad\qquad\qquad$ X and that the efficiency ratio of the turbine is 0·75 throughout, find the weights of steam bled and the thermal efficiency of the turbine.   (*U. Lond.*)

[Total heats of bled steam = 1,185 and 1,095 B.T.U. respectively ; $w_1 = 0·104$ lb. ; $w_2 = 0·1226$ lb. ; W.D. = 329 B.T.U. per lb. of steam passing through boiler ; $\eta = 32·4\%$.]

4. A boiler supplies 20,000 lb. of steam per hr. at 230 lb./in.^{2} abs. 140° F. superheat to a triple expansion engine and its auxiliaries. Expansion takes place to 3·3 lb./in.^{2} abs., and 10% of the total boiler steam is required for its auxiliaries, the exhaust steam from which is used to raise the feed water temperature to 200° F. If the efficiency ratio for the engine is 0·72, calculate its thermal efficiency.

An exhaust steam turbine interposed between the L.P. cylinder and the condenser enables the vacuum to be raised to 29 in. with a barometric height of 30 in. If the turbine is coupled to the main driving shaft of the engine, and its efficiency ratio is 0·65, calculate the saving in lb. steam/hr./h.p. output, assuming that bled steam at 3·3 lb./in.^{2} abs. is used to raise the condensate temperature to the saturation temperature at 3·3 lb./in.^{2} abs., and the exhaust steam from the auxiliaries is available to heat the feed water, as in the case of the engine before the addition of the turbine.   (*U. Manch.*)

[$\Delta H_U = 226$ B.T.U. per lb. ;   thermal $\eta = 18·2\%$;   0·0590 lb. of steam are bled at 3·3 lb. per sq. in. per lb. of boiler steam ;   W.D. = 261·7 B.T.U. per lb. of boiler steam ;   saving = 2·78 lb. per h.p.-hr. Assume condensate from heaters is returned to feed.]

5. A multi-stage steam turbine has to be provided with two stages of bleed heating. The temperature rise of the feed has to be divided equally between the two heaters. Initial steam pressure is 400 lb. per sq. in. abs. with 160° F. of superheat. Exhaust pressure is 1 lb. per sq. in. abs. Temperature of condensate is 95° F. The first tapping is made at 30 lb. per sq. in. abs. Determine the pressure for the second tapping point and the quantities to be tapped at each point. Determine the gain in efficiency due to bleed heating and the increase in consumption rate. Use a stage efficiency of 70%.   (*U. Witw.*)

[P for second tapping = 6·4 lb. per sq. in. ; $w_1 = 0·0770$ lb. ; $w_2 = 0·0706$ lb. per lb. of main flow ; with bleed heating W.D. = 155 + 69·2 + 65·6 = 289·8 B.T.U. per lb. of main flow ; $\eta = 26·6\%$; without bleed heating, but still with 3 stages W.D. = 307 B.T.U. per lb. ; $\eta = 24·6\%$; increase = 2·0% ; increase in consumption rate = 0·50 lb. per h.p.-hr.]

6. Discuss partial admission in connection with turbine stages. A marine turbine receives steam at 400 lb. per sq. in., 170° C. superheat and exhausts at 0·7 lb. per sq. in., 0·9 dryness fraction. The shaft horse-power is 10,000, the loss of work due to steam tapped to heat the feed water 12% and the external losses 6% of the isentropic heat drop. Determine the steam flow in lb. per sec.

The inlet end of the H.P. cylinder consists of a two-row velocity-compounded stage followed by a group of reaction stages of uniform blade height and uniform diameter. The turbine speed is 2,500 r.p.m. and the pressure drop due to adiabatic throttling in the inlet valves is 25 lb. per sq. in. The velocity-compounded stage has a mean diameter of 38 in., the value of ρ which is the ratio blade velocity to velocity corresponding to isentropic heat drop in the nozzles is 0·23, the effective exit angle of the nozzles 20°, the nozzle velocity coefficient 0·98, the steam admitted over a nozzle arc of 100°, and the stage efficiency 70%. The group of reaction stages has a mean diameter 22 in., blade exit angle 20°, effective ρ 0·80 approximately, exit pressure from group 170 lb. per sq. in. and internal efficiency

85%. Determine (a) the exit pressure and the nozzle exit height for the velocity-compounded stage, (b) the number of stages and the blade height for the group of reaction stages.

Assume, for the reaction stages, that the relative velocity at exit from the blades is equal to that corresponding to the isentropic heat drop in the blade ring, and for superheated steam $PV = 2 \cdot 24(I - 464)$ where P is in lb. per sq. in., V in cu. ft. per lb. and I in C.H.U. per lb. (U. Camb.)

[$\Delta H_T = 478 \cdot 7$ B.T.U. per lb. ; external losses $= 86 \cdot 2$; $\Delta H_U = 393 \cdot 4$; W.D. on shaft $= 307 \cdot 2$ B.T.U. per lb. ; $\underline{W = 23 \cdot 0 \text{ lb. per sec.}}$

Impulse : Assume $0 \cdot 98$ is nozzle efficiency (i.e. $\Delta H_U = 0 \cdot 98 \Delta H_T$) ; $\Delta H_T = 64 \cdot 7$; by trial : $\underline{P = 217 \text{ lb. per sq. in.}}$ at exit from nozzles ; do. $V = 2 \cdot 83$ cu. ft. per lb. ; total normal area of nozzles $= 5 \cdot 25$ sq. in. ; $\underline{\text{height of nozzles} = 0 \cdot 462 \text{ in.}}$, neglecting division plate.

Reaction : H entering stage $= 1,344 \cdot 6$ B.T.U. per lb. ; $\Delta H_U = 24 \cdot 9$; from velocity dia., $cw = 324$ ft. per sec. ; diagram W.D. per lb. $= 3 \cdot 1$ B.T.U. per lb. ; $\underline{\text{no. of stages} = 8}$; H at exit $= 1,319 \cdot 7$; V at exit $= 3 \cdot 54$ cu. ft. per lb. ; $\underline{\text{blade height} = 1 \cdot 66 \text{ in.}}$]

7. Two stages of feed heating are employed in a steam turbine installation, steam being bled for these at pressures of 50 and 10 lb. per sq. in. It may be assumed that the temperature of the feed is raised to that of the bled steam and that the condensate from each heater is returned, by means of separate drain pumps, to the feed water at points immediately upstream of each heater. The condensate from each heater may be taken as being at the same temperature as the feed entering the heater.

The steam is supplied to the turbine at 250 lb. per sq. in. with 40° F. superheat, and the condenser pressure is 1 lb. per sq. in. The stage efficiency between 250 and 50 lb. per sq. in. is $0 \cdot 7$, and in the other two stages $0 \cdot 65$.

Estimate :

(a) the weight of steam bled for each heater per lb. of steam supplied to the turbine ;
(b) the total work done per lb. of steam supplied to the turbine ;
(c) the overall thermal efficiency of the cycle. (Batt. Poly.)

[Stage ΔH_T's 130, 112, 135 B.T.U. ; ditto ΔH_U's 91, $72 \cdot 8$, $87 \cdot 8$; H entering heaters, 1,137, 1,064 B.T.U. ; $w_1 = 0 \cdot 0914$ lb., $w_2 = 0 \cdot 0837$ lb. ; W.D. per lb. supplied to turbine $= \underline{229 \cdot 5 \text{ B.T.U.}}$; $\underline{\eta = 23 \cdot 5\%}$.]

8. Give a brief explanation of the objects of regenerative feed heating as applied to a multi-stage steam turbine.

A four-stage pressure-compounded turbine is supplied with steam at 160 lb. per sq. in. (abs.) and of 20° F. superheat, the pressure at exhaust being $2 \cdot 5$ lb. per sq. in. (abs.). The stage efficiency is 73%, the reheat factor is $R = 1 \cdot 03$, and the work done in each stage per lb. of steam is the same. If steam for regenerative feed heating is tapped off after the first three stages, estimate the quantity of steam to be withdrawn in each case and the theoretical gain in thermal efficiency through use of the heaters. (U. Birm.)

[Rankine $\Delta H = 278$; ΔH_U per stage $= 52 \cdot 2$; H of bled steam 1,156, 1,103, 1,051 respectively at 65, 24, and 8 lb. per sq. in. Assuming that the condensate from each heater is cascaded to the succeeding heater and finally into the hot-well, $w_1 = 0 \cdot 0688$ lb., $w_2 = 0 \cdot 0570$ lb., $w_3 = 0 \cdot 0375$ lb. per lb. of main feed ; (N.B., h of hot-well $= 110 \cdot 1$ B.T.U. per lb.) W.D. $= 190 \cdot 3$ B.T.U. per lb. of main feed ; $\eta = 20 \cdot 2\%$, an increase of $1 \cdot 3\%$ over the efficiency without heaters.]

CHAPTER XIX

REFRIGERATION

Introduction

It is assumed that the student has already acquired some understanding about the general methods of refrigeration and the types of refrigerants commonly used. Only vapour-compression refrigerators are usually considered in connection with numerical examples in courses of the scope described in the preface. The so-called " Bell-Coleman " type of machine is, of course, readily amenable to theoretical investigation as it only consists of an air compressor in conjunction with an air motor ; this type of machine is not now used very extensively.

A student's ability to master this topic is greatly dependent upon an understanding of the general properties of vapours (cf. chapter I) together with a sound knowledge of temperature–entropy, total heat–entropy, and total heat–pressure diagrams for the vapours concerned. Ample sketches of these diagrams are given below and, wherever applicable, solutions should not be attempted until a diagram has been drawn and understood.

Reference was made in chapter I, page 16, to the matter of choosing a datum for E for refrigeration vapours. The datum of E for steam is invariably taken at 32° F. and this is generally satisfactory for engineering applications. But refrigeration vapours will commonly be at temperatures lower than 32° F., so that we shall have to deal with negative values of internal energy, total heat, and also of entropy. This usually presents an artificial difficulty to learners and often leads to arithmetical complications due to the method of construction of a T–ϕ diagram. Consequently, it is becoming more customary, both in the trade and examinations, to refer E to some lower datum which will, in general, be below the lowest working temperature of the refrigerant in an engineering application. The temperature chosen is − 40° F. (which is the same as − 40° C.), and the internal energy of refrigerants is now commonly referred to that temperature. For steam it was shown in chapter I that H at 32° F. was negligibly small, due to the small value of saturation pressure. The same conclusion does not necessarily apply to refrigerants. In each case the value of $\dfrac{PV}{J}$ must be found at datum in order to find the magnitude of

$H = E + \dfrac{PV}{J}$ at datum. Examples will be worked with the datum at − 40° F. and also at + 32° F.

Definition :

$$\text{Coefficient of Performance} = \frac{\text{Heat abstracted}}{\text{Work required}}.$$

This ratio will normally be greater than unity, hence it is not called an efficiency. As a ratio it merely indicates the number of B.T.U. abstracted from the cold space or body per B.T.U. of work done to produce this effect.

The cycle of events for vapour-compression machines resembles a reversed Rankine cycle and may be traced on three forms of chart, (a) temperature–entropy, (b) total heat–entropy, and (c) pressure–total heat. The $T\phi$ chart (a) is generally used in a descriptive manner only, and modern practice turns to the use of the PH chart (c) for numerical values rather than the $H\phi$ chart (b). The shape and proportions of these charts naturally depend upon the physical characteristics of the refrigerating fluid and the three charts shown below are to be considered as generalizations only. The pressure scale of the PH chart is often logarithmic.

The wet fluid at B at the lower pressure P_2 is compressed adiabatically and isentropically to the state A, chosen in this case as dry saturated vapour at the upper pressure P_1. The work done during this isentropic compression is $H_A - H_B$, since the process is a flow-process involving the introduction and delivery of the fluid as well as the phase-work of compression (cf. I,37). $H_A - H_B$ is easily read off charts (ii) and (iii), but is represented by the " Rankine cycle area " ABFCA on (a) which would necessitate the use of a planimeter for direct measurement, or could be calculated as explained in chapter XIV. The vapour at A is passed into the condenser and the latent heat is removed by the cooling water, bringing the fluid to a saturated liquid at C. Generally, this liquid is undercooled at the pressure P_1 to the point D. This high-pressure liquid at D is usually passed through a throttle-valve to the lower pressure P_2, the process being one of constant total heat readily shown on (b) and (c) as D to E. Notice that the work done in the cycle is $H_A - H_B$, and this is not in any way affected by the throttling conditions, and the area on (a) BACDE is *not* equal to the work done.

The very wet vapour at E now absorbs heat at the lower temperature in the evaporator (producing the refrigeration effect), and leaves the evaporator in the state B. The refrigeration effect produced is $H_B - H_E$.

For " dry "[1] compression, when the vapour is superheated at delivery from the compressor, the compression is denoted by B'A'. For " wet " compression, the conditions are shown by B"A". Generally in practice the vapour is moderately superheated after compression and the liquid is undercooled as much as possible before throttling.

In general, the phase CD is virtually coincident with the liquid line on the $T\phi$ and $H\phi$ diagrams but, being at constant pressure, is shown as a distinct horizontal line on the PH diagram.

[1] In some countries, the term " dry " compression is used when the vapour is dry saturated at suction to the compressor.

The constant temperature lines in the liquid region of the PH diagram (e.g. t_D in diagram (c)) are very nearly vertical for some refrigerants and may be virtually coincident with lines of constant total heat.

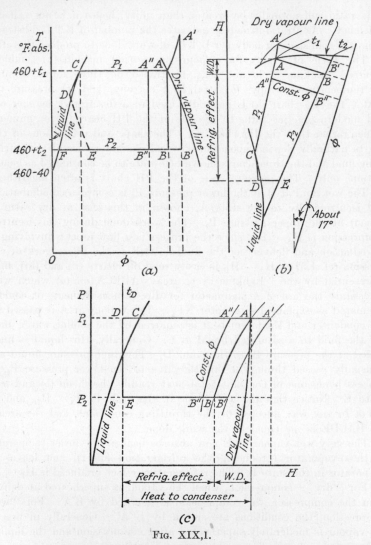

Fig. XIX,1.

If the T–ϕ diagram is used for numerical work, it should be remembered that the refrigeration effect = area under EB is $(\phi_B - \phi_E)\, T_E$, where T is in degrees F. *absolute*, i.e. the area must be measured down to zero degrees absolute. This is entirely independent of the datum for ϕ and E, and applies equally to the heat removed in the condenser from A to D.

1. *An ammonia refrigerator operates on the simple throttling cycle. The liquid ammonia before throttling is at 175 lb. per sq. in. abs. and its temperature is 81° F. (27·2° C.). The evaporator pressure (assumed uniform throughout) is 36 lb. per sq. in. abs. and the gas leaves the evaporator at 15° F. (— 9·5° C.). The i.h.p. of the compressor is 2·84. The weight of ammonia circulating per min. is 0·96 lb.*

Calculate : (a) the dryness fraction of the gas after passing through the throttle ; (b) the heat absorbed per min. in the evaporator ; and (c) the coefficient of performance of the refrigerator. Use the data given below :

Pressure, lb. per sq. in. abs.	Saturation temperature, ° F.	Total heat, B.T.U. per lb. liquid	gas
36	7·1	49·5	614·0
175	88·0	139·5	—

The specific heat of the liquid at 175 lb. per sq. in. abs. is 1·14. The specific heat of the vapour at 36 lb. per sq. in. abs., at constant pressure, is 0·60.

(*I.Mech.E.*)

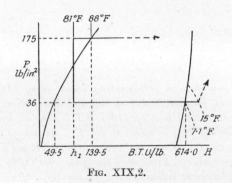

Fɪɢ. XIX,2.

All the available information should be recorded on a diagram, as above.

Before reaching the throttle the temperature is $88 - 81 = 7°$ F. below the saturation temperature. So the total heat of the liquid before throttling is

$$139·5 - 1·14 \times 7 = 131·5 \text{ B.T.U.} = h_1.$$

The total heat of the fluid when throttled to 36 lb. per sq. in. will have the same value, and since the liquid heat at this pressure is 49·5 B.T.U., some of the liquid will have been vaporized. Let the dryness be x, then :

$$131·5 = 49·5 + x(614 - 49·5).$$

$\underline{x = 0·145 \text{ dry.}}$ **Ans.** *(a).*

On leaving the evaporator the fluid must be superheated, since the temperature is 15° F. whereas the saturation temperature is 7·1° F.

$$\therefore \text{ Total heat leaving evaporator} = 614 + 0.6 \times 7.9$$
$$= 618.7 \text{ B.T.U.}$$

$\therefore$ Refrigeration effect per lb. $= 618.7 - 131.5 = 487.2$ B.T.U.
$\therefore$ Heat absorbed per min. in the evaporator $= 0.96 \times 487.2$

$$= \underline{468 \text{ B.T.U.}} \quad \text{Ans. } (b).$$

The W.D. per min. by the compressor $= 2.84 \times 42.4 = 120.5$ B.T.U.

$$\therefore \text{ Coefficient of performance} = \frac{468}{120.5} = \underline{3.88}. \quad \text{Ans. } (c).$$

It is not possible to plot the complete cycle on a diagram since there are insufficient data to find the state of the vapour after compression. Almost certainly the compression would not have been isentropic, since this would have resulted in excessive superheat.

2. *A vapour compression refrigerating plant using CO_2 as the working agent, works between pressure limits of 960 and 360 p.s.i.a. The CO_2 leaves the compressor with a total heat of 110·5 B.T.U. per lb. and entropy 0·200. After condensation, the CO_2 is cooled to 70° F. Assuming compression to be adiabatic, find the work done and the refrigerating effect per lb. of CO_2, and the coefficient of performance. Find also the mass of CO_2 to be circulated per min. and the displacement volume in cu. ft. per min. of an ideal compressor for a refrigerating effect of 1,000 B.T.U. per min.*

Data from CO_2 tables :

Pressure, p.s.i.a.	Saturation temperature ° F.	Total Heat of		Entropy of		Specific volume of	
		Liquid	Vapour	Liquid	Vapour	Liquid	Vapour
960	80	37·2	84·7	0·065	0·154	0·024	0·062
360	10	−9·7	103·0	−0·022	0·218	0·017	0·245

Specific heat of liquid CO_2 at 960 p.s.i.a. can be taken as 1·2. In the above tables, total heats and entropies are reckoned from 32° F.

(U. Melb.)

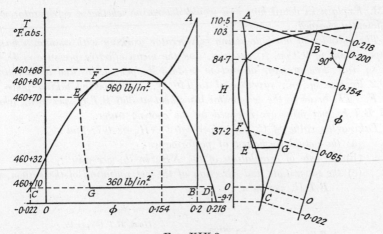

Fig. XIX,3.

This problem demonstrates the case when the datum is at 32° F. and the liquid heats and entropies below this temperature are negative.

First, note that the CO_2 after compression is superheated as the total entropy is greater than that for saturation.

$$H_B = h + xL = h + CB \times 470$$
$$= - 9.7 + (0.200 + 0.022)470 = 94.7.$$

∴ W.D. per lb. of CO_2 = $H_A - H_B$ = $110.5 - 94.7$ = $\underline{15.8 \text{ B.T.U.}}$ Ans.

The liquid is undercooled to the point E,

and $h_E = h_F - 1.2 \times 10 = 37.2 - 12.0 = 25.2.$

EG is a throttling process, so that $h_E = H_G$.

Refrig. effect per lb. = $94.7 - 25.2 = \underline{69.5 \text{ B.T.U.}}$ Ans.

$$\text{Coeff. of Perf.} = \frac{69.5}{15.8} = \underline{4.40.}$$ Ans.

$$\text{Mass of } CO_2 \text{ per min.} = \frac{1,000}{69.5} = \underline{14.4 \text{ lb.}}$$ Ans.

$$x_B = \frac{CB}{CD} = \frac{0.022 + 0.200}{0.022 + 0.218} = 0.925.$$

Vol. per lb. at B = $0.245 \times 0.925 + 0.017 \times 0.075 = 0.228$ cu. ft.

Swept vol. per min. = $0.228 \times 14.4 = \underline{3.28 \text{ cu. ft.}}$ Ans.

This assumes 100% volumetric efficiency and is therefore applicable to an " ideal " machine.

3. *Explain in detail how you would determine whether a refrigerator was sufficiently charged.*

The cylinder of a single-acting refrigerator working with ammonia has a swept volume of 9·9 cu. ft. per min. and the mean effective pressure is 48 lb. per sq. in. The pressure at suction is 34·3 lb. per sq. in. and at discharge 169·2 lb. per sq. in., superheated to 140° F., undercooling taking place to 68° F. The brine in the evaporator loses heat at 356 B.T.U. per min., while 453 B.T.U. per min. are removed by the cooling water.

Taking the value of C_p for superheated NH_3 as 0·7, find :

    (a) *the actual coefficient of performance ;*

    (b) *the rate of circulation of the NH_3 in lb. per min. ;*

    (c) *the magnitude and direction of the net radiation of the system, in B.T.U. per min.*

P lb. per sq. in.	Saturation temperature, ° F.	Heat, B.T.U. per lb.	
		Liquid h	Latent L
169·2	86	138·9	492·6
124·3	68	118·3	510·5
34·3	5	48·3	565·0

(U. Lond.)

If the total charge is small, then the amount of liquid in the evaporator will be small and refrigeration will only be taking place at the section near the throttle-valve, the remainder of the evaporator being ineffective. Also, with too small a charge, the compressor suction becomes starved and the suction pressure falls. This causes a large range of compression in the compressor, and the delivery may become excessively superheated.

The W.D. per min. = m.e.p. × volume per min.

$$= (48 \times 144) \times \frac{9 \cdot 9}{778}$$

$$= 87 \cdot 9 \text{ B.T.U.}$$

Since the refrigeration effect is 356 B.T.U. per min., the coefficient of performance is

$$\frac{356}{87 \cdot 9} = \underline{4 \cdot 05}. \quad \text{Ans. } (a).$$

(Note especially that the 68° F. temp. line is practically vertical, so that $h_B = h_A = H_C$.)

The heat removed per lb. in the condenser is (i) superheat, (ii) latent heat, (iii) sensible heat at 169·2 lb. per sq. in.

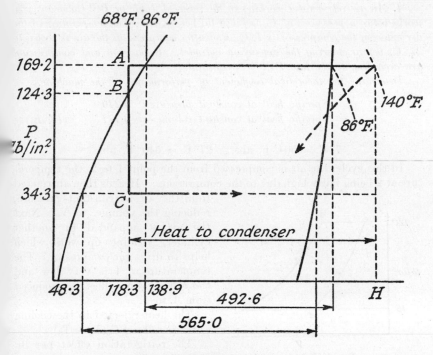

Fig. XIX,4.

$$\therefore \text{ Heat per lb. to condenser} = 0.7(140 - 86) + 492.6 + (138.9 - 118.3)$$
$$= 37.8 + 492.6 + 20.6$$
$$= 551.0 \text{ B.T.U. per lb.}$$

$$\therefore \text{ Weight of NH}_3 \text{ per min.} = \frac{453}{551}$$
$$= 0.822 \text{ lb. per min.} \quad \text{Ans. } (b).$$

The heat input *into* the system is the refrigeration effect plus the work supplied to the compressor. The heat *output* is that to the condensing water.

$$\text{Heat outwards per min.} = 453 \text{ B.T.U. per min.}$$
$$\text{Heat inwards per min.} = 356 + 87.9$$
$$= 443.9 \text{ B.T.U. per min.}$$
$$\therefore \text{ Radiation } \textit{into} \text{ the system} = 453 - 443.9$$
$$= 9.1 \text{ B.T.U. per min.} \quad \text{Ans. } (c).$$

4. *An air refrigerator working in the reversed Joule or Bell-Coleman cycle works between pressures of 15 and 120 lb. per sq. in. The temperature of the air entering the compressor is 7° C., and after compression the air is cooled to 27° C. before entering the expansion cylinder. Expansion and compression are according to the law $PV^{1\cdot35} =$ constant.*
Determine the theoretical coefficient of performance of the machine.

$$\text{Specific heat at constant pressure} = 0\cdot240$$
$$\text{Specific heat at constant volume} \;\; = 0\cdot171 \qquad (I.C.E.)$$

$$7° \text{ C.} = 504° \text{ F. abs. ;} \quad 27° \text{ C.} = 540° \text{ F. abs.}$$

In this cycle, the air is compressed from the point 1 to 2, the temperature at 2 being fairly high due to the compression. Heat is then abstracted

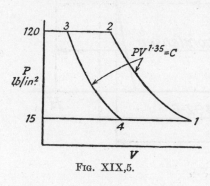

FIG. XIX,5.

from the air at constant pressure, reducing the volume to V_3. Next the air is expanded in another cylinder, yielding up work which helps to drive the compressor. The temperature at 4 is very low and the refrigeration effect is produced from 4 to 1.

The heat rejected to the cooling water per lb. $= C_p(T_2 - T_3)$.

The refrigeration effect per lb. $= C_p(T_1 - T_4)$.

The net W.D. per lb. is the area of the indicator diagram, and must not be taken as the difference between the above quantities of heat, since neither the compression nor the expansion is adiabatic. If the compression and expansion had been adiabatic, it would have been possible to evaluate the W.D. in this manner. From (III,2)

$$\text{W.D. per lb.} = \frac{n}{n-1}\cdot R\Big[(T_2 - T_1) - (T_3 - T_4)\Big].$$

$$T_1 = 504 \quad \text{and} \quad T_2 = 504 \times \left(\frac{120}{15}\right)^{\frac{0\cdot35}{1\cdot35}}, \text{ by (I,18)}$$

$$= 865° \text{ F. abs.}$$

$$T_3 = 540 \quad \text{and} \quad T_4 = 540 \div \left(\frac{120}{15}\right)^{\frac{0\cdot35}{1\cdot35}}$$

$$= 315° \text{ F. abs.}$$

$\therefore$ Refrigeration effect per lb. of air $= 0\cdot24(504 - 315)$
$$= 45\cdot4 \text{ B.T.U. per lb.}$$

$$R = (0\cdot24 - 0\cdot17)J = 0\cdot07J.$$

$$\therefore \text{ W.D. per lb.} = \frac{1 \cdot 35}{0 \cdot 35} \times 0 \cdot 07 \times [(865 - 504) - (540 - 31 \, 5)]$$

$$= 36 \cdot 75 \text{ B.T.U. per lb.}$$

$$\therefore \text{ Coefficient of performance} = \frac{45 \cdot 4}{36 \cdot 75}$$

$$= \underline{1 \cdot 24 \text{ nearly.}} \quad \text{Ans.}$$

It should be noted that the refrigeration effect per lb. of air is relatively small compared with that produced by 1 lb. of fluid on the vapour compression cycle, so that the size of plant required on the Bell-Coleman cycle is disproportionately large in the case of reciprocating machines.

5. *An ammonia vapour compression refrigerator works between the pressures of 50 and 160 lb. per sq. in. ; and the temperature at which the vapour leaves the compressor is 120° F., the total heat under these conditions being 657·8 B.T.U. per lb. After condensation the liquid at a temperature of 60° F. with a liquid heat of 109·2 B.T.U. per lb. is passed through a throttle valve to the evaporator.*

Sketch the cycle on a pressure–total heat diagram giving the values for the various stages of the cycle. Find the refrigeration effect per h.p.-hr. and compare this value with that which would have been achieved if the vapour left the compressor in a dry saturated condition.

The saturation temperatures for the above pressures are 21·67° F. and 82·64° F. respectively. At 160 lb. per sq. in. the total heat and total entropy under saturation conditions are 631·1 B.T.U. per lb. and 1·1952 ; and at 50 lb. per sq. in. the liquid heat and liquid entropy are 66·5 B.T.U. per lb. and 0·1475. (U. Lond.)

When the diagram has been drawn and all available information recorded on it, the problem largely resolves itself into finding H_4 ; this in turn depends on ϕ_4 which equals ϕ_1 and we must work from first principles ; for

$$d\phi = \frac{dQ}{T} = \frac{C_p \, dT}{T} \text{ per lb., at const. pressure, except during evaporation,}$$

i.e., here
$$\phi_1 - \phi_5 = C_p \log_e \frac{T_1}{T_5}, \text{ fig. XIX,6,}$$

where C_p is the mean specific heat of the vapour at 160 lb. per sq. in. between 120 and 82·64° F.

But, $$H_1 - H_5 = C_p(T_1 - T_5)$$

$$\therefore C_p = \frac{657 \cdot 8 - 631 \cdot 1}{120 - 82 \cdot 64} = 0 \cdot 715$$

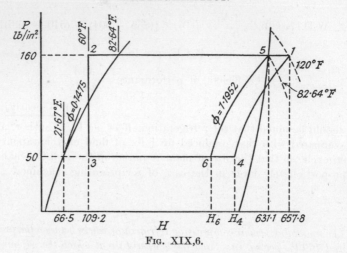

Fig. XIX,6.

whence, $\qquad \phi_1 - \phi_5 = 0\cdot715 \log_e \dfrac{580}{542\cdot6} = 0\cdot715 \log_e \dfrac{2}{1\cdot87}$

$$\phi_1 = 1\cdot1952 + 0\cdot715 \times 0\cdot068 = 1\cdot2438 = \phi_4.$$

Now, $\qquad\qquad \phi_4 = \phi_l + x_4\phi_L = \phi_l + x_4\dfrac{L}{T},$

where ϕ_l refers to the entropy of the liquid,

i.e. $\qquad\qquad 1\cdot2438 = 0\cdot1475 + \dfrac{x_4 L}{481\cdot7} \; ; \quad x_4 L = 528.$

$$H_4 = 66\cdot5 + 528 = 594\cdot5.$$

Refrigerating effect $= 594\cdot5 - 109\cdot2 = 485\cdot3$ B.T.U. per lb.

$\qquad\qquad$ W.D. $= 657\cdot8 - 594\cdot5 = \;\; 63\cdot3$ B.T.U. per lb.

$$\therefore \frac{2,546}{63\cdot3} \times 485\cdot3 = \underline{19{,}550 \text{ B.T.U.}} \text{ of refrig. effect per h.p.-hr.} \quad \text{Ans.}$$

Also, $\qquad\qquad x_6 L = (1\cdot1952 - 0\cdot1475)481\cdot7 = 505$

$\qquad\qquad\qquad$ $H_6 = 66\cdot5 + 505 = 571\cdot5.$

$\qquad \therefore$ New W.D. $= 631\cdot1 - 571\cdot5 = 59\cdot6.$

$\qquad\qquad$ New R.E. $= 571\cdot5 - 109\cdot2 = 462\cdot3$

and $\qquad\qquad \dfrac{2,546}{59\cdot6} \times 462\cdot3 = \underline{19{,}750 \text{ B.T.U.}} \text{ of R.E. per h.p.-hr.} \quad \text{Ans.}$

6. *A vapour compression refrigerator works between the temperatures of 23° F. and 50° F., the vapour being just dry saturated at 50° F. at the end of compression. The liquid is cooled to 45° F. before being throttled to the evaporator pressure. Assuming that the compression is carried out adiabatically, determine the refrigeration effect produced by 1 lb. of the working fluid in passing through the cycle.*

The latent heat of the working fluid is 556 B.T.U. at 50° F. and 574 B.T.U. at 23° F., and the mean specific heat of the liquid is 0·91 over this range of temperature.

If, at the lower temperature, the pressure–temperature curve has a slope such that

$$\frac{dT}{dP} = 0.88,$$

P being in lb. per sq. in., find the volume entering the compressor per min. when the refrigeration produced is 200,000 B.T.U. per hr. Neglect the volume of the liquid. (*U. Lond.*)

In this problem it will be easiest to use the temperature–entropy diagram. 32° F. will be taken as the datum, but the student is strongly advised to rework the problem using 23° F. as the datum ; the datum should not here be chosen at − 40° F., as the mean specific heat of the liquid is only given between 23 and 50° F. and a small error will be introduced by using the figure of 0·91 over the range − 40 to 50° F.

It will be necessary to calculate the entropy at A, fig. XIX,7,

$$\phi_A = \phi_l + \phi_L$$

$$= 0.91 \log_e \frac{510}{492} + \frac{556}{510}$$

$$= 0.0325 + 1.09 = 1.1225.$$

At 23° F., $\qquad \phi_l = 0.91 \log_e \frac{483}{492} = -0.017.$

$$H_B = h + xL, \quad \text{but } xL = \text{area under DB,}$$
$$\therefore \ H_B = -(0.91 \times 9) + 1.1395 \times 483 = 542.2 \text{ B.T.U.}$$
and $h_C = 0.91(45 - 32) = 11.8$ B.T.U., assuming C is on the liquid line.
$$\therefore \text{ Refrigeration effect per lb.} = H_B - H_C$$
$$= 542.2 - 11.8$$
$$= \underline{530.4 \text{ B.T.U. per lb.}} \quad \text{Ans.}$$

To produce 200,000 B.T.U. per hr.,

$$\text{Weight of fluid} = \frac{200,000}{530.4} = 378 \text{ lb. per hr.}$$

and $\qquad$ Dryness at B $= \dfrac{1.1395}{574} \times 483 = 0.961.$

The volume per lb. of the dry saturated vapour may be found from Clapeyron's equation (I,40)

$$V_s = \frac{JL}{T} \cdot \frac{dT}{dP} = 778 \times \frac{574}{483} \times \frac{0\cdot88}{144} = 5\cdot65 \text{ cu. ft. per lb.}$$

$\therefore$ Volume entering compressor per min. $= \dfrac{378}{60} \times 5\cdot65 \times 0\cdot961$

$$= \underline{34\cdot2 \text{ cu. ft. per min.}} \quad \text{Ans.}$$

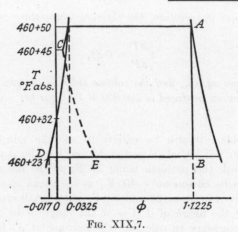

Fig. XIX,7.

7. *A vapour compression refrigerating plant uses ammonia as the working fluid, and the pressure and temperature of delivery from the compressor are 160 lb. per sq. in. and 100° F. After condensation, the liquid at 60° F. is passed through a throttle valve to the evaporator in which the pressure is 35 lb. per sq. in. Using the following information abstracted from tables using − 40° F. as datum, find the coefficient of performance. Sketch the total heat–pressure diagram for the cycle.*

P_{sat}, lb. per sq. in.	t_{sat}, ° F.	h (liquid), B.T.U.	Entropy (liquid), B.T.U.	$\dfrac{L}{T}$
160	82·64	135·0	0·2804	0·9148
35	5·89	49·3	0·1113	1·2123

At 160 lb. per sq. in. and 100° F., the total heat is 643·9 B.T.U. and the total entropy 1·2186 ; at the same pressure the liquid heat at 60° F. is 109·5 B.T.U.

If the throttling process had been carried out by first throttling to 60 lb. per sq. in. and then throttling the liquid only to the evaporator, the vapour being passed back to the compressor, find the increase in the refrigeration effect per lb. of the fluid passing through the evaporator. Assume the vapour leaves the evaporator in the same condition as previously, and at 60 lb. per sq. in., the liquid heat at the saturation temperature of 30·2° F. is 75·9 B.T.U.

(U. Lond.)

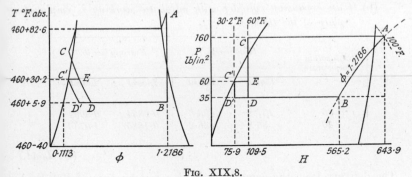

Fig. XIX,8.

From reference to the diagram, the total heat at B is $h + xL$, but as only $\dfrac{L}{T}$ is given,

$$xL = (1\cdot2186 - 0\cdot1113)465\cdot9.$$
$$\therefore \ H_B = 49\cdot3 + (1\cdot2186 - 0\cdot1113)465\cdot9$$
$$= 565\cdot2 \ \text{B.T.U.}$$
$$\text{W.D. per lb.} = H_A - H_B$$
$$= 643\cdot9 - 565\cdot2 = 78\cdot7 \ \text{B.T.U.}$$

Now
$$H_D = h_C = 109\cdot5$$
$$\therefore \text{Refrigeration effect per lb.} = H_B - H_D$$
$$= 565\cdot2 - 109\cdot5 = 455\cdot7 \ \text{B.T.U.}$$

$$\therefore \text{Coefficient of performance} = \frac{455\cdot7}{78\cdot7} = \underline{5\cdot79.} \ \text{Ans.}$$

When, however, the liquid is first throttled to 60 lb. per sq. in. only, the temperature being 30·2° F., some of this liquid is turned into vapour at the point E. The liquid *only* at the point C' at 30·2° F. is throttled to the lower pressure, and this liquid has a total heat of 75·9 B.T.U.

∴ Increase of refrigeration per lb. fluid passing the evaporator

$$= 109\cdot5 - 75\cdot9 = \underline{33\cdot6 \ \text{B.T.U.}} \ \text{Ans.}$$

Although this does not arise in the question, the vapour at E is led back to the compressor, which draws in a cylinder volume at the lower pressure (state B), and then the higher pressure vapour is admitted after the start of compression. Thus, more work is needed in the compressor per lb. passing the evaporator, but the overall coefficient is improved by this " compound " expansion.

8. *The working substance in a heat pump is ammonia. Heat is taken in* *at 40° F. after which the vapour is compressed adiabatically to 100° F., while* *condensation takes place at 85° F. There is no undercooling.*

Find the theoretical value of the heat delivered in B.T.U. per min. for an *input of 1 h.p., given that C_p for superheated ammonia is 0·7 :*

(a) *if a throttle valve is used to reduce the pressure ;*

(b) *if an expansion cylinder with adiabatic working is employed in* *place of the throttle.*

Saturation temperature, ° F.	Heat per lb.		Entropy per lb.	
	Liquid	*Latent*	*Liquid*	*Latent*
85	*137·8*	*493·6*	*0·2854*	*0·9064*
40	*86·8*	*536·2*	*0·1885*	*1·0733*

(U. Lond.)

The delivery from the compressor is at a temperature of 100° F., but since condensation occurs at 85° F., the condition at 100° F. must be superheated. Also, since the pressures are not given, it will be necessary to use the temperature–entropy diagram.

The problem is really that of the vapour-compression refrigerator, in which the heat delivered to the condenser equals the sum of the work done in the compressor and the refrigeration effect, if there are no losses. Being a heat pump, however, the point of view to be taken is that the compression work causes heat to be absorbed at 40° F. and to be delivered partly at 85° F. and the remainder over a temperature range from 85° to 100° F. The heat delivered per lb. is $H_2 - H_3$, and the W.D. per lb. is $H_2 - H_1$. The cycle is 1 2 3 6 1, fig. XIX,9.

The entropy of the superheated vapour, ϕ_2, is given by :

$$\phi_2 = \phi_l + \phi_L + (\phi_{sup} - \phi_s)$$
$$= 0·2854 + 0·9064 + 0·7 \log_e \frac{560}{545}$$
$$= 1·2107.$$

This equals the entropy of the wet vapour before compression, and if the dryness be x, we have :

$$1·2107 = 0·1885 + x \times 1·0733$$
$$\therefore x = 0·9524.$$

Now $H_1 = 86·8 + 0·9524 \times 536·2 = 597·5$ B.T.U.

and $H_2 = 137·8 + 493·6 + 0·7(100 - 85) = 641·9$ B.T.U.

$\therefore$ Work per lb. $= H_2 - H_1 = 44·4$ B.T.U.

The heat delivered per lb. $= H_2 - H_3 = 641·9 - 137·8$
$$= 504·1 \text{ B.T.U.}$$

$\therefore$ Heat delivered per min. per h.p., i.e. per h.p.-min.

$$= 504 \cdot 1 \times \frac{42 \cdot 4}{44 \cdot 4} = \underline{481 \cdot 2 \text{ B.T.U.}} \quad \text{Ans. } (a).$$

When an expansion cylinder is used to expand the liquid at 3 down to the lower pressure, the work done by the expansion is used to help drive the compressor. This expansion work is the isentropic heat drop 3 to 4, and is equal to $h_3 - H_4$ and represented by the area 3 4 5. The cycle is now represented by 1 2 3 4 1 and the net W.D. per lb. is now 1 2 3 4 instead of the whole shaded area 1 2 3 5 1. Since 1–2 and 3–4 are adiabatic and reversible, the net W.D. may now be obtained as the difference between the heat delivered to the condenser and the heat absorbed.

The area below 4 1 = 500 (1·2107 − 0·2854),

i.e.   Heat absorbed = 462·7 B.T.U.

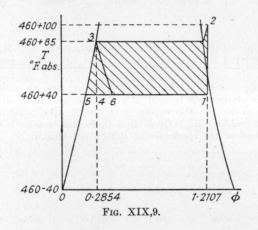

Fig. XIX,9.

and $H_2 - h_3 = 504 \cdot 1$ as before = heat delivered.

$$\therefore \text{ Net W.D.} = 504 \cdot 1 - 462 \cdot 7$$
$$= 41 \cdot 4 \text{ B.T.U.}$$

(The expansion work $h_3 - H_4 = 44 \cdot 4 - 41 \cdot 4 = 3 \cdot 0$ B.T.U.)

$\therefore$ Heat delivered per min. per h.p.

$$= 504 \cdot 1 \times \frac{42 \cdot 4}{41 \cdot 4} = \underline{516 \cdot 5 \text{ B.T.U.}} \quad \text{Ans. } (b).$$

It is possible to calculate $h_3 - H_4$ directly, as $\phi_3 = \phi_4$, whence x_4 and H_4.

1. Describe how you would decide whether the correct amount of working substance was present in a vapour compression refrigerator.

After adiabatic compression, the ammonia in a refrigerator is at 140° F. Condensation takes place at 86° F. and evaporation at 5° F. Given that C_p for superheated NH_3 is 0·7 and that there is no undercooling, determine, for a cooling effect of 1,000 B.T.U./min. :

(a) the i.h.p. required to drive the compressor ;

(b) the corresponding amount of heat to be removed in the condenser.

Saturation $t°$ F.	h	L	ϕ liquid	ϕ latent
86	138·9	492·6	0·2875	0·9029
5	48·3	565·0	0·1092	1·2161

(*U. Lond.*)

[ϕ leav. comp. = 1·2571 ; x ent. comp. = 0·944 ; per lb. NH_3, R.E. = 442·4 and W.D. = 88·0 B.T.U. ; (a) 4·69 i.h.p. ; (b) 1,198 B.T.U. per min.]

2. Discuss the relative merits of CO_2, NH_3 and SO_2 as refrigerants.

An ammonia refrigerator is used as a heat pump, taking in heat at 40° F. and condensing at 90° F. The vapour is at 140° F. after adiabatic compression and there is no undercooling. Given that C_p for the vapour is 0·72, determine the heat delivered to the condenser in B.T.U. per i.h.p.-hr.

Saturation temp. ° F.	Heat per lb. above − 40° F.			Entropy	
	Liquid	Latent	Vapour	Liquid	Vapour
40	86·8	536·2	623·0	0·1885	1·2618
90	143·5	488·5	632·0	0·2958	1·1846

(*U. Lond.*)

[ϕ during comp. = 1·2474 ; x at comp. suction = 0·986 ; W.D. = 52·2 B.T.U. per lb. ; 25,600 B.T.U. per i.h.p.-hr.]

3. A vapour compression refrigerating plant using ammonia works between pressure limits of 150 and 40 p.s.i.a. and circulates 3 lb. of ammonia per min. The ammonia leaves the compressor in a superheated condition with total heat 672·3 B.T.U./lb. and entropy 1·2745. After condensation the ammonia is undercooled to 70° F. Assuming compression to be adiabatic, find the work done, and the refrigerating effect per lb. of ammonia, and the coefficient of performance. Sketch qualitatively how this cycle would appear on the temperature–entropy chart.

If the compressor is single acting, and runs at 200 r.p.m., find a suitable cylinder size, making your own assumptions where necessary.

Data from Ammonia Tables :

Pressure p.s.i.a.	Saturation temp. ° F.	Total Heat of		Entropy of		Spec. Vol. of Vapour
		Liquid	Vapour	Liquid	Vapour	
150	78·8	130·6	630·5	0·2724	1·2009	1·994
40	11·7	55·6	615·4	0·1246	1·3125	7·047

The specific heat of liquid ammonia can be taken as 1·1.   (*U. Melb.*)

[H at comp. suction = 597·5 B.T.U. ; H during throttling = 120·9 B.T.U. ; C.O.P. = 6·37 ; neglecting vol. of liquid, V = 0·1024 cu. ft. per stroke ; assuming vol. η = 80% and L = 1·2D, D = 6·17 in. ; L = 7·40 in.]

4. An ammonia refrigerating machine operates between the temperatures 75° C. and − 15° C. The following data refers to latent and specific heat values at these temperatures.

$$L_{75} = 273 \text{ lb. calories per lb. ; } L_{-15} = 314 \text{ lb. calories per lb.}$$
$$C_l = 1·02 \text{ ; } C_q = 0·5.$$

Determine the degree of superheat at the end of compression and the C.O.P. λ when the vapour is 98% dry at the beginning of compression.   (*U. Witw.*)

[Take h and ϕ_l at − 15° C. = 0, then H at throttle = 91·8 C.H.U. ; H at comp. suction = 307·7 C.H.U. ; $\Delta\phi$ for dry sat. vapour at 75° C. and state leaving comp. = 0·103 ; ° C. of superheat = 80 ; H at comp. discharge = 404·8 C.H.U. ; C.O.P. = 2·22.]

5. A vapour-compression refrigerator, fitted with an expansion valve, worked between the pressures of 900 and 300 lb. per sq. in. The properties of the working substance at these pressures are given below. At the end of compression the vapour had a temperature of 50° C. and a total heat of 61 C.H.U. per lb. ; the liquid left the condenser at a temperature of 18° C. Assuming adiabatic compression, constant specific heat for the superheated vapour, and a specific heat of 0·5 for the liquid, find the coefficient of performance.

Pressure lb./sq. in.	Temp. °C.	Total Heat C.H.U./lb.		Entropy of Liquid
		Liquid	Vapour	
900	24	16	49	0·053
300	− 18	− 8·2	57	− 0·033

(*U. Lond.*)

[C_p = 0·462 ; ϕ during compression = 0·203 ; x at comp. suction = 0·922 ; H ditto = 51·9 C.H.U. ; H during throttling = 13 C.H.U. ; C. of P. = 4·27.]

6. Show that a reversed heat engine can be used for refrigeration. Air is withdrawn from a cold chamber at − 5° C. and atmospheric pressure into the cylinder of a compressor and is compressed adiabatically to 5 atmospheres pressure. The gas is then cooled at constant pressure to 15° C., and finally expanded adiabatically to atmospheric pressure and returned to the cold chamber. Find the refrigerating effect per lb. of air and the work done on the air to obtain this refrigerating effect.

(Specific heat at constant pressure = 0·235.)   (*I.C.E.*)

[Take γ = 1·4 ; temp. rise, comp. = 282° F. ; temp. drop, exp. = 191·4° F. ; R.E. per lb. = 36·5 B.T.U. ; W.D. per lb. = 21·3 B.T.U.]

CHAPTER XX

HEAT TRANSFER

Introduction

1. The treatment of heat transfer, within the scope of this book, must be confined to the more elementary type of example which, nevertheless, is of real value to the engineer. However, example no. 7 will be found to supply a pointer in the direction of the more advanced work, some of which is of recent origin.

2. The fundamental equation for the *conduction* of heat is

$$Q = -kA\frac{d\theta}{dx} \text{ B.T.U. per unit time} \quad . \quad . \quad (XX,1)$$

which, upon integration for a flat plate of uniform thickness x ft., leads to

$$Q = -\frac{kA\theta}{x} \quad . \quad . \quad . \quad . \quad (XX,1a)$$

where Q is the heat conducted in B.T.U. per hr., A the area in sq. ft. measured at right angles to Q, θ the temperature difference in ° F. in the direction of Q and measured across the thickness x. The negative sign indicates that θ decreases in the positive direction of Q.

k is the thermal conductivity, assumed constant, and has the units $\dfrac{\text{(B.T.U.)(ft.)}}{\text{(hr.)(sq. ft.)(° F.)}}$. Another way of writing (XX,1a) numerically is

$$Q = \frac{\theta}{\dfrac{x}{Ak}} = \frac{\theta}{R} \quad . \quad . \quad . \quad (XX,1b)$$

R being termed the resistance to heat flow. This is analogous to Ohm's law in electricity, Current $= \dfrac{\text{Potential}}{\text{Resistance}}$.

If a number of plates are placed in series, it is readily seen that Q must be the same through each plate once the steady state has been reached, and letting θ denote the overall temperature difference

$$Q = \frac{\theta}{R_1 + R_2 + \ldots} = \frac{\theta}{\sum \dfrac{x}{Ak}} \quad . \quad . \quad (XX,2)$$

The above may safely be applied to thin pipes, but a separate integration is required to deal with the case of the thick cylinder, e.g. lagged steam pipes. This case is dealt with in example no. 2 in this chapter.

3. In many practical cases, heat transfer is a combination of conduction and *convection*. Without considering in detail questions involving surface effects, we have

$$Q = h \dot{A} \theta \text{ B.T.U. per hr.} \qquad . \qquad . \qquad . \qquad (XX,3)$$

where A sq. ft. is the *surface* area from which heat is being lost (before or after being conducted through a thickness of material), $\theta°$ F. is the temperature difference between the *surface* and the fluid surrounding it, and h is called the coefficient of heat transfer and has units $\dfrac{\text{B.T.U.}}{\text{(hr.)(sq. ft.)(° F.)}}$. The student may meet the term "coefficient of emissivity" applied to h ; this practice is, however, going out of use, as the term emissivity is correctly used only in relation to radiation phenomena.

The overall coefficient of heat transfer, U, is similarly defined by

$$Q = UA\theta_0 \text{ B.T.U. per hr.,}$$

where A sq. ft. is the heat transfer surface area, and θ_0 the *overall* difference in temperature between warmer and colder fluids. It can again be shown that

$$\frac{1}{UA} = \Sigma\frac{1}{Ah} + \Sigma\frac{x}{Ak},$$

when several layers are concerned in conduction and convection.

The heat loss, by natural convection, from a body in air, is given approximately by $Q = cA\theta^{1\cdot25}$ B.T.U. per hr., the average value of c for plane and cylindrical surfaces being 0·30. The heat transfer coefficient h is then given by $h = \dfrac{Q}{A\theta} = c\theta^{0\cdot25}\dfrac{\text{B.T.U.}}{\text{(hr.)(sq. ft.)(° F.)}}$.

4. The mean effective temperature difference for parallel flow between a fluid in a pipe and another fluid surrounding it can be shown to be

$$\theta_M = \frac{\theta_1 - \theta_2}{\log_e \dfrac{\theta_1}{\theta_2}} \qquad . \qquad . \qquad . \qquad . \qquad (XX,4)$$

where θ_1 and θ_2 are the temperature *differences* between the fluids at the two ends of the pipe. An example of its use will be found in example no. 5 in this chapter. θ_M is known as the logarithmic mean temperature difference.

5. The third factor in heat transfer is *radiation* and the quantity of heat radiated per unit time from a surface whose temperature is equal to T_1 at all points, the surface being in surroundings at a temperature T_2

$$Q = E \times 0\cdot172 \times 10^{-8} \times A[T_1{}^4 - T_2{}^4]$$

or $\qquad Q = E \times 0\cdot172A\left[\left(\dfrac{T_1}{100}\right)^4 - \left(\dfrac{T_2}{100}\right)^4\right]$ B.T.U. per hr. (XX,5)

where E is the emissivity.

This equation is known as the Stefan–Boltzmann equation, the constant $0.172 \times 10^{-8} \dfrac{\text{B.T.U.}}{\text{(hr.)(sq. ft.)(}^\circ\text{ F. abs.)}^4}$ being also known by that name. Without further constants the equation can only give approximate answers, as the factor E, which is less than 1, is introduced to allow for deviation from complete " blackness " in terms of which the Stefan-Boltzmann law is expressed ; further constants may be required to allow for the angle through which one surface " sees " another when both are of comparable size. Some idea of the magnitude of E is given in example no. 6 in this chapter.

6. Many students will recall Newton's law of cooling which states that the heat loss from a body to the surroundings is proportional to the excess temperature of the body above its surroundings, providing the excess temperature is small. Taking the natural convection loss as proportional to $\theta^{1.25}$ and the radiation loss in accordance with the Stefan-Boltzmann equation, we have a total surface loss

$$Q = \alpha\theta^{\frac{5}{4}} + \beta[(T + \theta)^4 - T^4]\frac{\text{B.T.U.}}{\text{(sq. ft.)(hr.)}},$$

where α and β are constants, T is the temperature of the environment in $^\circ$ F. abs., and θ the temperature of the body above T° F.

Now, $Q = \alpha\theta^{\frac{5}{4}} + \beta[T^4 + 4T^3\theta + 6T^2\theta^2 + 4T\theta^3 + \theta^4 - T^4]$

$$= \alpha\theta^{\frac{5}{4}} + \beta T^4\left[4\frac{\theta}{T} + 6\left(\frac{\theta}{T}\right)^2 + 4\left(\frac{\theta}{T}\right)^3 + \left(\frac{\theta}{T}\right)^4\right]$$

Generally T will be of the order of 500° F. abs. or more ; hence for small values of θ, $\dfrac{\theta}{T}$ is small and powers of $\dfrac{\theta}{T}$ become insignificant.

$$\therefore\ Q \simeq \alpha\theta^{\frac{5}{4}} + 4\beta T^3\theta.$$

Now $\alpha\theta^{\frac{5}{4}}$ is often considered linear in θ, and in any case this term is usually the smaller of the two. Then, for a system in given surroundings (constant T),

$$Q \simeq (\alpha + 4\beta T^3)\theta \simeq C\theta.$$

which is Newton's Law of Cooling. It is clear that this simple linear law will give good approximate answers when e.g. $T = 500$, $\theta = 50$, a case which many would not have classified as being applicable to " small " excess temperatures. The criterion is, in fact, mainly that powers of $\dfrac{\theta}{T}$ are of a negligible order and that the convection loss may be considered linear with θ.

1. *A cold room has one of the walls which measures 15 ft. by 7 ft. 6 in. constructed of brick $4\frac{1}{2}$ in. thick, insulated externally by cork slabbing 3 in. thick. The cork is protected externally by wood 1 in. thick.*

Estimate the heat leakage through the wall per 24 hr. if the interior temperature is 28° F. and the exterior 65° F.

The thermal conductivities of brick, cork and wood are 6·5, 0·3 and 1·2 respectively, these values being measured in B.T.U. per hr. for an area of 1 sq. ft., thickness 1 in., and a temperature gradient of 1° F.

What will be the temperatures at the interfaces?

(U. Lond.)

This is a straightforward question on conduction through flat plates and is readily solved by applying (XX,1a).

$$Q = -\frac{kA\theta}{x} \text{ B.T.U. per hr.}$$

or (XX,2)
$$Q = \frac{t_1 - t_4}{\frac{1}{A}\Sigma\frac{x}{k}},$$

FIG. XX,1.

the area being constant here at 112·5 sq. ft.

Resistance of brick, $R_a = \frac{x_a}{k_a} = \frac{4\cdot5}{6\cdot5} = 0.692$

,,   ,, cork, $R_b = \frac{x_b}{k_b} = \frac{3\cdot0}{0\cdot3} = 10\cdot0$

,,   ,, wood, $R_c = \frac{x_c}{k_c} = \frac{1\cdot0}{1\cdot2} = 0\cdot833$

$$\Sigma R = 11\cdot525\frac{\text{(hr.)(sq. ft.)(° F.)}}{\text{B.T.U.}}.$$

$$\therefore \text{ Heat Leakage} = \frac{(65-28)\times112\cdot5}{11\cdot525}\times24$$

$$= 8,670 \text{ B.T.U. per 24 hr. Ans.}$$

Now, equation (XX,1b) shows that the temperature difference is proportional to the resistance, if Q is constant through each layer (Ohm's law analogy); i.e.

$$\frac{\theta_1}{\Sigma\theta} = \frac{R_1}{\Sigma R},$$

whence,
$$\frac{65-t_2}{65-28} = \frac{0\cdot833}{11\cdot525}.$$

$$t_2 = 65 - 37\times\frac{0\cdot833}{11\cdot525} = \underline{62\cdot3° \text{ F.}} \text{ Ans.}$$

Also,
$$\frac{t_3 - 28}{65 - 28} = \frac{0 \cdot 692}{11 \cdot 525}.$$

$$t_3 = 28 + 37 \times \frac{0 \cdot 692}{11 \cdot 525} = \underline{30 \cdot 2° \text{ F.}} \quad \text{Ans.}$$

As a check,
$$\frac{62 \cdot 3 - t_3}{65 - 28} = \frac{10}{11 \cdot 525}; \qquad \text{i.e. } t_3 = 30 \cdot 2° \text{ F.}$$

2. *A steam pipe, 4 in. outside diameter, is covered with two layers of insulating material, each 1 in. thick, the thermal conductivity of one material being three times that of the other.*

Working from first principles, show that the effective conductivity of the two layers is 15% less when the better insulating material is on the inside than when it is on the outside.
(*U. Lond.*)

When heat flows radially outwards through a thick cylinder of length l the conduction equation (XX,1) may be applied to a cylindrical element of radius r and radial thickness dr, thus

$$Q = k \frac{2\pi r l(- d\theta)}{dr},$$

the negative sign being due to a decrease in temperature in the positive direction of Q.

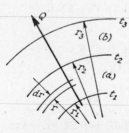

$$-\frac{dr}{r} = \frac{2\pi l k}{Q} d\theta$$

$$\log_e \frac{r_2}{r_1} = \frac{2\pi l k}{Q}(t_1 - t_2)$$

$$Q = \frac{2\pi l k(t_1 - t_2)}{\log_e \frac{r_2}{r_1}} \text{ B.T.U. per hr.}$$

FIG. XX,2.

Applying this to the present example per ft. length, fig. XX,2,

$$t_1 - t_2 = \frac{Q}{2\pi k_a} \log_e \frac{r_2}{r_1}$$

and
$$t_2 - t_3 = \frac{Q}{2\pi k_b} \log_e \frac{r_3}{r_2}.$$

Adding,
$$t_1 - t_3 = \frac{Q}{2\pi}\left\{ \frac{\log_e \dfrac{r_2}{r_1}}{k_a} + \frac{\log_e \dfrac{r_3}{r_2}}{k_b} \right\}.$$

Now, $r_3 = 4$ in.; $r_2 = 3$ in.; $r_1 = 2$ in.
Better insulator on *inside*,

$$t_1 - t_3 = \frac{Q_1}{2\pi}\left\{\frac{\log_e 1\cdot5}{k} + \frac{\log_e 1\cdot333}{3k}\right\}.$$

Better insulator on *outside*,

$$t_1 - t_3 = \frac{Q_2}{2\pi}\left\{\frac{\log_e 1\cdot5}{3k} + \frac{\log_e 1\cdot333}{k}\right\}.$$

$$\therefore \frac{Q_1}{Q_2} = \frac{\frac{1}{3}\log_e 1\cdot5 + \log_e 1\cdot333}{\log_e 1\cdot5 + \frac{1}{3}\log_e 1\cdot333} = \frac{\dfrac{0\cdot40547}{3} + 0\cdot28764}{0\cdot40547 + \dfrac{0\cdot28764}{3}}.$$

$$\frac{Q_1}{Q_2} = \frac{0\cdot42280}{0\cdot50135} = \underline{0\cdot843.} \quad \text{Q.E.D.}$$

3. *A sphere (surface area $4\pi r^2$) of radius 16 in. is lagged to a radius of 20 in., the inner and outer surface temperatures of the lagging being $450°$ and $150°$ F. respectively.*

Find the rate of heat leakage if K for the lagging is $0\cdot46$ B.T.U. per sq. ft. per hr. per ° F. difference per in. thickness.

If you use a formula, develop it.

(*U. Lond.*)

We now apply (XX,1) to a thin spherical shell at a general radius r, radial thickness dr, so that

$$Q = k\frac{4\pi r^2(-d\theta)}{dr}$$

$$-\frac{dr}{r^2} = \frac{4\pi k}{Q}d\theta.$$

Integrating, $$\frac{1}{r_1} - \frac{1}{r_2} = \frac{4\pi k}{Q}(t_1 - t_2)$$

where suffices 1 and 2 refer to internal and external conditions respectively.

$$Q = 4\pi k(t_1 - t_2)\frac{r_1 r_2}{r_2 - r_1} \text{ B.T.U. per hr.}$$

$$= 4\pi \times 0\cdot46 \times 300 \times \frac{320}{144 \times 4}.$$

$$Q = \underline{963\cdot5 \text{ B.T.U. per hr.}} \quad \text{Ans.}$$

4. *A pipe of outside diameter d_1 is lagged with insulating material and the outside diameter of the lagging is d_2. Deduce an expression for the logarithmic mean radius.*

A 2 in. diameter steam pipe, with an outside diameter of $2\frac{3}{8}$ in., is lagged with composition to a diameter of $4\frac{1}{2}$ in. The pipe is 150 ft. long, and conveys wet steam at 120 lb. per sq. in. Estimate the heat loss per hr. if the surrounding temperature is $65°$ F. The thermal conductivity of the composition is $3·5 \times 10^{-5}$ and the emissivity per degree $7·0 \times 10^{-5}$, the units in both cases being B.T.U., ft., sec., $°$ F.

(*U. Lond.*)

It has already been shown in example no. 2 in this chapter that for a thick cylinder

$$Q = \frac{2\pi lk(t_1 - t_2)}{\log_e \dfrac{r_2}{r_1}}.$$

The " mean " radius r_m is such that the area $2\pi r_m l$ produces the same heat flow in the same material, so that

$$\frac{k(2\pi r_m l)(t_1 - t_2)}{r_2 - r_1} = \frac{2\pi lk(t_1 - t_2)}{\log_e \dfrac{r_2}{r_1}}$$

$$r_m = \frac{r_2 - r_1}{\log_e \dfrac{r_2}{r_1}} = \underline{\frac{d_2 - d_1}{2\log_e \dfrac{d_2}{d_1}}}.\quad \text{Q.E.D.}$$

$t_1 =$ inside temp. of lagging $= 341·3°$ F., the saturation temp. at 120 lb. per sq. in. and neglecting the effect of the pipe itself,

$t_2 =$ outside temp. of lagging,

$t_3 = 65°$ F. $=$ surrounding air temperature.

For conduction, $Q = \dfrac{2\pi \times 150 \times 3·5 \times 10^{-5}(t_1 - t_2)}{\log_e \dfrac{2·250}{1·188}}$

$$t_1 - t_2 = 19·36Q \qquad . \qquad . \qquad . \qquad . \qquad . \qquad . \qquad (i)$$

For surface heat loss, using the value of the " emissivity " as given, *per* $°$ F. (see note in introduction to this chapter, page 327, article 3).

$$Q = hA(t_2 - t_3)$$

$$= 7·0 \times 10^{-5} \times \pi \times \frac{4·50}{12} \times 150 \times (t_2 - t_3).$$

$$t_2 - t_3 = 80·9Q \quad . \qquad . \qquad . \qquad . \qquad . \qquad . \qquad . \qquad (ii)$$

Adding (i) and (ii), $t_1 - t_3 = 100·3Q$

$$Q = \frac{341·3 - 65}{100·3} = 2·757 \text{ B.T.U. per sec.}$$

$$\underline{Q = 9,920 \text{ B.T.U. per hr.}} \quad \text{Ans.}$$

5. *Find the surface area required in a surface condenser dealing with 60,000 lb. of steam per hr., 92% dry, at 0·6 lb. per sq. in. abs. The temperature of the condensed water leaving the condenser is 84° F. The cooling water is heated from 56° to 75° F. in passing through the condenser. Assume that the mean coefficient of heat transmission is 620 B.T.U. per sq. ft. per hr. per ° F.*

If this condenser is to have two water passes, composed of tubes $\frac{3}{4}$ in. outside diameter and 0·048 in. thick, with water speed 5 ft. per sec., determine the length and number of tubes in each pass. (*I.Mech.E.*)

For incoming steam,

H = 53·2 + 0·92 × 1,045·4 = 1,015 B.T.U. per lb., $t = 85\cdot3°$ F.

Heat gained by cooling water = 19 B.T.U. per lb.

Heat lost by steam = 1,015 − 52 = 963 B.T.U. per lb.

∴ lb. of cooling water per lb. of steam $= \dfrac{963}{19} = 50\cdot6$

lb. of cooling water per hr. $= 60,000 \times 50\cdot6 = 3\cdot04 \times 10^6$

By (XX,4), Log. mean temp. difference $= \dfrac{(84-56)-(85\cdot3-75)}{\log_e \dfrac{28}{10\cdot3}}$

i.e. $\theta_M = \dfrac{17\cdot7}{\log_e 2\cdot72} = 17\cdot7°$ F., nearly.

Now, $Q = UA\theta_M$

$$A = \frac{(963 \times 60,000)}{620 \times 17\cdot7} = \underline{5,260 \text{ sq. ft.}} \quad \text{Ans.}$$

Now, $A = \pi \times \dfrac{0\cdot750}{12} \times L$

where L is the total tube length

∴ L = 26,800 ft.

Taking the specific volume of water as 0·016 cu. ft. per lb.,

cusecs flowing through tubes $= \dfrac{3\cdot04 \times 10^6}{3,600} \times 0\cdot016.$

∴ area for water flow $= \dfrac{3\cdot04 \times 10^6 \times 0\cdot016}{3,600 \times 5} = 2\cdot7$ sq. ft.

Let $x = $ number of tubes in each pass, then

$$2\cdot7 = \frac{\pi}{4} \times \left(\frac{0\cdot654}{12}\right)^2 \times x$$

$x = \underline{1,160 \text{ tubes per pass.}}$ Ans.

The length of the tubes, l, will now be given by

$$l = \frac{26,800}{2 \times 1,160} = \underline{11\cdot55 \text{ ft.}} \quad \text{Ans.}$$

6. *Give a brief account of the effects of temperature and surface condition, on emissivity.*

A polished brass pipe, outer diameter 2 in. and emissivity 0·15, in surroundings at 60° F., carries hot water at 180° F. Calculate the heat loss per ft. length of pipe, natural convection from its outer surface being given by 0·400$^{1·25}$, where θ is the temperature difference between pipe and air.

If the pipe were covered with ¼ in. thickness of insulation, of thermal conductivity 0·10 B.T.U. per ft.-hr. ° F. and emissivity 0·9, what would be the percentage change in the heat loss by convection from the outer surface ?

(U. Lond.)

Emissivity, E (a radiation phenomenon).

Metals.—Polished metals have very low emissivities, and it is found that the better the electrical conductivity of the metal, the lower is its emissivity in the polished condition. Rough metals and oxidized metals have higher emissivities which may vary widely for any particular metal. A thin film of oil or grease will considerably increase the emissivity of polished metals ; similarly, a thin coat of lacquer may effect a five- to ten-fold increase in E, so that the low heat loss from a polished metal cannot be preserved by this means.

Increase in temperature increases the emissivity of metals ; in the case of polished metals, the increase is by about 50% to 400% between 100° F. and 2,000° F.

Non-metals.—Practically all non-metals (bricks, wood, paints, paper, etc.) have a high value of E at moderate temperatures, and even white paper is almost " black " in the thermal sense. Roughening and pitting of a surface increases E.

Increase in temperature reduces E of non-metals ; thus, for a white refractory brick E falls from 0·9 to 0·3 when its temperature is raised from 100° F. to 2,000° F.

It is important to note, that practically all surfaces, except polished metals, have values of E between 0·8 and 0·9 at moderate temperatures, and a figure of this order can always be assumed in calculating the heat radiated from lagged surfaces, and room heating installations. A conspicuous exception to this general rule is aluminium paint, for which E is about 0·3.

Surface area of pipe $= \pi \times \dfrac{2}{12} \times 1 = \dfrac{\pi}{6} = 0{\cdot}525$ sq. ft. per ft. run.

By (XX,5), radiation loss,

$$Q_R = 0{\cdot}172 \times 0{\cdot}15 \times 0{\cdot}525 \left[\left(\frac{640}{100} \right)^4 - \left(\frac{520}{100} \right)^4 \right]$$

$$= 0{\cdot}172 \times 0{\cdot}15 \times 0{\cdot}525 \times 946{\cdot}5$$
$$= 12{\cdot}8 \text{ B.T.U. per hr.}$$

Also, natural convection loss,

$$Q_C = 0.40 \times 0.525 \times (180 - 60)^{1.25}$$
$$= 0.40 \times 0.525 \times 397 = 83.4 \text{ B.T.U. per hr.}$$

Total heat loss from unlagged pipe, Q = <u>96·2 B.T.U. per hr. per ft. Ans.</u>

When ¼ in. insulation is added, the heat conducted through the lagging per ft. length is

$$Q' = \frac{2\pi k(t_1 - t_2)}{\log_e \dfrac{r_2}{r_1}}$$

in accordance with the expression derived in example no. 2 in this chapter;

i.e. $\quad Q' = \dfrac{2\pi \times 0.1}{\log_e 1.25}(180 - t_s) = 2.81(180 - t_s)$ B.T.U. per hr. per ft.,

where t_s is the surface temperature of the lagging. The heat conducted through the lagging must be equal to the sum of the convection and radiation loss.

$$\text{New surface area} = \pi \times \frac{2.5}{12} \times 1 = 0.655 \text{ sq. ft. per ft.}$$

$$\therefore \; Q'_C + Q'_R = 0.655 \times 0.4(t_s - 60)^{1.25}$$
$$+ \, 0.172 \times 0.9 \times 0.655 \left[\left(\frac{t_s + 460}{100} \right)^4 - \left(\frac{520}{100} \right)^4 \right].$$

This must equal Q', and may be solved by assuming a series of values for t_s and plotting Q' and $(Q'_C + Q'_R)$ against t_s until an intersection is obtained.

Say, $t_s = 120°$ F., then $Q' = 168.6$, and $Q'_C + Q'_R = 84.4$.

$\therefore \; t_s > 120°$ F., as Q' decreases with increasing t_s.

Say, $t_s = 150°$ F., then $Q' = 84.3$, and $Q'_C + Q'_R = 138.7$.
Say, $t_s = 130°$ F., then $Q' = 140.5$, and $Q'_C + Q'_R = 101.7$.

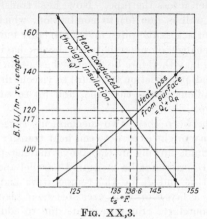

FIG. XX,3.

The graph of Q' is, of course, a straight line, and it can be seen that $Q'_R + Q'_C$ is almost linear (cf. introduction to this chapter, article 6). The point of intersection is

$$t_s = 138 \cdot 6° \text{ F.}, \quad Q' = 117 \text{ B.T.U. per hr. per ft.}$$

The new convection loss alone,

$$Q'_C = 0 \cdot 655 \times 0 \cdot 4 \times (138 \cdot 6 - 60)^{1 \cdot 25} = 61 \cdot 4 \text{ B.T.U. per hr. per ft.}$$

$$\% \text{ reduction in convection loss} = \frac{83 \cdot 4 - 61 \cdot 4}{83 \cdot 4} = \underline{26 \cdot 4\%}. \quad \text{Ans.}$$

(Note also, $\% \text{ increase in rad. loss} = \dfrac{55 \cdot 6 - 12 \cdot 8}{12 \cdot 8} = 334\%$.

$$\% \text{ increase in total loss} = \frac{117 - 96 \cdot 2}{96 \cdot 2} = 21 \cdot 6\%.)$$

7. *Discuss Reynolds's analogy as applied to the heat transmission between a fluid flowing in a pipe and the wall of the pipe. Derive an expression relating Nusselt's Number, Prandtl's Number, Reynolds's Number and Euler's Number (i.e. "f", the pipe friction drag coefficient). Give definitions of these " Numbers " which are consistent with the expression you have given.*

Discuss the validity of the theory and the limitations of the expression. Indicate the improved formula due to Taylor and Prandtl (i.e. that based on taking into account the existence of a laminar layer as well as a turbulent core). Indicate, in general terms, the further improvement due to von Kármán.

$$(U. \ Dur.)$$

When fluid flows through a pipe and heat is transferred between the fluid and the pipe, both the fluid temperature and the axial velocity vary in an ordered manner across the pipe. Now, heat transfer between a fluid in a pipe and the wall is due (*a*) to conduction, which depends on the temperature gradient across the pipe, and (*b*) to eddy motion, which causes a continuous interchange of mass between layers having different axial velocities and which may therefore be described as a transfer of momentum.

On the other hand, pipe friction is due (*a*) to viscous drag, which depends on the velocity gradient across the pipe, and (*b*) to eddy motion of the same type as above.

The similarity between these two mechanisms suggested to Reynolds that a proportionality might exist between heat transfer and fluid friction.

Consider some fluid, flowing in the above manner past a solid boundary ; let x and y co-ordinates be measured parallel and perpendicular to the boundary. Let dt and dv be the temperature and velocity increase respectively across a layer of unit area between planes distant y and $y + dy$ from the boundary. Suppose that, due to eddy motion, a mass

m of fluid is exchanged across the layer in unit time. Then, the frictional resistance R across this unit area of the layer is given by

$$R = \mu \frac{dv}{dy} + m\, dv \qquad . \qquad . \qquad . \qquad . \qquad (1)$$

μ being the viscosity, and $m\, dv$ the rate of momentum transfer due to eddy motion.

The total heat transfer across the same layer will be

$$Q = - k \frac{dt}{dy} - mc\, dt \qquad . \qquad . \qquad . \qquad . \qquad (2)$$

where k is the thermal conductivity and c the specific heat of the fluid at constant pressure.

Dividing (1) by the density of the fluid ρ, and (2) by $c\rho$,

$$\frac{R}{\rho} = v \frac{dv}{dy} + \frac{m}{\rho} dv \qquad . \qquad . \qquad . \qquad . \qquad (3)$$

$$\frac{Q}{c\rho} = - \alpha \frac{dt}{dy} - \frac{m}{\rho} dt \qquad . \qquad . \qquad . \qquad (4)$$

where $v =$ kinematic viscosity $= \dfrac{\mu}{\rho}$; and $\alpha =$ thermal diffusivity $= \dfrac{k}{c\rho}$.

If we let $\dfrac{m}{\rho} dy = \varepsilon$, (3) and (4) may be written

$$\frac{R}{\rho} = (v + \varepsilon) \frac{dv}{dy} \qquad . \qquad . \qquad . \qquad . \qquad (5)$$

$$\frac{Q}{c\rho} = - (\alpha + \varepsilon) \frac{dt}{dy} \qquad . \qquad . \qquad . \qquad . \qquad (6)$$

Now, *if and only if* $(\alpha + \varepsilon) = (v + \varepsilon)$, and assuming R and Q to be constant relative to y,

$$v_2 - v_1 = \frac{R}{\rho} \int_{y_1}^{y_2} \frac{dy}{v + \varepsilon} \qquad . \qquad . \qquad . \qquad . \qquad (7)$$

$$t_2 - t_1 = - \frac{Q}{c\rho} \int_{y_1}^{y_2} \frac{dy}{v + \varepsilon} \qquad . \qquad . \qquad . \qquad (8)$$

Thus, the laws of distribution of v and t are the same; this will also be true, if Q and R vary in the same way relative to y. Hence,

$$\frac{\rho(v_2 - v_1)}{R} = \frac{c\rho(t_1 - t_2)}{Q} \qquad . \qquad . \qquad . \qquad (9)$$

or, if v and θ are the difference in velocity and temperature respectively, between y_1 and y_2,

$$\frac{v}{R} = \frac{c\theta}{Q}$$

or

$$\frac{Qv}{Rc\theta} = 1 \qquad . \qquad . \qquad . \qquad . \qquad . \qquad (10)$$

This is the form in which Reynolds's analogy is commonly presented; it may also be expressed in terms of dimensionless numbers as follows:

Nusselt's No., $$\text{Nu} = \frac{Qd}{k\theta}$$

where d is a characteristic dimension of the system, taken as the diameter for a pipe.

Prandtl's No., $$\text{Pr} = \frac{c\mu}{k} = \frac{\mu}{\rho} \times \frac{\rho c}{k} = \frac{\nu}{\alpha}$$

i.e. $$\text{Pr} = \frac{\text{kinematic viscosity}}{\text{thermal diffusivity}}.$$

Reynolds's No., $$\text{Re} = \frac{vd\rho}{\mu}.$$

Euler's No. f is given by $$\text{R} = f \times \frac{\rho v^2}{2}.$$

Hence, $$\frac{Q}{\theta} = \text{Nu} \times \frac{k}{d}$$

$$v = \text{Re} \times \frac{\mu}{d\rho}, \quad \therefore \ \text{R} = f \times \frac{\text{Re}^2 \mu^2}{2d^2\rho}$$

But, $$c = \text{Pr} \times \frac{k}{\mu}.$$

Substituting in equation (10),

$$\frac{\left(\text{Nu} \times \dfrac{k}{d}\right)\left(\text{Re} \times \dfrac{\mu}{d\rho}\right)}{\left(f \times \dfrac{\text{Re}^2\mu^2}{2d^2\rho}\right)\left(\text{Pr} \times \dfrac{k}{\mu}\right)} = 1$$

or $$\text{Nu} = \frac{f}{2} \times \text{Re} \times \text{Pr}. \quad \text{Ans.} \qquad . \qquad . \qquad . \quad (11)$$

Validity.—This depends on the assumptions made in deriving (8) and (9), viz. $\alpha + \varepsilon \backsimeq \nu + \varepsilon$, and that R and Q vary in the same manner with y. The latter is generally found to be approximately true.

Now, $$\alpha + \varepsilon \backsimeq \nu + \varepsilon,$$

if (a) $\alpha \backsimeq \nu$, or (b) if ε is very large compared with α and ν.

(a) If $\alpha = \nu$, then $\dfrac{\nu}{\alpha} = \text{Pr} = 1$. This is approximately true for many gases and Reynolds's analogy (10) or (11) is then valid.

(b) ε is large compared with ν and α in any turbulent region for liquids and gases, in which case (10) and (11) hold.

For laminar flow of liquids $\text{Pr} \gg 1$, and ε is not large cf. with ν so that Reynolds's analogy is not valid. For flow of liquids in a pipe, there is always a laminar boundary layer even if the flow as a whole takes place at Reynolds's numbers well above the critical (i.e. the flow is mainly turbulent); the analogy cannot then be used directly.

G. I. Taylor modified the theory for liquids by supposing the flow to be divided into a fully turbulent core in which Reynolds's analogy applied, and a purely laminar layer in which (1) and (2) reduce to $R = \mu\dfrac{dv}{dy}$ and $Q = -k\dfrac{dt}{dy}$.

(10) then becomes $\qquad \dfrac{Qv}{Rc\theta} = \dfrac{1}{1 + x(\mathrm{Pr} - 1)} \qquad . \qquad . \qquad . \qquad . \qquad$ (12)

where x is the ratio

$$\frac{\text{Axial velocity where turbulent and laminar zones meet}}{\text{Axial velocity of turbulent core}}.$$

If $x = 0$, or if $\mathrm{Pr} = 1$, (12) reverts to (10), which is to be expected, since $x = 0$ signifies that there is no laminar boundary layer, while $\mathrm{Pr} = 1$ means that $\nu + \varepsilon = \alpha + \varepsilon$.

Prandtl further developed the Taylor theory by obtaining a value for $x = \beta \mathrm{Re}^{-0.125}$, where β is a constant, so that

$$\frac{Qv}{Rc\theta} = \frac{1}{1 + \beta \mathrm{Re}^{-0.125}(\mathrm{Pr} - 1)} \qquad . \qquad . \qquad . \qquad (13)$$

Experiments show that (13) is true for small values of $(\mathrm{Pr} - 1)$, up to about 1; as Pr increases further, there is an increasing discrepancy. For water at $40°$ F., $\mathrm{Pr} = 11 \cdot 1$; and at $200°$ F., $\mathrm{Pr} = 1 \cdot 9$.

von Kármán does not assume ε to be negligible in the boundary layer, as Taylor does, but von Kármán does assume R to be constant across the boundary layer. A theory is developed which is based on experimental data for turbulent flow. Correlations of measured heat transfer data show that von Kármán's modified analogy gives correct results for Pr up to 10, and a fair approximation for Pr up to 25.

Examples

1. A spherical vessel of 20 in. radius contains a liquefied gas at $-297°$ F. It has two jackets of lagging, each 4 in. thick. The inner layer has a conductivity of $0 \cdot 35$ and the outer of $0 \cdot 45$ in B.T.U./ft.^{2}/hr./$°$ F. difference/*inch* thickness.

Find the rate of heat leakage into the container if the outermost surface is at $60°$ F.

Establish any formula used. (*U. Lond.*)

[Mean effective area for a spherical vessel $= 4\pi r_1 r_2$; total resistance $= 0 \cdot 424$ hr. $°$ F. per B.T.U.; $Q = \dfrac{357}{0 \cdot 424} = 842$ B.T.U. per hr.]

2. Calculate the heat loss per 100 ft. length of pipe when the pipe is insulated by corrugated asbestos for which the thermal conductivity k_{av} is 0·060 B.T.U./(hr.)(ft.^{2})($^\circ$ F./ft.). The pipe temperature may be taken as 300° F. and its outside diameter as 1$\frac{1}{2}$ in. The thickness of the lagging is 2 in., and its external temperature is 100° F.

Also, prove that the maximum heat loss in such a case is when the outside diameter of the lagging is given by

$$D = \frac{2 \cdot k_{av}}{h_c + h_r} \text{ ft.}$$

h_c and h_r are the convection and radiation losses in the usual units. State what these units are.   (*U. Melb.*)

[$Q = 5,800$ B.T.U./hr. ; Q is max. when overall " resistance " R is a minimum ; find $\dfrac{dR}{dr_1}$ and equate to zero.]

3. Derive an expression giving the maximum rate of heat loss by radiation from a surface at a high temperature and emissivity E, to a surrounding surface at a lower temperature.

Calculate the minimum temperature of an incandescent fuel bed which burns coal of C.V. = 13,500 B.T.U.s/lb. at the rate of 25 lb./hr./ft.^{2} of grate area, assuming that combustion is complete at the surface of the fuel bed. The coal is supplied with 17 lb. of air per lb. of coal, at 60° F., the temperature of the surrounding surface is 400° F. and the emissivity of the surface of the fuel bed is 0·9.   (*U. Manch.*)

[Heat loss by radiation is a maximum when either the surroundings are black (absorptivity = 1), or if the surroundings are large compared with the body ; $Q_{max.} = 0.172 \times 10^{-8} \times E_1 \times A_1(T_1^4 - T_2^4)$ B.T.U. per hr.—Assuming C_p for all products = 0·24, the required temp. is given by $394,547 = 0.1548\left(\dfrac{T_1}{100}\right)^4 + 108T_1$; whence by trial $t = 2,325^\circ$ F.]

4. Calculate the thickness of insulating material of conductivity 0·06 B.T.U. per ft. per hr. per $^\circ$ F. necessary to reduce the heat loss from a hot-water tank to 25% of the unlagged loss. Assume the coefficient of surface heat transfer by radiation and convection to be 1·5 B.T.U. per sq. ft. per hr. per $^\circ$ F. for the unlagged tank, and 1·2 B.T.U. per sq. ft. per hr. per $^\circ$ F. for the exposed surface of the lagging.   (*U. Lond.*)

[Assume surface area, unlagged $\fallingdotseq$ surface area, lagged $\fallingdotseq$ area for conduction ; for lagged tank $U = \frac{3}{8}$; $\dfrac{1}{U} = \dfrac{x}{0.06} + \dfrac{1}{1.2}$; $x = 1.32$ in.]

5. In a communal hot-water distribution scheme, it is proposed to use a ring main of 6 in. outside diameter clothed with lagging 2 in. thick. The total circuit of the main is 2,000 yd. and it is laid in a conduit in which the air temperature may be assumed constant at 20° C. The temperature of the inside of the lagging may be taken to be the same as that of the water in the main. The coefficients of conductivity and emissivity for the lagging are 2.5×10^{-4} and 10×10^{-4} respectively in in., min., lb., $^\circ$ C. units.

When no water is being tapped from the main, a circulation must be maintained to keep up the temperature. Under such conditions, show that if the water leaves the pumping station at a temperature of 80° C., about 291 lb. of water must be circulated per min., in order that the temperature of the water returning to the pumping station may not be less than 50° C.

The specific heat of the water may be taken as 1.   (*U. Camb.*)

[Log. mean $r = 3.91$ in. ; total resistance at any cross-section per in.
length $= 325.3 + 31.8$; log mean overall temp. diff. $= 43.3°$ F. ; $\underline{W = 290.5 \text{ lb.}}$
per min.]

6. Calculate the leading dimensions of a condenser for 1,000 lb. of saturated
steam per hr. at 5 lb. per sq. in. gauge using cooling water at 60° F. It is suggested that the velocity of water through the tubes should be in the order of
3 ft. per sec. The condensate is not to be cooled.

The heat transfer coefficient for the condensing steam is to be taken as
1,000 B.T.U./sq. ft. hr. 1° F., and the water film coefficient is to be taken from
the following equation.

$$h = 150(1 + 0.01t)\frac{V^{0.8}}{D^{0.2}}$$

where h is the water film coefficient in B.T.U./sq. ft. hr. ° F.
t is the mean temperature of the water in ° F.
D is the internal diameter of the tube in inches.
V is the water velocity in ft. per sec.   (*I.Chem.E.*)

[Assume : water outlet temp. $= 120°$ F., two water passes using tubing $\frac{5}{8}$ in.
O.D. $\times$ 16 S.W.G., neglect conductivity resistance (this being very small) ; hence,
16,000 lb. of water per hr., 18 tubes per pass, actual water velocity $= 2.90$ ft.
per sec. ; water film coefficient $= 766$; total resistance $= \dfrac{0.000894}{l}$, where l is
the total tube length in ft. ; log. mean temp. diff. $= 135.7°$ F. ; $l = 6.32$ ft. ;
i.e. effective length of tubes per pass $= \underline{3 \text{ ft. 2 in.}}$]

7. Discuss, with a diagram of temperature against thickness of metal, why
the heat flow from steam to cooling water through a condenser tube may be
regarded as independent of the thickness of the tube itself.

The formula $\left(\dfrac{Qd}{k\theta}\right)\left(\dfrac{Cv}{k}\right)^{0.5} = 0.03\left(\dfrac{vcd}{k}\right)^{0.8}$ has been derived for the heat
transmission from a tube of diameter d to a fluid, of conductivity k, flowing in
it at a velocity v, where Q = heat flow in unit time per unit surface ; θ = temperature difference between tube and fluid ; C = specific heat of the fluid per
unit volume ; $\nu = \dfrac{\mu}{\rho}$, the kinematic viscosity of the fluid.

Prove that each bracket contains a dimensionless quantity, by considering
each symbol in terms of the dimensions, length, time, temperature and heat.
                                                    (*U. Lond.*)

8. Explain what is meant by the term *logarithmic mean temperature difference*
and derive an expression for it in terms of the temperature differences at inlet
to and exit from a tubular air cooler placed in a large stream of water which
may be assumed to remain at a constant temperature.

A tubular cooler is required to cool 3,000 lb. of liquid per hr. from a temperature of 220° F. to 150° F., the specific heat of the liquid being 0.58. The
water supply temperature is 55° F. and the rise in temperature is not to exceed
75° F. Estimate the saving in sq. ft. of the surface area of the tubes when a
counter-flow cooler is used in place of a parallel-flow cooler. The overall coefficient
of heat transfer may be assumed to be 230 B.T.U. per sq. ft. hr. ° F. in both
cases.   (*U. Lond.*)

[Q = 121,800 B.T.U. per hr. ; for parallel flow : log. mean temp. diff. $= 68.7°$ F.,
A = 7.70 sq. ft. ; counter-flow : $\theta_M = 93.5°$ F., A = 5.66 sq. ft. ; $\underline{\text{saving} = 2.04}$
sq. ft.]

INDEX